ABOUT THE AUTHOR

Daniel M Dorothy was born i[...] up in Harpswell Maine, a lobste[...] Bay. He also lived in Hawaii for several years before eventually emigrating to Thailand in 1991.

He has worked with Pattaya Mail Publishing since its inception in 1993, and in 1996 became executive editor of Pattaya Mail Publishing Co. Ltd., a position he still holds today. In 2002, Dan became a founding partner in the Chiang Mai Mail newspaper in Northern Thailand and served as its president for three years. He still sits on the Chiang Mai Mail board of directors.

Mango Rains is his first book.

MANGO RAINS

MANGO RAINS

The true story of a Thai mother's lifelong search for
her abducted daughter.

DANIEL M DOROTHY

PUBLISHED BY MAVERICK HOUSE PUBLISHERS.

Maverick House Publishers, Office 19, Dunboyne Business Park, Dunboyne, Co. Meath, Ireland.

info@maverickhouse.com
http://www.maverickhouse.com

ISBN: 978-1-905379-66-8

5 4 3 2 1

The paper used in this book comes from wood pulp of managed forests. For every tree felled, at least one tree is planted, thereby renewing natural resources.

A CIP catalogue record for this book is available from the British Library.

DEDICATION

Mango Rains is dedicated to my late mother, Eva Minot. May she rest in peace.

ACKNOWLEDGEMENTS

Many people have given me ideas and encouragement throughout the writing of this book. It would be impossible to name them all but I would like to give special thanks to:

Jean Harrington at Maverick House for taking me under her wing and guiding me through the publishing process; Dr. Iain Corness, author of the *Farang* series of books, for proofreading the manuscript; my late mother Eva Minot (may she rest in peace) for convincing me not to give up on this project; Dave Sparks Jr. for bugging me to finally dust off the manuscript and make the finishing touches; Tom Gingerich for being a good sounding board off which to bounce ideas; Peter Malhotra, 'father' of the Pattaya Mail publishing family who goes above and beyond the call of duty for his extended family; and finally to 'Lek' and 'Nid', without whom there would be no *Mango Rains*.

INTRODUCTION

The following is a true story based on the recollections of Lek, one of the two main characters in *Mango Rains*, as recounted to me in dozens of interviews conducted in Bangkok and Pattaya. The names of the main characters have been changed to protect their privacy.

I met Lek in the early 1990s in Bangkok. We became good friends and had many long conversations, mostly her talking about her past and her mother's story, but also her dreams and aspirations. Unfortunately, after about three years we went our separate ways. Last I heard she had married and started a family. Nid has since retired from the music business. She too finally married, then moved to Europe.

I was quite moved by this remarkable life story, and felt compelled to spread the message that there is so much more behind the famous Thai smile, so much hidden away from the casual eye. And although their story is unique in its details, it is synonymous with so many others in Thailand, not only to those who eventually end up in the bar trade, but with the many who work in factories, in hotels and restaurants, doing menial labor for pittance, barely able to exist, much less get ahead in life. There are many more similar stories that end in tragedy. Lek and Nid's story was inspirational to me as it ended in triumph.

Perhaps in it there is hope for others.

CHAPTER I

A warm breeze blew, causing the tops of the rice seedlings near her to quiver. In early June 1971, with the rainy season having just begun, Nid Sawang lay in pain on the edge of a rice paddy just outside a small town in northeast Thailand, near the Cambodian border. She had just turned 16 years of age. Although that accomplishment wouldn't make it into anyone's history book, it was a small miracle for Nid.

The ground was moist, but she didn't care. It couldn't be much longer now. She was nearing the end of her pregnancy, yet it had become clear to her that starvation was most likely going to come first. Her stomach pain kept her awake even though she wanted nothing more than to slip into a comfortable sleep, to make all her troubles go away.

She accepted her conditions. If this is what fate had planned for her she wouldn't fight it. She would just lie there and try to shut out the pain. Alone and helpless, with no one around to hear her cries of pain, she finally shut her eyes and let her mind drift away.

The hooves of a water buffalo made soft clomping sounds on the gravel road that cut through the center of Somchai's farm. The shackles of its harness jingled rhythmically, keeping an ever so slow beat as it strained under the pressure of pulling a wooden cart behind.

Somchai barely had to steer the beast, for it had been down this path a hundred times before. This gave him plenty of time to gaze upon the land that stretched out before him as far as he could see. It was his farm now, had been since his father passed away. The land he would someday pass on to his eldest son Thawanee, had been in his family for many generations.

Life had never been easy for his family. Farm life never was. There had been droughts, there had been territorial struggles with the Khmer, there had even been countless changes of government over the years, but somehow Somchai's family had managed to hold on to this precious plot of fertility.

'Your great-grandfather almost lost this farm back in the drought of 20-21,' Somchai spoke over his shoulder. His son Thawanee had come along on this trip to repair a broken paddy dam and lay resting in the back of the cart.

'Back in those days entire villages were like extended families,' Somchai continued. 'Farmers helped farmers, families helped families, and everyone looked out for one another. There wasn't any competition because rice wasn't sold. Traded sometimes, but it was mostly grown only for families to eat,' he said.

Thawanee recognized what was coming by the tone in his father's voice. 'Everything was changing and nothing was as good as it was in the old days.' How many times had he heard it? Never mind, Thawanee loved and respected his father and knew how much tradition meant to him, so he sat up to listen.

'The drought years were tough times. If it wasn't for the fact that everyone helped each other, many good people would have lost their farms. I shudder to think what would happen if we had a drought now. Sure, there are still a few old timers left, but we're a vanishing breed.'

As he listened to his father's fond memories of days gone by, Thawanee stared aimlessly at the long road ahead. Suddenly, something caught his eye. 'What do you suppose that is, *Por*?' Thawanee pointed to the spot where the object rested.

Somchai strained his eyes to see what he was pointing at. 'I don't know. It almost looks like a person.'

'What do you suppose he's doing way out here?'

'I don't know. I guess we had better find out.' Somchai took his switch and gave the buffalo a hard smack on its hind quarters. The gesture was futile. The buffalo had no interest in picking up the pace.

As they made progress toward the intruder, Somchai and Thawanee stared intensely at the person who lay prone beside their road. It had been a while since they had had a visitor, and both pondered who it might be that was interrupting their day and why they had done so. Finally, the wooden spoke wheels creaked to a halt when the wagon got close enough for the riders to see what appeared to be a young pregnant woman lying motionless.

'Hello,' Somchai called out to her. When she didn't respond, it became apparent that something was wrong. 'Go check on her,' he commanded his son.

Apprehensive, Thawanee took a deep breath before he jumped out of the wagon and walked over to where she was lying. 'Hello, can you hear me?' He asked as he took her by the hand. Her arm was limp and cold and she still didn't respond.

'Is she alive?' Somchai asked.

Thawanee knelt down and put his head on her chest. 'She's barely breathing.'

'Get her in the wagon,' Somchai commanded.

Nid was slowly jostled out of her unconsciousness by the uneven sway and bumpy ride of the makeshift ambulance as it made its way past rice paddies on one side of the path and a tapioca grove off in the distance to the other. Just before reaching the farmhouse, she blinked open her eyes. Patches of dark clouds crowded the sky. It would rain soon.

Was this some sort of holy chariot sent to take her into her next life? Was this what it was like to die? Her stomach began to hurt again.

'Hey *Por*, she's awake!' Nid heard someone say.

Was this a holy person sent to ease her journey? She turned to see who had spoken. He was just a boy. He couldn't be much older than she, Nid thought, as she tried to sit up to talk with him.

'Just lie back and rest. We're almost there,' Thawanee tried to sound reassuring.

Almost where? Nid thought. Her angel of mercy didn't much look the part. He appeared to be just a poor farm boy.

'Soam, come quick! We need your help,' Somchai yelled.

Nid slowly turned to see where the new voice was coming from. She could only see what looked like the back of an older man driving the cart.

'Who is she?' An older woman joined the two men after the wagon came to a stop outside a small farmhouse.

'I don't know,' Somchai said to his wife. 'We found her lying by the side of the path not far from the village road. She looks very sick.'

Sick? Nid thought. I'm not dead?

'She's pregnant,' Soam said, astonished.

Pregnant? Nid looked down to her belly. Yes, my baby. Again she tried to sit up. This time Thawanee helped steady her.

'Where am I?' Nid asked. She felt dizzy and thought she might faint at any moment.

'You're on the Somchai farm. Who are you? What happened?' Soam asked her as she guided her out of the wagon.

'Hungry,' was all that Nid could muster. Her eyes felt heavy. Maybe she should just go back to sleep.

'She's starving,' Soam exclaimed. 'We have to feed her, quickly. Get her inside.'

Somchai and Thawanee carefully carried Nid into the family's small wooden farm house. Once inside, Soam instructed the men to place her on the sitting mats and use pillows to prop her up. As they did so, their eldest daughter Wan brought her a bowl of hot rice soup.

'How long have you been at the edge of my farm?' Somchai asked after Nid had finished her second helping. The entire family, which now included several younger children, had gathered around to stare at this mysterious young woman.

'I don't know,' Nid replied. She could feel the warm liquid and rice bring back her strength as the meal slowly passed into her depleted system.

'Why was it on my farm that you chose to die?' Somchai blurted out. Soam gave him a curious glance.

'I don't know that either,' Nid answered, seemingly unfazed by the question. She looked down at her belly and sighed. 'I may have been very bad and perhaps deserve to die, but not yet. My fate is in the hands of Buddha and if I could ask him to grant me a dying wish, it would be to give life to my unborn child.'

'Do you have a husband or family that may help grant you this wish?'

'I do not. I am alone and an outcast.' Even though her strength was returning, Nid couldn't bear to look her saviors in the eyes.

Somchai cast a glance over at Soam. She was slowly shaking her head and had a pained expression on her face. 'What have you done to deserve this fate?'

Nid's stare was fixed firmly on the floor in front of her. 'I'm sorry, I don't mean to be rude. You have been very kind to me. You brought me into your home and served me this delicious soup. You saved my life, at least for now. I do not wish for your good deed to become bad in your mind so please don't ask me to tell you what it is that I have done. When I finish this soup I will be on my way again. I don't want to bring any bad tidings to you or your family.'

'Where will you go?' Somchai asked.

'I don't know,' Nid replied.

Somchai looked over at Soam again, then looked around at the rest of his family before returning his attention to Nid. A moment of silence passed before he began.

'Last night I had a dream,' Somchai spoke slowly and chose his words carefully. 'I dreamt of a fire in our barn. In my dream a woman bearing a child came and used magic to bring water to extinguish the fire.

'As you might know, to dream of fire will bring bad luck, but to dream of water conquering fire foretells good luck. You may think I'm just a simple farmer but I believe in these things. They have been a way of life for farmers like me for many generations.

'Today we found you on the edge of our farm near death. I'm convinced it wasn't a coincidence. It had to have something to do with my dream last night. It must be some sort of sign from the mother of water asking repayment for her help. I cannot say no to something that's much more powerful than any of us can imagine. Please accept my invitation to stay in my home until you are recovered enough to find your way.'

'I . . . I don't know what to say. I have no money and I am too weak to work for you. I wouldn't have any way to repay you.'

'You need not worry. It has been a good year so far and we have more than enough food to share. I believe you are an omen of good luck. That will be payment enough.'

'What about your friends and neighbors? I'm sure they will wonder about me.'

'If anyone should ask we will tell them you are my cousin from Korat who has fallen upon misfortune. I won't worry about that and neither should you,' the farmer said.

CHAPTER 2

Somchai's eldest daughter Wan was only a year younger than Nid and in the ensuing weeks proved herself to be a loyal nurse and an unwavering friend. She spent hours by Nid's side feeding her and making her comfortable. And when the rest of the family were busy working the farm, she would press Nid for the truth of her story.

'Not everyone believes you are *Por*'s cousin. In fact, there has been some talk around town that you are his minor wife. Some people are saying that he got you pregnant and now he has to take care of you. I don't think many people believe it, though. Most people know that *Por* loves *Mae* too much to have a minor wife. Just the same, the stories are being told.'

'It's not true. I never met your father until he found me on the edge of your farm. He's a good man and you mustn't let people believe I'm his mistress.'

'But then, who are you? Where did you come from?'

'I'm a nobody.' Nid finally gave in. 'I've spent the last three years in Surin trying to pay off the *mamasan* of a *songh* for the price of a water buffalo. You have to promise me you won't tell anyone until after I'm gone.'

'A water buffalo? I don't understand.'

'First, you have to realize that I come from a very poor family. About three years ago my father died just before the planting season began. It was a very hard year for our small farm. Earlier in the year my father sold our water buffalo so we could buy food and supplies. He had hoped that when the time came to plow he would be able to borrow one from the headman of our village. After he died, my mother took my sister Nok and I into the village to see the headman to ask him for the loan of a buffalo. He refused, saying there were none to spare. He told us we could probably buy one from the next village. But we had no money. My mother was desperate, we might have starved.

'There happened to be a rich looking couple standing nearby as we had our conversation with the headman. As we turned away in distress, they stopped us and told us they had overheard our talk. The woman told my mother she sympathized with her and wanted to help. She said she could offer my sister and I good jobs in Surin, and if we agreed to go they would buy a water buffalo for our family. Even though the man was looking at us strangely, the woman assured us we would be well cared for and able to return someday to help our family.

'We had two other sisters and five brothers, no money and very little food. My mother saw how wealthy the couple looked and didn't hesitate.'

'So, what happened next?' Wan asked. At last, maybe her mystery could be solved.

'They had a car and put us in the back seat right away, before my mother had a chance to change her mind. They gave her enough money to buy a water buffalo, then drove us away. We didn't even have time to say good-bye. As Nok and I looked out the back window my mother never even turned around to wave to us. We were so scared we were in tears.'

'What did you do?'

'What could we do? We huddled together as the couple drove us away. After a while we began to calm down because despite all that was going on, the couple did seem nice. The woman introduced herself as Khun A and her husband as Khun

Chatchai. Khun A looked us over and said the first thing she was going to have to do was buy us some better clothes to work in. We came from a large and poor family so all our clothes were passed down and shared with our brothers and sisters. It had been a while since we'd bought new clothes. Maybe this sounds stupid, but the thought of getting new clothes made leaving our family a lot less frightening.

'We rode for a long time in that car. We had never been outside our village and as we passed mountains and rice fields we thought for sure we were going to the edge of the world. After a couple of hours we started to see more buildings and more people. We thought this must be the biggest city in the world!'

'Where were you?'

'We had come to Surin.'

'Surin? I've never been to Surin even though it's only a couple of days walk from here. Someday I want to go. I want to see the shops, eat in a restaurant. It must be beautiful.'

The two girls continued to talk. 'It was both beautiful and ugly. There were shops everywhere selling clothes and things we had never seen before. But there was garbage, too. In the streets, on the sidewalks, in the alleys behind the shops. It smelled.

'We stopped at a restaurant and ate some delicious curry and rice, and eel soup, then Khun A took us to one of the shops and bought us the most beautiful clothes I'd ever seen. Nok and I thought we were in a dream. We must have been rewarded for being good people in a previous life.

'Then it came time to go to the house where we would be working. Khun A seemed to change. It's difficult to describe, but all of a sudden she seemed cruel. When she told us from now on we belonged to her and if we did as we were told there would be no problems, she said it in almost a sadistic way. She said she bought us from our family so now we had no family, only her.

'As we stopped the car in front of the house I could see eyes peering out from behind the curtains upstairs. Khun A told us we would be staying with other girls and must do as they say, listen to them and learn from them. If we did as we were told we would be fed. If we didn't, we wouldn't be able to eat. Simple rules.'

'That doesn't sound too bad, so far. My friend Aram's mother tells her the same thing. Sometimes Aram gets angry but she realizes her mother loves her and is just trying to teach her to work hard so that when she has her own family she'll be able to take care of it,' Wan replied.

'Sure, I can understand discipline too, but this was different. When we went inside the house and saw the other girls we realized we wouldn't be working in the rice fields. They were all putting on make-up and brushing their hair. Some were half naked and they all looked very tired. There was one who looked a little older then the rest and Khun A told her to get us ready.'

'Ready for what?' Wan inquired.

'At that time we didn't know. The girl's name was Dang and she looked angry when told that she had to be the one to get us ready. The first thing she did was give us each a towel and tell us to go to the klong jar and wash. I remember it was a very hot day and the cold water felt refreshing. While we were washing, Nok and I tried to figure out what was happening and what kind of work we were to do. Between the two of us we couldn't find an answer.

'When we got out of the shower, Dang took our towels away and made us stand in front of her, naked. Nok was a year older then me and a little more developed and as Dang reached over and fondled her breasts, the other girls laughed. She said, "Oh, you're going to bring *mamasan* a lot of money."

She then looked at me, told me I was very pretty and asked if I had ever been with a man before. I was only thirteen years old and didn't understand what she meant. Dang only shook her head and smiled, then showed us how to put on make-up and chose the clothes we were to wear.

'We were just about finished when Khun A started calling us to join her downstairs. All the girls dropped what they were doing, got up and walked down to a big room on the first floor. On one side of the room there were two well dressed local men sitting on a couch talking with Khun Chatchai. On the other side of the room they had chairs lined up against the wall facing the couch with the men on it. Dang sat Nok and I on either side of her in the chairs with the other girls. After a couple of minutes of talking and pointing, the men got off the couch and were joined by a couple of the girls. Then they left. That was it. The whole thing took about ten minutes. The rest of the girls started laughing and joking and we all went back upstairs.

'About thirty minutes later we repeated the process, only this time the men were different. About an hour later, when we were just about to do it again, I noticed the first two girls had come back. I didn't see them come in, but I knew it was them.

'That night no one told us anything directly but we could hear some of the returning girls talking. They were saying things like "very quick" and "too strong" and when they got back they all looked as if they hadn't slept in days. Although we were hoping it wasn't true, we were beginning to realize what was going on.

'After three or four days of marching up and down the stairs we both started to believe we might be lucky and not have to go with a man. But one day Khun A, who we now called *mamasan*, came upstairs by herself and told me to follow her downstairs, alone. I was so scared I didn't want to let go of Nok's arm, but Dang tore us apart and dragged me over to *mamasan.* Before she let me go Dang whispered in my ear that I was a lucky girl, and beautiful too, and not to ever forget it.

'A well dressed older man with big gold chains around his neck was waiting for us downstairs. He smiled at me nicely but I was too scared to breathe.'

'"Are you sure she's a virgin?" he said.'

"Yes. I'm sure you'll be very pleased," Khun Chatchai told him. The man nodded his approval and the next thing I knew, Khun Chatchai grabbed me by the arm and led the two of us across a courtyard to a small room behind the house. I try to forget that night, but I can't. The door of the room had the number one on it and was locked from the outside. Once inside I could see it was only big enough for a bed and a night stand with a dim light on it. Khun Chatchai mumbled something to the man that I couldn't hear then locked us inside. I was so scared, I didn't know what I was supposed to do. I didn't even know what he was doing, I only remember how sweaty he got and how much it hurt. I also remember the look on his face when he finished. I thought he was going to die. But after a few minutes he started to smile and sing some stupid song about releasing the dragon or something. He started trying to tickle me, but it didn't tickle, only hurt. I felt as if I couldn't move.

'I was still lying naked on the bed when Khun Chatchai returned to let him out. After the man left, Chatchai told me to be quiet and not tell anyone. Then he did it to me too.'

'How awful! Did you tell anyone? Did you try to get away?'

'I told my sister and we both vowed we would leave that next day and never come back. But Dang heard us talking and pleaded with us not to try. Everyone there wanted to get out but the last girl to try was easily caught, brought back and beaten. We didn't believe her until she showed us the scars she had on her head covered by her hair. Dang had been the last one to try.'

'So you stayed and did nothing?'

'What could we do? They never gave us any money and even if they did, none of us knew anything about the town of Surin and we had no place to go.

'But we didn't just stay there and do nothing, we dreamed. Everyone dreamed. We dreamed and prayed that someday a good man with lots of money would come and get us and take us away. We would talk for hours about our dreams and what we'd do when it was over. Those dreams kept us alive, got us through the bad times and promised us hope for the future.'

'Then one day *mamasan* came upstairs and told Dang she had finished paying her debt and was free to go. Dang had been there for four years. She was bought from her family for ten thousand baht and had brought *mamasan* over forty thousand baht. I found out later that usually if you bring in three times your purchase price you are allowed to go, but our *mamasan* had kept her on much longer. At that time Dang was only seventeen years old yet she had been to bed with men over six hundred times. She began to cry. She cried and cried and we thought she would die. We couldn't tell if she was crying for joy or sorrow, I think maybe it was both.

'"What am I going to do now?" was all she could say between sobs, "what am I going to do now?" We all started to cry. Some of the girls gathered her things for her and *mamasan* handed her five hundred baht. She said it was to get her started in her new life. We all knew it was a pitiful amount after all the time Dang had been there. Still crying, Dang walked downstairs for the last time and out the front door.

'The rest of us looked out of the upstairs window and watched as Dang stood by the road looking in both directions. She sat down by the side of the road and we could tell she was still crying. After about an hour, I watched her start to walk in one direction, then turn and walk the other way. She never came back.'

As the sun set over the rain soaked fields, the pastel sky left an eerie orange glow in and around Somchai's small wooden farm house. It would soon be time to start the cooking fire and prepare the evening meal.

'What ever happened to your sister, Nok? Is she still there?' Wan asked after noticing a faraway look in Nid's eyes.

'No, about a year ago a foreigner came into the house.' Nid seemed a little hesitant to tell this part of her story.

'It was the first foreigner we'd ever seen. The first time he came he took Nok for an hour. When she got back she told me how kind he was and how they didn't even have sex. She said he could speak Thai fairly well and they just joked and talked for the whole hour. He taught her a couple words of English and said he was from America. He even tried to give her some money. She knew *mamasan* wouldn't let her keep it, though, so she gave it back to him.

'A week later he returned and took Nok again. Then he returned the next day and the next, every day for a week and always the same, no sex, only talk. *Mamasan* liked him a lot because he paid two hundred fifty baht every time he came. The Thai men usually only paid fifty baht. At the end of the week he talked *mamasan* into letting him take her back to his hotel room for the night. At first she said no, so he offered her five hundred baht. I couldn't believe it, five hundred baht for my sister! *Mamasan* couldn't refuse.

'Nok and I were so excited that she was going to be able to get out of the house, even if it was only for one night. It had been a long time since any of us had seen the outside world other than the small view we had from our upstairs window. Nok was so nervous I practically had to push her out the door.' Nid paused. 'That was the last time I saw her.'

Wan took a deep breath. She could see this wasn't an easy thing for her new friend to talk about. She tried to find some comforting words but couldn't come up with any. 'Do you miss her?'

'Yes, I miss her very much.' Nid paused again. 'This may seem strange to you, but even though I missed her terribly, at times she helped me almost as much by being away as she did when she was with me. I know that sounds cruel, but it's true. Do you remember I told you how we used to dream about a rich man coming and taking us away? Well, we had to believe that's what happened to Nok. And if it could happen to her, then maybe, just maybe it could happen to one of us. It made our dreams seem a little more real.

'From then on, whenever I went with a man I would imagine that I was my sister and that the man was the foreigner that took her away. I could imagine the rooms out back were actually the bedroom of his big house in America. It made it so much easier for me to do what I did. At times it was almost even enjoyable.'

Thawanee momentarily broke up the conversation when he came crashing through the front door with a fresh load of wood and a bucket of charcoal for the evening fire. He wore a silly smirk as he stole a glance at Nid. When Nid caught his glance and returned his smile he quickly looked away and rushed back outside. Wan caught the exchange. With raised eyebrows, she smirked her approval. 'And what about you?' she asked after the flirtatious moment had passed. 'How did you get away?'

'Not long after my sister left I had a problem. When it came time for my monthly visit, I was late. At first I didn't think much about it, it was actually a relief not to have to bother with it. At the time I didn't really know what it meant. When the second month came and went, though, I thought maybe there was something wrong with me. I started to feel sick every day, sometimes I would even throw up. After the third month I started to get really sick and I lost all my energy. *Mamasan* thought I might have caught something from one of the men so she finally took me to see a doctor to check for disease. When he finished his check-up he said the three words that changed my life: "You are pregnant."

'I was shocked and *mamasan* was enraged. At first she acted very nice and thanked the doctor, but as soon as we got back to the house she struck me across the face and started yelling and screaming at me. How could I have let this happen to myself? Why didn't I tell her sooner? My sister ran off with a foreigner, and now I was pregnant. She cursed the day she went to my village.'

'She sounds very cruel,' Wan said with conviction.

'That's not all. She told me I would have to keep working and continue going with men. And when my belly began to get bigger she would tell the men that it would be an exotic experience to have sex with a pregnant woman. It didn't work, though, none of them wanted to go with me anymore.

'Finally, about a month ago, she became very angry again. She started yelling that I was no good, that I was only eating her food and not bringing her any money. When she stopped yelling she threw me one hundred baht and told me to get out of her house.

'Of course I had no place to go. I thought about going home to my family, but after what I've been doing the past three years I could never go back. Never. I'd be too ashamed.

'It was a scary thought going out into the real world after all those years in captivity. I even tried pleading with *mamasan* to let me stay. She said absolutely not and wanted me to leave immediately. So I left. Even if I die today, leaving that house was the best thing I ever did. It was both the happiest and saddest day of my life. I was free but alone, let out of my cage of captivity into the trap of poverty, and I had an unborn child to care for.'

'How did you end up here at the edge of our farm? Surin is a two day walk from here for a healthy person and you're carrying a child.'

'It wasn't easy. I wandered around Surin for most of last month eating what food I could find or beg, and sleeping behind the shops and restaurants. Many of the local men had visited the *songh* so the townspeople knew where I'd come from. None of them were anxious to help a pregnant whore. I didn't know where to go. I only knew that in order to survive I would have to leave Surin. Not knowing or caring where I was going, I started walking in this direction. Along the way I begged food and slept in the fields and in the forest. I was very scared. All I thought about was how I would be able to save my baby.

'At one point I knew my life was over. I hadn't eaten in days and all my strength was gone. I lost all hope. I just wanted to sleep, sleep for a long time. Maybe I would wake up and find this was all just a bad dream. Maybe I would wake up in my own bed next to my brothers and sisters back home. That's when your father found me.'

CHAPTER 3

The loud creak of the farmhouse door announced Soam's entrance. Wan quickly ran over to help her bring in the vegetables for the evening meal.

Nid wished she could help but the sharp pains in her stomach, which she had been having all afternoon, prevented her from doing so. She was afraid to say anything to anyone about the pain because she didn't know what it was. After all they had been through, she hoped she wasn't losing the baby.

As Soam and Wan went about the task of preparing dinner, Nid began to feel dizzy. She tried to steady herself by concentrating on the crackling fire that was working hard to boil the rice and cook the fish curry. The wonderful smell of curry permeated the air. It was a smell she had enjoyed many times before, each time bringing the eager anticipation of a good meal. That same smell was now only making her sick to her stomach. What was happening? Another pain in her stomach, this time so bad it made her groan.

Soam was an experienced midwife. When she heard Nid's groan, her head snapped up from her cooking. A quick look was all she needed. She knew exactly what was happening. She calmly walked over and sat next to Nid.

'Does your stomach hurt?' she asked tentatively.

'Sometimes very much,' Nid replied.

'How long have you been in pain?'

'Off and on all afternoon.'

'And how often have you been having this pain?'

'Before, not so much. But now, fairly often.'

The time was at hand. Why didn't she say something sooner? Soam thought to herself. She didn't realize the contractions had already begun, although she knew they could start any day now. There were a lot of preparations that needed to be done, not only for the birth of the child but for the *yoo fai* ceremony as well.

The *yoo fai* is an ancient Thai ceremony performed to help a new mother regain her strength. The ritual has been passed down from generation to generation, and in most small towns and villages it is as big a part of childbirth as the birth itself. Soam knew that everything must be done and timed just right. Good luck or bad luck depended on it.

The evening meal would just have to wait, there were more important things that needed to be done.

Preparations for the delivery would be rather simple and Soam called out to a couple of her younger children to get them boiling water and gathering clean linen.

Preparations for the *yoo fai* ceremony were more complicated and would take more time. Knowing full well how critical the timing was, Soam started barking out orders like a sergeant on the front line.

She sent Wan off to get the local monk and Thawanee to get Somchai so they could cut up the bamboo stocks and banana tree stumps for the new mother's bed next to the fire. After her younger children brought in the clean linen, she sent them back out to find some thorny branches to put under the house and stuff in the cracks in the walls and ceiling to keep away evil spirits. Soam then dug through her old wooden chest to find the pieces of cloth that needed to be hung around the room. Each one had a magic charm drawn on it, also to keep bad spirits away.

When Wan returned with the monk, he blessed the *sai-sin*, a string that no evil spirits can cross, then encircled the room with it.

Everything began falling into place. It was now up to Nid and nature. Nid had seen, indeed taken part, in these same preparations during the delivery of her younger brothers and sisters on her family farm. She recognized the *yoo fai* ceremony and now knew that her baby was about to be born. She also knew that as part of the ceremony she would be living next to the fire on that bed made of bamboo and banana tree trunks for seven days and nights after her child was born.

The monk was still sprinkling holy water around the room when the delivery began. Soam immediately ordered all the men to leave and instructed Wan to close the door behind them. They all obeyed her without question, she was the expert.

The monk sat in one corner outside the delivery room and chanted ancient Sanskrit mantras for the safe delivery of Nid's child.

Everyone waiting outside cringed each time the awful screams emanating from behind the closed door pierced their ears. Everyone knew the dangers of childbirth. Many things could happen, most of them bad.

Yet, despite what the people outside were thinking, inside everything was happening rather smoothly. As deliveries go, this one was fairly easy and relatively painless. Nid didn't think so. She was so very young, and this being her first child, every pain, every delay, every look of concern by the women who were helping her was multiplied tenfold. Soam, being an expert at both deliveries and reassurances, was able to keep Nid, and the rest of those in the room for that matter, relatively calm throughout the birth.

The newborn was very small, weighing barely over five pounds. Otherwise, the baby seemed quite healthy. When it began to exercise its lungs in a most obstreperous manner, as most newborns do, Nid began to panic, thinking something must be wrong. Again Soam's reassuring voice calmed the nervous mother.

'Don't you want to know?' she asked as she cleaned off the child.

'Know wha . . . of course I do!' Nid exclaimed.

'It's a beautiful, healthy baby girl,' she replied, as she handed the baby to her young mother.

'So this is what's been growing inside me for so long. This precious little bundle of life is what has kept me going, allowed me to escape my hell and brought me to this wonderful family. I love you my little girl. I love you so much.'

Wan burst through the doors that led into the waiting room outside. 'It's a girl!' she announced excitedly.

'Is she okay?' Thawanee's face was wrought with concern.

'Yes! Everybody is fine.'

Thawanee had already started to enter the room when Somchai caught him by the arm. 'Don't go in there empty handed. We have work to do.'

As the two men set about the task of finishing the *gadarn*, the makeshift bed Nid would occupy near the fire as part of the *yoo fai*, Soam began the ceremony. She knelt in front of the fire, pressed her palms together and held her hands up near her face, then bowed her head slightly forward in what is called a *wai*. In this position, she prayed to the god of the fire and asked for his help to bring Nid's strength back.

When she finished, the monk, who by now had stopped chanting, blessed a mixture of salt and rice which Soam then chewed to soften. She spit it out three times onto Nid's uncovered belly and three times into the fire, then slowly backed away.

The monk then walked over, dipped a wisp into a bowl of holy water and said a prayer in ancient Sanskrit as he sprinkled the water onto the fire.

Wan waited patiently in the background with a tray of food, flowers, a candle and some joss sticks she wished to give as an offering.

Still lying on the floor where she had delivered her child, Nid watched silently with her newborn cradled in her arms. Each part of the ritual happening in front of her was full of tradition and meaning, and each part was performed to perfection. She was in awe of it all, especially since it was being done for her. Barely two weeks had passed since she thought her life was over. Tonight she realized it had just begun.

Wan knelt down beside her, gave her a warm smile and slowly took the baby from her arms. Nid didn't want to let her go, yet the power of the moment was so great she couldn't help but trust her. Soam then calmly rolled Nid on her side and gently stood on her, a part of the ritual performed to try and help put the new mother's body back into its normal shape. Nid knew it was coming and silently dreaded it, but Soam's practised feet attached to her light frame actually turned the ordeal into nothing more painful than a strong massage.

When Soam was through, she quietly backed away. The next step was up to Nid. The entire family watched as she struggled to get up. With sweat rolling down her face and her knees shaking, she gingerly walked over and knelt down in front of the fire. She made a long, deep *wai*, said a silent prayer, then climbed up onto the *gadarn*.

To finish the ceremony for the night, the monk blessed a mixture of ground turmeric and betel, then Soam spread the two pastes over Nid's body to keep her skin moist.

CHAPTER 4

As the week wore on, Nid was surprised at how many of the local village women stopped by to wish her well. Every day a group of women would sit with her by the fire, talk with her and comfort her. It was unbearably hot in that room, yet none of the women complained about the heat or how uncomfortable it was.

Occasionally a few of the husbands would stop by too. Mostly they stayed outside to talk with Somchai and lend a hand in the chores. Toward the end of the week, though, one of them came inside for a glass of water.

He and Nid immediately recognized each other. He was one of the many men who had at one time or another bought her services at the *songh* in Surin. Without saying anything to Nid, he quickly went back outside—without his water.

Nid strained to look out the window to see where he went and what he would do. It was no surprise, yet no less painful, when she saw that he went directly over to talk with Somchai. As the two men talked, Somchai could not look his friend in the eye. His gaze alternated between the ground and the house, and as he slowly shook his head, Nid knew her secret was out.

Somchai knew what a *songh* was. He and all his male friends had been to one at least once. It was just the way things were. When there was a good harvest and a little extra money in their pockets, they would buy a bottle of lao-kao rice whiskey and sit out in front of the Sam Jet Sam Cafe where they would talk, eat ants wrapped in leaves, hard boiled eggs, and rice until the whiskey was gone. Then they'd stroll over to Soi Three where Khun El had the prettiest girls in town, none of whom were more than seventeen years old. No one gave much thought to the girls. Although they were pretty enough they had all been with other men, so they weren't good for anything else. Now he had one staying in his home.

Ever since the day Nid arrived, Somchai secretly suspected that she may have come out of a *songh* from one of the nearby towns. He had hoped that it wasn't true and that if it was, no one would ever recognize her. If she stayed a secret, as far as Somchai was concerned, she could stay with his family forever. He liked her. His whole family liked her. She had shown tremendous strength by making it to his farm alive and had even brought them good luck.

Their little ruse had almost worked, too. Most people did believe she was his cousin from Korat. That was until Meechum came along. He was sly, though. Sly as a snake. In only one afternoon he somehow managed to let the maximum number of people know where Nid had come from with the minimum number finding out how he knew.

Nonetheless, her secret was out. If Somchai didn't act on the situation his whole family would lose face. People might believe it was he who got her pregnant. Soam would be castigated for allowing her husband's minor wife to live with the family, something that is only done if the wife has done something bad enough to warrant it. He just couldn't let that happen.

He would just have to plead ignorance and tell everyone he didn't know she was a whore. If he acted quickly enough, maybe the townspeople would believe his story. After a while the controversy was bound to subside and life would return to normal. The sooner he acted the sooner this would happen.

He knew it would be rough on Nid, she had no place to go. What could he do? He had his family to think about.

The next day was the seventh and final day of the *yoo fai* ceremony and sure enough, no one from the village came by to see Nid. Rumors spread fast in small towns.

Avoiding the inevitable, Somchai kept himself busy working in the fields all day. His reluctance to confront the issue was not shared by Soam, however. By late in the afternoon she paid Nid a visit and told her what they had heard from Meechum on the previous day. 'Is it true?' she asked her.

Although Nid didn't want the hospitality of this family to end, they had been too good to her for her to lie. 'I'm afraid it is,' she answered solemnly.

With obvious sincerity Soam explained, 'I feel very sorry for you and for what you have been through. I think you should know that a few of the villagers are beginning to believe the rumors about you being Somchai's minor wife. Somchai has worked hard all his life to become a respected member of our village. It is a small village and relationships in small villages are very delicate sometimes. A controversy like this could upset the balance and cause irreparable damage to our family. We depend on the help our neighbors give us and thrive on helping them. As much as we like you and want to help, you just can't stay. I'm sorry. I don't know, perhaps you can go back and stay with your own family. I'm afraid that whatever it is you can do, you will have to do it soon.'

Nid silently nodded her agreement.

After dinner when the family retired for the night, Nid had difficulty trying to sleep. Minutes passed like hours as she laid in bed trying to figure out what she would do. The answer never came.

When the roosters began to crow and the sky began to change from dark black to light blue, Nid gathered her baby and what little she had, then left the house and began to walk away from the rising sun.

She hadn't gotten very far when Wan caught up with her. 'Where are you going?'

'Honestly? I don't know.'

'Let me go with you,' Wan pleaded.

'I'm sorry Wan, but you can't go. Believe me, wherever it is I am going, you don't want to end up there. Why would you? Your family loves you and your life is good here. You have food to eat and a home to live in. I have nothing but my baby and the clothes on my back. Whatever the future holds for me is not for you.' Nid paused. 'You have been a good friend and I will always remember you, Wan. So you have got to promise me that you will stay here and live the life you're supposed to. Never do what I have done.'

'I can't bear to see you go, Nid. You're my best friend in the world!'

'Promise me!'

'Okay, I promise. Here, take this, it's only a hundred baht I've saved up. I wish I could give you more but it's all I have. Take it, please.'

'Wan, you're the best friend a person could ever have. Thank you. I promise someday I'll pay you back. I'll miss you.'

'I'll miss you too, Nid. Take care of yourself and your baby. You know, you never told me what you'll call her. Haven't you thought of a name?'

'I have. She's so small and precious, I've decided to call her Lek.'

CHAPTER 5

By early December, after months of begging, borrowing and doing whatever she could to survive and keep on the move, Nid had found her way to Bangkok where she earned a modest living doing the only job she could get. She had joined a group of girls with similar backgrounds who were working out of a coffee shop on Petchburi Road, selling their bodies to whoever would pay their paltry fees. She had found and moved into a small, cheap room next to the coffee shop, and although it wasn't much, it was the only home she could afford.

For a six-month-old baby having to live in the conditions that she did, Lek didn't cry often. It was a good thing she didn't, for she was often left alone, sometimes for hours, while Nid tried to pick up customers next door. On rare occasions one of Nid's friends from the coffee shop would take a night off to baby-sit. Unfortunately, none of them had much money and none could be trusted. It was often for the better to leave her alone. It was one of these so-called friends that began a new chapter in Lek and Nid's lives.

'Nid, I know you're not going to like what I have to say to you,' Pom began. 'It's dangerous to leave Lek here by herself when you go to work. What would happen if there was a fire or a hungry rat loose in your room?'

'I know it's not good,' Nid agreed. 'I have no choice. I can't afford to pay someone to watch her every day and if I don't work, both Lek and I will starve.'

'This is where I think I can help you. I have a daughter a little older than Lek. She stays with my family in Korat. After seeing what you are going through, I took the liberty of talking with my mother. She agreed that if you send her money she will take care of Lek. Rest assured, she is very good with children.'

'Are you saying I should give up my baby to someone I've never met? I couldn't do that.'

'You wouldn't be giving her up, you'd be allowing her to grow up on a farm and in a safe environment. After a while you could go see her and if you ever made it to where you didn't have to work like this anymore, you could take her back. Think about it. It would be the best thing you could do for Lek and yourself.'

'She's all I have. What would I do without her?'

'I know how you feel. I felt the same way when I left my baby with my mother. The first few days were really tough. I now know she's getting things I would never be able to give her. She's safe and happy and I don't have to worry about her all the time. Now that she's gone I make more money, too. I can go with more customers without having to rush home and check on her. I can even stay with them longer. You know as well as I do that staying with a man overnight pays better than going with him for a short time.'

'I don't know, Pom. Maybe you're right. I don't want to be a bad mother. I only want what's best for my baby. I can't just give her up without thinking about it though. I'll have to let you know, okay?'

'Sure, I understand. Just don't wait for something to go wrong before you do the right thing.'

Nid knew full well the dangers of leaving Lek alone every day. If anything ever happened to her, Nid wouldn't be able to live with herself. After all Nid had been through just so Lek could be born, Lek had become the only reason Nid had for living.

Yet Nid couldn't bear the thought of not seeing the pride of her life grow up, take her first steps, and say her first word. What bothered her most about Pom's idea was that if she did give Lek to Pom's mother, Lek would do all those things thinking someone else was her mother.

On the other hand, Nid remembered her own family and how easy life seemed growing up on the farm. She also thought about Somchai's family and what a normal life they seemed to live. Nid longed to be part of a family again, and even though she knew she could never have that for herself, she realized that maybe, through Pom, she would be able to give that to Lek. The two sides of the debate formed a confusing dilemma.

A few nights after her talk with Pom, Nid had a wild night with a British customer named Bill. Over the course of the evening, the two of them nearly finished an entire bottle of Mekong whiskey. They were so drunk that when he took her back to his hotel, neither could stop laughing. Nid had enjoyed herself so much that night, for a while she forgot all her problems.

When she finally remembered that she had to leave, Bill at first complained about her only staying with him for a short time. Disappointed with her early departure, he nonetheless paid her well and promised he'd go back to the coffee shop to see her.

When Nid returned home, she staggered into her room and went over to give Lek a kiss good night. When she got there she noticed that Lek had vomited all over herself. She was lying on her back and much of the vomit was still in her mouth, making it hard for her to breathe. Nid blinked her eyes, shook her head and tried to determine if the booze in her system was playing a cruel trick on her mind.

Lek stared up at her and seemed to plead for her life. Each breath she took was short and gurgling, obviously a major effort.

Nid stood frozen for a moment not knowing what to do. Her mind desperately fought the effects of the alcohol. Finally her maternal instincts took over and without even realizing what she was doing, she turned Lek over on her side and began digging the vomit out of her mouth.

Normal color slowly returned to Lek's face as she began to breathe again. Although a frightened look remained in her eyes, the panicked look dissipated. She never even cried. Nid picked her up, held her to her breast and let her own tears flow.

'I'm such a terrible mother! How can I be this cruel? You've done nothing to deserve this.' The conversation she had with Pom now seemed so important.

'I don't want to lose you, oh how I don't want to lose you. Maybe Pom was right. Maybe I should give you the life you deserve. I promise you I will never hurt you again.'

Nid bundled Lek in a blanket and rushed over to the coffee shop to find Pom.

'You were right,' she cried. 'Please give Lek to your mother. Please give her a good life.'

'Oh, you look awful. What happened?'

'Never mind. Just take Lek before I hurt her any more!'

'I can't take her now,' Pom replied. 'I can come by your room in the morning. You have her ready to go and I'll take care of everything else. You've made the right decision.'

Nid solemnly took Lek back to her room and held her for the rest of the night. She quietly whispered in her ear about the Sawang family up country and the farm they came from. She told her about the games she used to play as a child with her brothers and sisters. She talked about what it meant to be part of a family and how she would never be able to give that to her.

She apologized for where Lek had come from and told her she would always love her and always be her mother. She explained that she knew Lek was too young to understand that she was doing this for her, trying to give her the life she had lost somewhere along the way. Nid promised her that she would make good so that someday they could be together again and live the happy life they both deserved.

At about 10 a.m. Nid was awakened by a knock on her door. Seeing that it was Pom, she bundled up what few clothes she had for Lek and put them together with her diapers and a stuffed rabbit. She had saved up five hundred baht and with a strong resolve that she was doing the right thing, she handed it all to Pom.

'Promise me you will take care of her,' Nid pleaded.

'I promise,' Pom replied.

'And when you get back you'll tell me where she is so I can go visit her someday.'

'I promise,' Pom said, as she walked out the door.

It was over. The love of Nid's life and the reason for her being had just left for a better world. She had left her mother behind to find her own path through the maze that Nid hoped would eventually lead her back. She hoped it would be soon.

Nid stared for a moment at the closed door and felt as if someone had thrust a dagger into her abdomen. Still slightly drunk from the night before, she sat on the edge of her bed and looked around her room.

'So this is what I've come to,' she said aloud, although there was no one around to hear her. The dim light coming through her barred window barely revealed her few meager belongings. A half dozen dresses hung from a wire stretched across one wall, a scattering of make-up containers were heaped on a rickety wooden table in front of a cracked and stained mirror against another wall. The entire room was barely three square meters. It had no bathroom, that was down the hall. And finally, her little sagging, lumpy bed. The bed she had shared with her baby, her precious little Lek.

'What have I done!' she screamed and raced out the door. Bursting onto the sidewalk, she strained her eyes first right, then left. Pom and Lek had already disappeared into the crowded Bangkok streets.

'Bus or train? Bus or train?' Nid tried to determine the most likely form of transportation Pom might use to go to Korat. 'Why didn't I ask her? It has to be the bus. Maybe I can catch them before they leave.'

The people walking along the street gave a wide berth to the disheveled-looking teenager talking to herself. Paying no attention to them, Nid hailed a tuk-tuk and rushed to the bus station.

When she arrived, Lek and Pom were nowhere to be found. The ticket clerk said she hadn't sold a ticket to anyone that fitted their description, either. Thinking they hadn't arrived yet, Nid sat down to wait.

Meanwhile, in another tuk-tuk speeding in the opposite direction, Pom and Lek were heading toward the other side of town. Their destination was not Korat as she had told Nid, but Patpong, an area of Bangkok popular with foreigners where bars, coffee shops and massage parlors lined the streets.

Pom had been there a few times with some of her customers and had met a local man everyone called Chalarm. He was a short, pudgy man who always seemed to be angry about something. He ran a little food stall on the edge of the Patpong area and besides being a great cook, he was a sly, crooked businessman. To supplement his income he had set up a racket where he gave housing to the poor, elderly and crippled; in exchange they worked the streets for him, begging for money from tourists.

It was common knowledge among the people who worked in Patpong that all the foreigners who visited Bangkok were rich, otherwise how would they be able to afford to come from far away to visit Thailand? Many of these tourists who saw how poor some of the Thai people were wanted to help in their own small way. Chalarm couldn't pass up the opportunity to tap into this easy money market.

He had begun about a year ago by renting a room not far from his food stall to house his future employees. The room he found had been used for storage and when the company that owned it moved to a new location, they were more than happy to let Chalarm use it. It was rather small with a makeshift bathroom and washing area set up in one back corner. It had no windows and the paint was peeling off the walls, making it a dark and dingy place. Chalarm found some old mattresses that a hotel had thrown away, brought them to the room and put them on the floor. The place wasn't a mansion, but it would be enough to serve its purpose and, since it was all free, the price was right.

With the room set up and ready to be occupied, Chalarm next went into the Klong Toey slums in search of prospective employees. On the first day of his search he found four people willing to work for him: an old man, a young boy and a woman with a baby. They all looked famished and had all been living under a bridge that spanned a polluted canal. He offered them food and shelter if they would come work with him. Given their current living conditions, each was happy to oblige.

Each afternoon Chalarm would drop his crew off near the edge of Patpong, then go to work in his food stall. He had taught them how to search out foreigners, *wai* deeply in front of them, continually put one hand toward their mouths and extend their other hand. He had also taught them how to be persistent and recognize hesitancy in the foreigners' faces. If the foreigners thought about them at all, with a little persistence, they were easy targets.

It paid off. Soon Chalarm was earning anywhere from five hundred to one thousand baht a day from his little scam, and it only cost him twenty to thirty baht a day to feed his workers. Even though his employees were being grotesquely exploited, Chalarm reasoned the conditions they were working under were a vast improvement from where they had come from. Not that it really mattered to him.

At first he was hesitant about employing the woman and her baby because only the woman would be able to work and he would have two mouths to feed. Soon he came to realize that the mother and child appealed more to the foreigners' sense of charity than the boy and the old man, for the mother was bringing in almost twice as much money as the other two combined. The cost of feeding the baby was almost negligible, too.

After the first few months the boy ran off and the old man became lazy. The money he earned became less each day. Over the same time period, the woman and her baby never let him down. The mother seemed grateful for the care Chalarm showed her and her child and she would consistently bring in four to six hundred baht a day.

Chalarm quickly learned his scam would be a great success if he could only find more women and children to work for him. It didn't take him long to find out it would not be an easy task. Although there were plenty of women living in poverty, single women with one small child were much harder to find.

Then one day a prostitute brought her customer to his food stall to eat. Chalarm overheard them talking about an un-cared for baby and it gave him an idea. Maybe if he offered her enough money she would be willing to give up her baby, even if it was only for a short while. After all, why were the little whores in the business anyway? To make money, right?

Chalarm knew that the by-products of the sex trade, these illegitimate children, tended to get in the way of their mothers and limit their income. He rolled some figures around in his head and decided that two thousand baht would be affordable for him, and enticing for the little whore. If she agreed, he could pair up the baby with any available woman and could make up the purchase price in no time.

Pom listened to Chalarm's business offer with keen interest. Although she knew she could never convince Nid to give up Lek outright, Pom considered herself a smart woman and knew she could come up with a plan. The money Chalarm offered sounded too good to pass up, so she thanked him for his offer and told him she'd be back.

It took her about a week before she figured out how she was going to go about it. She had no trouble relaying to Nid the true story of her own child that she left with her mother. The difficult part was being convincing when she told the lie about how her mother had agreed to take care of Lek, too. She tried to look at every angle from Nid's point of view as she planned her story. Once she got started with it, one lie led easily into the next. When she was through, she'd done such a good job that she'd almost convinced herself.

But deep down she knew it was a terrible thing to do. She tried to justify it by thinking it wouldn't be any worse for Lek in Patpong than if she stayed with Nid. At least in Patpong she would have someone looking after her all day, every day. Even Nid would be better off thinking her child was being well cared for. Never mind if she didn't know the truth so long as everyone was happy. Besides, two thousand baht was a lot of money. She knew girls who worked for years and never saved two thousand baht. Nid had even given her five hundred baht, what a good day it had turned out to be!

Pom's plan was to drop off Lek with Chalarm, then hide out for a couple of days. With that much money she could even rent a room in a nice hotel on the outskirts of the city, where Nid wouldn't be able to find her. She could probably even pick up some business while she was there.

When she went back, Nid would never know the difference. Since the two women weren't that close to begin with, it wouldn't seem unusual if Pom avoided Nid as much as possible. She would only have to meet up with her every now and then when she wanted to implement the second part of her plan. She thought herself particularly clever when she thought up that part, how Nid needed to give her mother money to take care of Lek. Now she could get a few extra baht every month without having to work for it.

CHAPTER 6

Malee's ancestors migrated south from Tibet more then two centuries ago to live on the rugged mountain ridges along the Thai-Burmese border. They brought with them strong religious convictions of animism and ancestor worship, as well as a keen ability to cultivate rice, corn and opium poppies in the harsh yet beautiful terrain of this mountainous region. For hundreds of years they fiercely resisted assimilation into modern society, opting instead to perpetuate their ancient way of life. During this time they kept on the move, wandering around in search of fertile soil without regard for provincial or national borders.

Over the past few years, though, Malee's tribe had been increasingly caught up in something they knew little about and they didn't care to know more. Whereas for centuries they had grown opium for their own use, believing strongly in it's powerful medicinal purposes, the increasing international demand for heroin was changing the area where Malee lived. Unknown to Malee and her people, the mountainous area to where they had migrated was becoming known internationally as the Golden Triangle.

Small armies were being formed to try and take control of the lucrative opium trade, the strongest being the Shan United Army run by a half-Chinese, half-Shan warlord who went by the name of Khun Sa. Malee had seen a small part of Khun Sa's army once when it passed by her village. Although they were heavily armed, they didn't seem to be a threat to Malee or her people. She didn't realize that not far away, fierce battles were being fought to control the land she lived on. What she was aware of was that her people were growing less corn and rice and more opium poppies.

Malee didn't know that the opium coming out of the poppies her tribe grew was amongst the best quality available in the world. She also didn't know that it was for this opium that the battles around her village were being fought. Somehow, without trying, she and her tribe had become pawns in an international maze of corruption and deceit.

Oblivious to all that was going on around her, Malee had been living her life with the happy idea that she was never going to stray far from her family and her tribe. She had been born into this Akha hill tribe and had spent her entire life moving around these hills. They would work the land until it dried up or until an ancestor's spirit told the village headman it was time to move on. Such was the simple, innocent life of Malee and her nomadic Akha hill tribe.

Malee didn't care that she was still unmarried at the age of twenty-eight. There were no men in her village that her father thought worthy of her, at least that's how she viewed it. After all, he would know—he was the village headman. She also understood that being the tribal leader was a time consuming occupation. She, being one of seventeen children, understood that he was a busy man and she wouldn't dare to presume he would have any time left over to speak with her.

It didn't bother her either that the hut she and four of her brothers and sisters shared was far from the rest of the family, for it was situated just inside the upper village gate. This and the lower gate were the demarcation boundaries between the human world and the spirit world, and they kept the bad spirits away. She knew that if a bad spirit had somehow managed to jump onto her shoulder or into her basket, she only needed to re-enter the village through one of these gates and the bad spirit would be left behind.

The hillside village was a very close-knit community. Although many of their people came and went on a day-to-day basis as they roamed the surrounding territory in search of fertile soil, it wasn't often they would receive a visit from an outsider. There was one man who made an occasional visit to the village and each time he came his arrival generated curiosity and interest. He always brought gifts for the headman and the elders, spoke their language fluently and showed great interest in their crops. He usually left after a couple of days with samples of their opium.

No one in the village, except perhaps the tribal leaders, knew that Anan was one of Khun Sa's main men. The vast northern area he patrolled was made up of many villages with many different types of hill tribes. His job was to search the hillsides for villages like Malee's that could produce the highest quality and largest quantity of opium. He would take samples back to Khun Sa who would then give him instructions as to which tribal leaders he should approach to try and secure their crops.

Malee had seen him come and go and took no particular interest in him. She knew his name was Anan; other than that he was just a wayward traveler who liked to indulge in the village opium. This time his arrival seemed different, though. The entire village sensed it. When Malee's father called a village meeting for that night it confirmed that something big was about to happen.

When the entire village met it was usually an exciting, fun-filled happening. Not much work would get done that day, for the people would be too busy getting ready for the big event. Since there was so much to do, each and every person took on tasks according to their specialties and every person took pride in whatever it was they could contribute, no matter if it was big or small. Meals needed preparing, sitting mats placed in their proper places and the meeting area had to be cleaned and decorated. Instruments had to be tuned, opium pipes readied, chickens prepared for the cockfights, and costumes decorated.

When the night fell, a surrealistic scene unfolded. Scattered throughout the meeting grounds, small bonfires provided light in the jungle darkness and warmth in the cool mountain air. The flickering light from the flames reflected off the surrounding foliage, making it seem as though the jungle were alive. The smoke rose steadily toward the sky and danced in front of a full moon that shone down like a beacon in the night, as it played a game of hide and seek with clouds racing by.

The smell of burning opium permeated the village compound. Off to one side, a group of women moved rhythmically as they performed ancient tribal dances while local musicians played the eerie sounds of their favorite melodies. The women had outdone themselves in decorating their tribal uniforms. Gaily woven headdresses rose high into the air. Their basic black outfits came alive with the red, white and yellow embroidery skillfully woven into them.

The meeting place was bustling with activity as the men sipped locally brewed rice whiskey, passed opium pipes and gambled. The men loved to gamble. Card games, cockfights and dice; 1 baht coins were being won and lost at a feverish pace.

Both men and women alike flashed blood red smiles caused by the stains left on their teeth from chewing betel nuts from the areca tree, which produced a mild euphoric feeling. Sharing them was an expression of hospitality and a way to cement friendships. On this night they were being passed around like candy.

The tribal leaders and elders shared the sacred opium pipe that was reserved just for them and which was only used for special occasions like this. They had positioned themselves on a platform overlooking the proceedings and it was from this platform that the village headman sent a messenger off to summon his oldest daughter.

Malee had no idea why her father wanted to see her. Perhaps he wanted to thank her for the special ants she had gathered for the elders' snack. It didn't really matter what the reason was. Her father had hardly spoken to her in almost a year, so she jumped at the chance to be near him. He was easy to find. His seat on the platform with the other important people was at the center of the festivities.

As she approached him, he motioned her to come closer. She dutifully went over, made sure to keep her head at a level below his out of respect, knelt down in front of him, and bowed deeply. He turned to Anan seated next to him and smiled as she performed this time-honored ritual. Malee would never forget exactly what he said when he turned back to address her.

'Malee, you are my oldest daughter and hardest worker. I want you to know your contributions to this family have not gone unnoticed. That is why it is you I have chosen for this honorable task. Anan, here, has proven to be a good friend to me and our people. His boss, Khun Sa, has agreed with him that our opium is the best quality available and will buy all we can produce. This will bring enormous power and prestige to our people. We will be able to bring modern supplies into our village and buy guns to protect ourselves and our crops from bandits.

'I know that not everyone agrees with change, but change is inevitable. If we allow our lives to remain stagnant we will never reach our full potential. We must approach each change with an open mind and be willing to do our part to help better ourselves and our neighbors. I know you will agree with me when I tell you how you're not progressing toward reaching your full potential. You are getting old and you still haven't found a husband. I believe you never will find him if you stay here working in the poppy fields. Anan is a man of wisdom and travel; however, I do not expect you to marry him, at least not yet. That is up to you two to decide. I do expect you to obey him and work for him as hard as you have worked for us.'

With that spoken, he turned back to Anan and announced, 'With great pride, I hereby give to you and hope you will accept my oldest and hardest working daughter as a gift, to show my deepest appreciation for the great things you have done for my family and the people of my village. She has a strong body and a sound mind, I know she will serve you well.'

Anan looked almost as shocked as Malee. He wasn't prepared for such a proposition and was quite taken aback. He wasn't particularly attracted to her, nor was he overly excited at the prospect of having to take her with him when he traveled. His modest home already had a capable maid. He also guessed she was too old to sell to a *songh* and couldn't think of anything else he would be able to do with her.

At the same time, there was much riding on the deal he was trying to make with these people. He didn't dare disappoint his boss Khun Sa. Therefore, not wanting to insult the village headman, he took Malee by the hand and sat her next to him.

Malee was overcome by an urge to run to the nearest gate, to re-enter the village in case an evil spirit had somehow become attached to her. Not wanting to disappoint her father, she gathered her strength, resisted the urge, and dutifully yet solemnly took a place next to and slightly below Anan.

With a smile deeply rooted in satisfaction for successfully completing what he considered a supreme sacrifice, Malee's father rose to speak. The entire crowd stopped what they were doing and gathered around to hear what he was about to say. When the village headman had finished revealing to them their impending new found wealth, the entire village cheered in jubilation and the celebration took on a feverish pitch.

The party would last for days, yet on the second day Anan took his leave with a dazed and submissive Malee at his side. Malee's father assigned them a guide and his best elephant to take them down out of the mountains into Mae Hong Son. From there they could hire better transportation to take them the rest of the way toward civilization.

CHAPTER 7

The midday sun bore down mercilessly on the city of Bangkok on this early January day. Those who were unfortunate enough not to be hidden in the shade or tucked away in an air conditioned office sweltered piteously in its unrelenting heat. The volatile air above the scorched pavement created illusions of warped structures. The bus station in northern Bangkok was a sea of pavement and offered no relief to those who waited for arrivals and departures.

Nid waited there for over an hour before she finally gave up. Just in case, she took a quick trip over to the train station. Pom and Lek weren't there, either. Nid was now sick to her stomach for not being able to catch them before they left. Yet, in blatant disregard for her hangover (which was compounded by the midday heat), she stopped at a local shop and bought a bottle of Mekong whiskey before she hailed a tuk-tuk to take her home.

She sweated profusely as she climbed the stairs that led to her room on the second floor above the crowded and noisy Petchburi Road, and couldn't understand why all those people were still out in the unbearable heat. Anyone sane was already hidden away from its cruel reach. When she opened her door, the heat trapped inside came rushing out prompting Nid to wait a moment before entering. She couldn't remember a day as suffocating as this, and the hot season hadn't even begun yet.

She quickly traversed her small room, opened her tiny window, then walked back and kicked a pair of shoes in front of her door to keep the wind from blowing it shut. Her worries were unfounded. No wind was stirring.

Sitting down on the edge of her bed, Nid stared emptily at the floor by her feet. After a moment of quiet contemplation, she reached over, twisted the top off the bottle of whiskey and filled a glass. Without thinking, she drained half its contents down her open throat. Recoiling from the strength of its taste, she distorted her face beyond recognition. It burned all the way down where it ultimately crashed hard into her empty stomach. Within minutes, the shot of alcohol began to take its desired effect. The heat and her hunger combined to make it extra lethal.

Her second gulp emptied the glass and she lay back on her bed with one hand grasping the bottle, the other loosely gripping her depleted chalice. Her head began to spin as her mind tried desperately to escape the reality of her situation. Where had she gone so wrong to deserve the fate that life had handed her? Why, at a mere sixteen years of age, was she forced to deal with the cruel realities of her world alone?

Nid had never felt so forsaken. Being trapped in the *songh* in Surin was terrible and she didn't miss it one bit, but at least there she felt a bond with the other girls that was born from that desperate situation. At least there she still felt part of a family. Working out of the coffee shop was different. It was everyone for themselves. People constantly fought each other, theft was rampant and no one trusted anyone. Even the best of friends sometimes turned on each other. If it weren't for Pom, Nid might have lost all hope in humanity.

Pom, what a true friend she turned out to be. She made her see what she was doing to her precious baby and offered to help. At least Pom and her mother might be able to give Lek a fighting chance. Just the same, even though it had only been a few hours since she left, Nid already missed Lek terribly. She definitely looked forward to the day when she would be able to get her from Pom's mother and take care of her by herself.

A commotion in the hallway brought her out of her deep thoughts. Her neighbors were either arriving or leaving, she couldn't discern which, nor did she care. She sat up quickly and soon discovered that doing so was a big mistake. The room began to spin uncontrollably around her making her grab the edge of the bed to steady it. Once it stopped, she poured herself another glass of whiskey and took a large gulp. 'Medicine for the soul,' she told herself.

It was past midnight when she finally finished the bottle. She suddenly remembered she told the foreigner she had been with last night that she would meet him in the coffee shop tonight. She looked over at her empty bottle and thought it would be nice to have more, but when she tried to stand up and leave, she nearly fell over and had to sit back down on her bed. Her second attempt landed her on the floor, effectively ending her efforts to keep her appointment.

As she managed to crawl back into bed, she hoped none of the other women working in the coffee shop would try to steal her man. Knowing how competitive it was there, what a big spender and what an easy mark he was, Nid realized it would probably be asking too much to have him wait for her. She would just have to find another. 'I miss my baby,' she said to herself before the alcohol shut down her ability to think any more.

CHAPTER 8

Nid slept until noon the next day. When she awoke, she unconsciously reached over to where Lek normally slept. Feeling an empty space beside her, she panicked. Quickly jumping out of bed, Nid began looking around to find her missing child. It took her a few minutes to remember what she had done. When reality sank in, she fell back onto her bed and into a deep depression.

She stayed in that condition for almost an hour before hunger and thirst pried her from her self pity. She remembered she hadn't eaten at all the day before and all she could taste in her mouth was an unpleasant residual coating of whiskey. She was still dressed in the same clothes as yesterday and when she reached into her pocket to see if she had any money, all she could produce were a few one baht coins. It wouldn't be enough.

Trying to clear last night's overindulgence out of her fogged head, she walked downstairs to the noodle stand and dipped a cup into the bucket of drinking water reserved for customers. The proprietor gave her a look of disapproval, then recognized her as a regular and let it pass.

The cool water brought her back to her senses and she remembered she had some money stashed away in her room. She climbed back up the stairs and shut the door so no one could see where she hid her treasure. She only had one stuffed animal on her bed, an elephant, and she picked it up, turned it over and found the tiny hole in the back of its head. Marveling at her ingenuity, she pulled out two hundred baht. She could now justify her bold action of drinking the noodle shop's water by ordering a meal. When she was finished, she would have plenty of money left over to buy more whiskey. She could even buy some cola and ice to stretch it out.

By ten o'clock in the evening she was in a similar state as the night before, yet with more energy. She had been trying to snap out of her depression by drowning in her glass of whiskey. Unfortunately, she ran out long before reaching her goal.

'This is silly. I've got to go to work or I won't have any money for tomorrow,' she told herself.

In a futile attempt to regain her sobriety, Nid walked down to the bathroom at the end of the hall and splashed water on her face, then returned to her room and tried to concentrate on her image in her stained mirror. Who was she looking at? Who owned those puffy, bloodshot eyes that stared back at her?

Scared away from the mirror by her own reflection, she gathered momentum and managed to find her way over to the coffee shop.

She half-walked, half-staggered through the front door. Even though it was dimly lit inside, she immediately recognized Bill, the foreigner from two nights ago. He was now seated with Payow and Nong at a table near the back. Using the backs of chairs and an occasional shoulder of an unsuspecting customer to steady herself, she made her way over to their table.

'Ah, Bin, you like butterfly. No good,' she forced herself to say in her best English.

'Bill,' he replied. 'My name is Bill.'

'I know, Bin, that's what I said. Bin, Bin, Bin.'

'Where were you last night? I waited for you all night,' he said, shrugging off her mispronunciation.

'You wait me? I think maybe you butterfly.'

'What's that mean? I don't understand what you're trying to say.'

'That means you took another lady,' Payow chipped in. She and Nong were chuckling about Nid's current condition. They both knew he had waited for her. Neither was about to offer that information. They hoped now that he could see what shape she was in, he might change his mind about wanting only her. Of course either one of them would have been more than happy to fill in.

'No, I didn't "butterfly". I waited for you all night. I like you. When you didn't show up I got a little worried. What happened?'

'Never mind, I don't care if you sit with another lady, up to you. Let's drink!'

'I think maybe you've had too much already. Why don't you sit down and talk for a while?'

'I know, I'm sad. My friend, she go Korat yesterday and I miss her,' Nid told him. She didn't want to tell him about Lek or what she did to her. It had nothing to do with him, anyway, so why ruin a good time with boring details?

'I'm sorry, won't you sit down with me?' Bill responded.

'No, I don't want to stay here. Too many people,' Nid said nodding toward Payow and Nong. 'Let's go to your room. Do you have any whiskey?'

'I can get some.' Bill started thinking it might not be another lost night after all.

They made their exit from the coffee shop with Nid tucked under Bill's arm. Realizing it was probably a mistake, Bill nonetheless steered them into a store about a half a block away to buy a bottle of Mekong, a few colas and some ice.

Nid grabbed him by the crotch to show her appreciation and in her drunken stupor didn't realize she had waited until Bill was standing in front of the clerk paying for the goods. Bill recoiled from her untimely advance, put his hand on his brow to try and hide from the disgusted look the clerk gave them, and hurried them both out of the store.

Bill didn't respond to Nid's questions of what she had done wrong, opting to hail a tuk-tuk and get the two of them back to his room before any other embarrassing situations arose. As the tuk-tuk weaved its way through traffic, Nid swayed back and forth. More then once she almost fell out of the side which prompted Bill to put his arm around her shoulder to steady her. She responded with a silly grin and looked as though she was having trouble keeping her refreshments from making an early exit. Both remained silent the entire trip back.

Bill let go a sigh of relief when the tuk-tuk finally turned into the entrance of his hotel. The sooner he could get her into his room, the better off everyone would be. His euphoria was fleeting, though, as he almost literally had to carry her through the reception area and into the elevator. The bellhops and nighttime reception clerk stared them down as they made their grand entrance and subsequent exit from the lobby.

'Bin, you good man. I think I love you too much,' Nid slurred once the elevator doors closed and just before her knees gave out.

Bill could see that any response would be futile, so he just stood quietly watching the numbers of the elevator blink. Once the elevator stopped on Bill's floor, he half carried her all the way to the door of his room. As he tried to steady her against the wall while he fished for his keys, with each increasing second her body became more limp and harder to hold on to. Eventually finding his keys took priority and she slipped out of his grasp and collapsed on the floor.

Bill slowly shook his head as he opened the door, walked inside, and set down the bag of booze and mixer. He then returned to the hallway to carry her into the room where he sat her on the bed. She immediately rolled off onto the floor.

Despite his efforts to return her to the bed, she fought him off saying she liked it better down there.

'Up to you,' he said with resignation.

'I know. Up to me,' Nid replied belligerently. 'Bin you good man. Give me one more drink, please?'

'What? Don't you think you've had enough?'

'Just one more, Bin. I know you good man, can help me. One more and I promise I will finish. You can do that for me?'

'What the hell,' Bill resigned. He decided throwing sand on this beach wouldn't change things much, the situation was already out of control. He mixed a highball and passed it to her, needing to steady her hand to control it.

'Bin ... Bin ... '

'I know, I know, I'm a good man,' Bill said with a depressing tone. He was starting to feel sorry for himself. Why had he waited for her? The two had such a good time together a couple of nights ago, he wondered what had happened to this beautiful and happy young woman between then and now. Maybe the other night was a fluke. Maybe she was like this all the time.

'Bin, you have one cigarette?' Nid asked him.

'You don't smoke, do you?' He replied.

'No, but they look so good. Can you give me one?'

Bill reached into his pocket and pulled out a pack of Syphon menthol. He tapped the pack on his knuckles until one stuck out further than the rest, then sat down on the floor next to her. She reached over unsteadily and pulled out the protruding cigarette and placed it in her mouth. He struck a match, waited for the sulfur to burn off, then reached over to light her smoke.

'Bin, you know my life is not so good now,' Nid began as she tried to blink the smoke out of her eyes.

'I lose my sister. I don't know where she went. I think maybe she's dead.'

'I'm sorry to hear that,' Bill replied with sincere sympathy. 'Is that why you're drinking so much tonight?'

Nid began to cry. 'Yes. I want to find her. I don't know where she went.'

'Don't worry, it'll be okay.' Bill put his arm around her shoulder and held her. 'Things have a way of working themselves out. Plus, you've got me to help you. I promise I . . .'

Without warning, Nid cut him off in mid sentence by pushing him away from her. With a panicked look on her face, she groped around the floor until she found the trash can, stuck her head partly inside and threw up.

'What a night I'm having!' Bill said as he ran into the bathroom, soaked a towel in cold water and returned to put it on her forehead.

'Bin, you good man, really. Before, I have man I like very much. Sometimes he got very angry and hit me. It hurt so much, but who cares?'

'I care.' Bill started to feel like a jerk for questioning why he had waited for her. She was just having a rough night. A rough life for that matter.

'Bin, I hurt. I hurt so much. All my life someone want to sell me, someone want to buy me. Well, who want to sell me now? Who want to buy me now? I hurt so much.'

Nid began to sob. Bill felt as though someone had just reached through his chest and pulled out his heart. She needed someone to help her. Right now she needed him. He reached out and held her and began rocking her in his arms.

'Sing to me,' he said.

'What?'

'Sing to me, please. I love the way you sing. You have such a wonderful voice.'

'No, I'm too shy,' she replied. Her tears began to let up though.

'Don't be shy, you're with me. Nobody else can hear you. Even if they did, I know they'd love it.'

'What do you want me to sing?'

'Sing me one of those beautiful Thai songs that you sang the last time we were together.'

Nid thought for a minute before she began to quietly sing a song about missing her home. Bill didn't speak Thai well enough to understand what the song was about. Nonetheless, he liked the sad sounding melody and asked her to sing louder.

When she finished the first song, Bill managed to get her off the floor and onto the bed where she sang another song wrapped in his arms. Gradually her voice became softer and soon the two of them were sound asleep.

CHAPTER 9

Bill awoke first at around 11 a.m. and ordered a huge breakfast from room service. When it arrived he set it up on the dressing table at the end of the bed, then tried to wake Nid. She didn't want anything to do with food that early in the day and when Bill persisted, she ran into the bathroom to throw up again.

When she came out of the bathroom she lay back down on the bed and buried her head in a pillow. Dejected, Bill ate as much of the meal as he could, making sure to save some for her when she finally came to.

A couple of hours later, Nid woke up and acted as if nothing had happened the night before. She was bubbly and cheery and devoured what remained of the room service food.

By this time, Bill's head was pounding and his stomach was more then a little upset. He wished he'd taken her cue and slept longer into the day. Seeing her awake and as lively as she was, he couldn't figure out where she got all her energy, especially after being in such rough condition the night before.

With exaggerated vitality, Nid ran into the bathroom and took a shower. She came out a few minutes later wearing only a towel. Bill was still laying on his back staring at the ceiling, trying to recover from what he always described as 'tee many martoonies', when Nid made a flying leap and landed on top of him. With her knees straddling his body, she planted a big kiss on his lips. She then pulled her towel back and revealed her young yet fully developed body.

Bill bit his lip. She looked absolutely delicious. When she leaned over and began to sniff his cheek, he grabbed her by the shoulders and pushed her back up in front of him. 'How old are you?' It was the first time he had dared ask.

'Twenty two,' she lied with a smile. 'Why?'

She handled herself so well and was so good at her trade, he had no trouble believing her. 'You're an incredible woman,' he said as he pulled her back down on top of him and tried to kiss her neck.

It tickled and she sat back up in a hurry, giggling. 'Bin, you're a good man. Why don't you take care of me? Why you let me get too drunk?'

'You were drunk when I met up with you last night. How could I have prevented that?' he protested.

'No, I mean you have to take care of me all day, all night.'

'Yeah? I'd like that. I like you when you're not drunk. It's fun to be around you.'

Leaving her towel behind, Nid jumped up off the bed and began to rummage around the room.

'What are you looking for?' Bill asked even though he already had an idea. Before she woke up he hid the remaining whiskey for fear that she might want to start drinking again that day.

'Where's the Mekong?' she asked.

'We finished it last night,' he lied.

She bounced her naked body over and sat down next to him on the bed. Pointing to the phone, she hinted for him to order more from room service. 'Let's drrrrink!' she said cheerily.

'Let's not drink yet,' Bill calmly pleaded with her. 'I have something special planned for us tonight and I don't want us to be drunk.'

'Special?' Nid gave him a seductive look.

'Yeah, it's a surprise. I've been trying to take you there since the night after we met. You didn't show up two nights ago and we both know what happened last night, don't we?'

'What happened last night?' Nid said. Unfortunately for Bill, she really didn't understand what he was referring to.

'Never mind. Come here you gorgeous specimen of humanity.' Bill grabbed her and pulled her on top of him.

'What mean, gorgee speshluman hoomaty?' Nid giggled once she was firmly in his grip.

After an afternoon of fooling around, at around five o'clock, Nid announced she needed to go home.

'Why?' Bill asked, 'I thought we were going to stay together.'

'Don't worry, I just need to change my clothes and get cleaned up. I can meet you later in the coffee shop.'

'Okay,' Bill resigned. 'Remember I have something special planned for us tonight.'

'Special?' Nid wiggled her body and gave him a look. She had already forgotten.

'Ah! What am I going to do with you?' Bill said, flustered. He grabbed her and flung her onto the bed next to him.

She giggled and squirmed as he tried to give her a kiss. Managing to break away from his advances, she got off the bed and got dressed.

When she finished, she sat on the edge of the bed and looked at Bill as if she had suddenly gotten lost in deep thought. It finally occurred to him what she was waiting for and he quickly found his pants, pulled out his wallet and handed her five hundred baht.

'You're such a good man, Bin. I think I love you too much,' she said jokingly as she pocketed the money and started for the door. 'You have twenty baht for tuk-tuk?'

Bill was a little annoyed since he had just handed her five hundred baht. Now she wanted twenty more for the tuk-tuk?

Well, maybe the tuk-tuk driver wouldn't be able to change a five hundred baht note. He handed her the extra twenty baht with a smile and an understanding nod.

Nid gave him a big, appreciative kiss on the cheek before she pranced out the door and closed it behind her.

During the tuk-tuk ride back to her room, Nid began to feel good for the first time since Lek had left. As long as she could believe that Lek would be okay as she grew up on a farm in Korat, and therefore better off than staying alone in Nid's room, then Nid was happy. She rather enjoyed the extra freedom she now had without the worry of rushing home to see if her unattended child was still okay. She liked Bill, too. He took care of her when she needed it and paid her well.

She gave the driver the twenty baht when he pulled up in front of her building, then started toward her room. About half way through the downstairs door she changed her direction, walked over to the local store and bought herself another bottle of Mekong. Just to have around, she told herself.

CHAPTER 10

Around nine o'clock that evening, Nid walked down to the coffee shop to meet Bill. He was sitting by himself at a table not far away from Payow and Nong, prompting Nid to give her rivals a look that spoke of how she had won them out. Payow responded by showing Nid her middle finger and all three women chuckled as Nid pranced over and planted a big kiss on Bill's cheek. She had allowed herself a couple of pre-meeting shots of whiskey and didn't want Bill to know, so she chomped vigorously on a piece of spearmint gum.

'Ah, Nid, you're finally here. Good to see you,' Bill said as he returned her kiss on the cheek.

'Buy me drink, sailor?' Nid kidded him and sat down.

'Not now,' he replied. 'Let's get out of here.'

'Oh, Bin, you horny too much.' She gave him a sly look.

'No, not that. Did you forget about the surprise I told you about?'

'I like surprises. Where we go?"

'Follow me,' Bill said happily as he led her out the door and flagged down a tuk-tuk. 'Mueang Issan,' he told the driver and away they went.

'You like Lao music, eh, Bin?' Nid already knew about Mueang Issan. It was a restaurant and drinking place that had live upcountry Thai music. Southern and central Thais fondly referred to that style of music as Lao music because its origins were so close to the Laotian border. She didn't know how he knew that that was the music she sang when he asked her to. She had learned some of the songs working on her family's farm upcountry and more of them from the other girls when she was trapped in the *songh* in Surin.

'I love it,' Bill replied. He was a little disappointed that she had heard of the place. Now his secret was out.

'How about you?'

'I think you know already, Bin. That's why you're taking me there, right? I can sing all Lao songs."

'Good,' Bill said without elaborating.

The tuk-tuk pulled up in front of a one story building that had an entrance covered in a multitude of colorful blinking lights. After the two got out of the tuk-tuk, Bill handed the driver a twenty baht note. The driver quickly drove off without returning any change prompting a smile from Nid as if to say 'you should have let me handle it.' She then turned and walked ahead of him through the front door.

It was quite dark inside. The only lighting came from the stage, where the entertainment was already underway, and the dance floor, where a handful of entangled couples swung vainly about. Two flashlight bearing waitresses guided Nid and Bill to a table near the stage, took their drink orders, then followed the beam of their torches off into the darkness.

Almost as soon as they were settled in, Nid looked around for the washrooms. She had needed to go since they left the coffee shop and was now ready to burst. When she spotted the telltale signs above the door, she politely excused herself and made her way through the darkness and into the brightly lit interior of the women's bathroom. When she had finished and was primping herself in the mirror, she noticed one of the other stall doors opening. A surprised Pom emerged from behind it.

'Pom? What are you doing here?'

'Nid!' She gasped.

'What's the matter?'

'Nothing. You just startled me.' Pom had to think quick. 'I just got back today. I went over to your place. You weren't home so I came here just for fun.'

'Are you here alone? Where's Lek?'

'Yes, I'm alone. Lek's safely with my mother in Korat. They love each other. Lek was so cute when we got there, you should have seen her.' Pom was making it up as she went along and it seemed to be working.

'She cried on the bus but once we got there she was all right.'

'She cried? She never cries. I wonder what was wrong?' Nid said, then added, 'You went by bus? I rushed over to the bus station to try and catch you but they told me they hadn't seen you. I waited for hours.'

'We must have just missed you.' Pom was caught but she had to stick with her story. It was too late to change it now.

'Never mind,' Nid said to Pom's relief. 'Why don't you come join us at our table. I've got a real good-looking foreigner and he's got lots of money. It'll be fun.'

'Well, I don't know,' Pom replied indecisively. She couldn't hide anymore and she couldn't think of a good excuse not to join them. 'Why not?'

'Great. Come on, I'll introduce you. But do me a favor, don't tell him about Lek. I don't want him to know, okay?'

'No problem,' Pom said, relieved that she wouldn't have to discuss the matter further.

For Bill it was a perfect turn of events. Now he had a Thai speaking ally to help him implement his plan. He wouldn't have to fumble around with his inadequacies with the language to get things set up. Not only that, she was a pretty hot looking lady.

After a few minutes of friendly, introductory conversation, Bill leaned over and whispered into Pom's ear. Pom smiled, nodded her head, then gave Nid a sly grin and excused herself.

Nid gave Bill a jealous little bang on his knee under the table. 'No good, Bin. I think you like butterfly too much,' she said, disgusted.

'I only have eyes for you,' he sang to her pitifully.

Pom returned a couple of minutes later and whispered into Bill's ear that everything was set. Nid didn't like what was unfolding in front of her and let Bill know with another kick to his shins.

'So, you like this music Nid?' Bill said with a grin as he tried to ignore his sore shin.

'Yes, very much, Bin. Thank you,' Nid replied curtly.

'Do you think you could stand up there and perform in front of a crowd?'

'Of course!' she replied with exaggerated confidence. Given the current situation, she felt she had to regain some of his respect. She knew the chances of her actually having to perform were slim at best.

Bill smiled and looked at Pom, who returned his smile with a grin. Bill then turned back to Nid and said, 'Good, because you're next.'

'What? No way. You like joking too much, Bin. Why you joke like that?'

'I'm not joking,' Bill replied. 'I like the way you sing and I'm sure everyone else will, too.'

When the current song ended, the M.C. grabbed the microphone to make an announcement. 'Tonight we have a talented amateur performer in the crowd who wishes to make her first public appearance. Would everyone please welcome to the stage, Nid Sawang!'

'No, no, I can't,' Nid said to Bill, overtaken by sheer panic. The audience applauded and as Bill pushed her out of her seat, the beam of a spotlight swung down and landed on her, leaving her no place to escape. She tried to duck but it was too late. She now had to back up her talk with action.

Almost too nervous to breathe, she climbed onto the stage and took the microphone from the smiling and applauding M.C. He leaned over and told her not to worry, she'd do great, then directed her over to the band. He reassured her that they were quite good and could probably play any song she wanted.

She picked out the song she had sung to Bill about missing her home and when the band began to play, her natural instincts took over. She knew every word and sang with the style and grace of a professional. Although she sang the first half of the song only looking nervously at Bill, before she was done she gained enough confidence to face the audience.

When she finished, the crowd erupted into a loud and appreciative applause and called out for her to continue. Two well performed songs later, despite requests for more, she thanked the band, the M.C. and the audience and returned to her seat.

'That was great,' Bill exclaimed and gave her a big kiss on her cheek.

'Not so bad,' Nid replied humbly.

The two women spoke in Thai. 'I didn't know you could sing like that.' Pom was all choked up. 'You have real talent!'

'I know you're just saying that to make me feel good. Thanks anyway. It was fun.'

Nid had enjoyed herself but didn't think any more of it than a short-lived good time.

'On the house,' the waiter told Nid as he handed her a bottle of Red Label scotch. 'The owner enjoyed your performance very much. He said if you're interested, you can show up and sing any time you want.'

Bill tried to hide his smile. He didn't want to be smug about being the one to introduce her to the stage. He didn't know much about talent or what it took to make it in show business, but he had traveled around Thailand quite a bit and could tell that Nid was just as good as anyone he had ever seen.

The three spent the rest of the evening drinking, listening to the music and gorging themselves on Thai food. Pom and Bill continuously attempted to convince Nid how good she had been. Nid continuously denied it. Just before closing time, all three returned to Bill's hotel room for the night.

CHAPTER II

Chalarm loved to cook. He did it with a flair like none other. Customers from all around Patpong ignored his gruff personality and came to watch him perform. Why not? He had plenty of practice. Every single day for the past twenty years he had pushed his little cart around the streets of Bangkok. It had only been in the last few years that he had established himself in this area around Patpong, and establish himself he did. He was on a roll and he knew it.

For most of those twenty years he cooked over his little bucket of coals. Always keen to progress, he now had a small gas burning stove which enabled him to expand his talents as well as his menu. He even had to get a bigger cart to hold all the ingredients for the new dishes he could prepare. Sun dried beef, fish, pork rinds, chicken feet, and baby shrimp, along with a wide variety of fresh greens, fruits and cooking pastes were all displayed proudly for his customers to choose from. He kept his old coal bucket going to boil rice and make soup.

Yes, he spent twenty years of his life perfecting his trade and serving the people of Bangkok. What did he have to show for it? Not much. Not much at all, he thought. He deserved better.

Chalarm always wanted to be a boss. His dream was to open his own restaurant. If he did, he knew all his years of experience would surely make it successful. He also knew he would probably never be able to save enough money to make his dream a reality. Drinking and gambling had a way of preventing that from happening. No, it was just an unobtainable dream.

Actually, life wasn't all that bad. With his new operation in full swing, Chalarm could fulfill his fantasy of being a boss and earn plenty of money for his vices. Best of all, he could do both without investing much of his own time or money. The people he had working for him would be better off, too. They would have a roof over their heads, beds to sleep in, and food in their mouths. All the while, Chalarm could continue to do what he did best—cook.

It was all beginning to come together. Chalarm had now built himself a fairly sizable base of employees. His most recent discovery had been cripples. He now had a half-dozen paraplegics and amputees working the streets for him, and they raked in the baht. Foreigners were all suckers for cripples.

Still, his best earners were the woman and baby teams he had put on the streets. There was something about a famished baby with her head laid weakly on her mother's shoulder that got the baht out of people's pockets in a hurry. The babies didn't even have to belong to the women who held them. Chalarm found that out when his friend Anan brought him that tribal woman from up north. Malee? Yes, that was her name. Chalarm had paired her with the baby named Lek, the child the little coffee shop whore had brought him. Malee and Lek had taken to each other as if they were actually mother and daughter. It was working out quite well. The two were bringing in at least as much money as the real mother and child teams, sometimes more.

Chalarm was going to have to watch out for that tribal woman, though. She was a feisty one. Evidently she had been giving Anan some sort of trouble, so he had to stop feeding her about four days before they arrived. Anan, now there was a smart man. Chalarm could learn a lot from him if he paid attention. Anan knew how to handle bad situations. By the time he dropped off the tribal woman, she was thin and sad and willing to do almost anything for something to eat.

Chalarm had won her over easily by feeding her almost immediately after Anan had left. If he played it right, she and the baby would bring him in plenty of money over the next few years. He was still going to have to watch her, though.

Malee had other ideas. She was tired of being someone's slave to do with as they pleased. After all, she had Akha blood in her veins. She was the eldest daughter of a very respected village headman, and knew this wasn't what her father had in mind when he gave her to Anan. That was an important thought, too. Her father had given her to Anan, no one else. Especially not this cockroach Chalarm. Malee felt no obligation to stay with him any longer than it took to find a way to escape.

First things first. During the last four days with Anan she had learned a valuable lesson and a key to survival. She now knew she had to do whatever her boss wanted. She needed to keep him happy and earn his trust because she could never know what lengths these people would go to in order to destroy her. These people weren't like her tribe. These people didn't seem to have any honor or integrity. Chalarm tried to come off as a nice man, but anyone with a brain could see right through that little charade. So, if it was begging he wanted her to do, she would beg. She would make sure she got good at it, too. That way maybe she could earn his trust, and with it, a little freedom. Once she did that, then she could start to think about making her life better.

'Ten baht, baby eat.' With Lek cradled in her left arm, Malee stood in front of an older foreign couple and said the few words of English she had been taught. Out of the corner of her eye she could see the old man she worked with sitting on the sidewalk, leaning against a wall, with a plastic cup in front of him. He looked half-dead and only made an attempt to move when someone came near him, which wasn't often.

Patpong was a living, breathing entity of its own. Neon signs announcing the names of various watering holes, brothels and go-go bars bathed the street in a surrealistic reddish-orange glow. Barker's voices filled the air promising the fulfillment of fantasies to foreign punters. The combined smells of Thai cooking, garbage and stale beer created a strange odor that dominated every breath. Hand painted folding fans brought down from Chiang Mai were big sellers in Patpong, not only for their decorative appearance, but for their usefulness as well. The heat, even at night, was insufferable.

'Ten baht, baby eat,' Malee repeated to the older tourist couple. Malee's tribal outfit was now so dirty from working the streets that it was barely recognizable. She wished she could wash it. Chalarm wouldn't allow it, though, because it would take away from her image of being a poor beggar.

Lek's bare bottom rested on Malee's left arm. Her tattered top barely covered her torso and she spent much of her time resting her head on Malee's shoulder. When Lek was awake she spent most of her time smiling and taking in these strange surroundings with big curious eyes.

Malee had only worked the streets of Patpong for a couple of months, yet she had already become very attached to this baby girl. Malee resolved that when she made her escape she would take Lek with her and try to find her a good home. She didn't know where the baby came from but she loved her all the same.

The older tourist couple were talking to Malee in their strange tongue, motioning toward her and Lek with their camera. The two had already had their picture taken at least twenty times by tourists and Malee knew it was a sure way to get money from them. She kept a stern look on her face when she nodded her accession.

The flash from the camera stung her eyes. She always forgot to look away when the tourists took a photograph. She could hardly see the fifty baht the couple handed her, the most she had ever received at one time. She tried to blink the spots out of her eyes as she made a deep *wai* and said thank you as best she could.

From the undamaged corner of her eye she noticed Pii El moving through the crowd. Making a graceful leave from the couple, she set herself a path to cut off his progress.

'Pii El, Pii El!' she beckoned as she approached him, 'What have you found out?'

El was a tuk-tuk driver from up north that Malee had been trying to befriend. He seemed to know a little bit about everything that went on in Patpong. She had high hopes that he would be able to help her find a way out.

'Nothing yet,' he replied. The tone of his voice signaled to Malee that something was wrong. His eyes darted from person to person, alley to alley, and from shop to shop. Satisfied that no one was looking, he grabbed Malee by the shoulder and hurriedly said, 'I can't talk right now. You must get away from me, quickly!' He then rushed off into the crowd.

Stunned, Malee wandered into the path of some American G.I.s and began to beg. They smelled of whiskey and their bloodshot eyes tried vainly to bring her into focus. They all laughed as one of them said something to her in a language she didn't understand. All of them kept looking at her body and trying to touch her. She didn't understand what was going on and it scared her, so she ran away to hide behind some clothing vendors. She spent the rest of the night trying to avoid foreigners and wondering what was happening to Pii El.

At 2 a.m., when she returned to the room Chalarm had set up for his beggars, she found out. She was greeted at the door by a punch that sent her and Lek sprawling to the floor. The other beggars looked on in horror, too afraid to do anything about it, as Chalarm mounted his assault. Lek began screaming as Chalarm grabbed Malee by the front of her shirt. Half tearing it off, he slammed her against the wall and punched her in the stomach so hard it took her breath away. With the salty taste of her own blood in her mouth, she was so dizzy she almost blacked out and had a difficult time understanding what Chalarm was screaming in her ear.

'You dog! You no-good, trouble-making dog! I've treated you well. I've fed you, given you a bed to sleep in. What thanks do I get? What do you give me in return for all my trouble? More trouble, that's what! How dare you try to escape me! You think you can escape me? Do you think I can let you go? Of course not! The only way you're going to leave me is in an urn. From now on you're going to work the foreigners around my food cart where I can keep an eye on you. He threw her to the floor, kicked her in the shin and walked away.

'Shut that baby's mouth or I'll have to teach her a lesson, too!' he screamed as Lek continued to wail.

Malee gathered what strength she had and cradled Lek. She whispered in Lek's ear that she would never let him hurt her. Before long the warmth and coziness of Malee's body settled Lek's wailing down into a broken whimper.

CHAPTER 12

Three days after the beating, as Malee and Lek were working the sparse crowd of foreigners near Chalarm's food stall, Malee spotted Pii El over by the entrance to Patpong, motioning for her to come over to him.

Malee's lip was still swollen from Chalarm's punch. She could still feel his fist in her stomach and his foot on her shins. She quickly looked away from El and glanced over toward Chalarm. As if he sensed something, he looked up from his cooking and caught her eye. Again she quickly looked away and rushed over to a small group of tourists looking over the food at another stall about half way between Chalarm and El.

She glanced back toward Chalarm. Apparently satisfied, he had gone back to cooking and talking with the locals who were gathered to watch him perform. She turned to look back toward the entrance to Patpong but could no longer see El.

'Ten baht, baby eat,' she said mechanically to the tourists. They weren't paying much attention to her nor she to them. She was too busy trying to locate El so as to avoid him at all costs. As a punishment, Chalarm had only fed her once in the past three days and the smell of food was affecting her thinking. Escape was no longer a concern, at least not now. Survival was the main issue. If she did as she was told, maybe Chalarm would start feeding her again. After she regained her strength, then she could start worrying about finding a way out. Right now, running into El could ruin everything.

'Don't turn around,' El said. He was now standing directly behind her looking over some dried fish on the vendor's cart. The group of tourists effectively blocked him from Chalarm's view.

'I heard about what happened the other night and I'm very sorry. I feel the only way I can make it up to you is if I get you out of here. I've found out about a group of women working together to help other women in need, like you. I believe it's called the Red Cross and it's located south of here, in Pattaya. It's not too far from here, yet far enough away so that Chalarm could never find you. My tuk-tuk is parked around the corner and ready to go. I can have you there by midnight. I don't know if you can ever trust me again, but I promise you I will do my best to get you there safely. Just remember, the streets can hear so we must go soon. The choice is yours. I can't wait very long.'

Malee didn't turn to face him, nor did she respond to his words. Slightly bent over from the hunger pain in her stomach, she sucked on her fat lip, held onto Lek a little more tightly and stared blankly into the small crowd of tourists in front of her. El bartered with the vendor over the price of the fish, eventually bought some and moved away.

Lek was sound asleep on Malee's shoulder. The tourists began to shuffle toward the entrance to the Patpong area which brought Malee out of her empty stare. Her first thought was to walk back toward Chalarm. It would be the safest and easiest thing to do. Yet when she looked over in his direction, she saw that he was busy entertaining his customers and oblivious to her whereabouts. Instinctively, she began to walk with the tourists.

Suddenly everything seemed to slow down. Her senses began to burst. She could hear every car and every rickshaw that passed by. She could hear people laughing across the street. The lights around her seemed incredibly bright and clear. The smells of the streets became vivid. She could feel Lek's warm breath on her neck. Malee had never before felt so alive.

'Ten baht, baby eat,' she said to the tourists, although she hoped none of them would give it to her. They were laughing and joking, totally oblivious to what was happening around them.

'Ten baht, baby eat,' she repeated as she looked back toward Chalarm. He was still busy with his customers.

'Ten baht, baby eat.' They were slowly getting closer to the edge of Patpong and further away from Chalarm. There was still no sign that he was looking in her direction. Still no sign of El, either.

'Ten baht, baby eat.' One of the tourists finally noticed her and slowly turned in her direction. She looked right past him because El had suddenly appeared. His tuk-tuk was running and he had a panicked look on his face.

'Ten baht, baby eat,' she repeated mechanically. All of a sudden Lek woke up, raised her sleepy head off Malee's shoulder and pointed. Malee had never seen her do that before. She followed the direction of her finger to see what she was pointing at, only to discover that Chalarm had dropped his utensils and had started to run towards them.

'Malee!' Chalarm screamed as he broke into a full gait.

Seeing Chalarm rushing toward her, Malee took a step back and stumbled into the foreigner. He had to grab hold of her arm to keep her from falling. Chalarm was gaining.

Malee looked back over toward El. 'Come on!' he screamed as he involuntarily raced the engine.

Chalarm was now only about ten paces away and closing fast. Malee could see the crazy anger in his eyes, the same madness she had seen three nights ago. She pulled away from the foreigner with such force it knocked him to one knee. Chalarm was moving too fast to change his direction and bowled right into him. Both crashed hard onto the pavement.

The fear that motivated her to pull away from the foreigner now gave Malee the strength to grasp Lek tightly and race over to El's tuk-tuk. When she got close enough, El reached out and pulled her into the passenger seat. She was barely inside when he slammed it into gear and screeched out into traffic.

As they raced away, Malee looked back and saw the tourist trying to help Chalarm get up. He was pushing the foreigner away, cursing Malee and her family, yelling that he would find her and El and make them pay.

CHAPTER 13

In the thick darkness of the tropical night, the tuk-tuk's single headlight barely illuminated small patches of the long road ahead. The loud, steady hum of the engine was all that was necessary to keep the baby Lek in a deep sleep. Both adult minds were busy, quietly trying to sort out what had just taken place and what they would do next.

Nothing was spoken during the first hour of the trip. The further south they traveled, however, with each increasing kilometer they put between themselves and Bangkok, the tension began to decrease and their minds moved toward other important issues.

'What will you do with the baby?' El broke the silence.

'I don't know,' Malee replied. 'If I had a home and a job I would keep her and raise her as my own. But I don't have either so I don't know what to do.' Malee looked down at Lek as she slept in her arms.

She wondered where she had come from and how she could have fallen into the hands of Chalarm. Who were her real parents? If they were still alive, they must be looking for her.

'A friend of mine who drives a tuk-tuk in Bangkok, the same one who told me about the Red Cross, said he spent part of his childhood in a place in Pattaya where they take in orphaned children,' El said with a touch of hesitancy. 'It is kind of like an orphanage and it's run by some Buddhist nuns. I'm sure they would take good care of her. She'd have other children to play with, regular meals, and when she got older they'd send her to school. I can tell how attached you've become and how hard it would be for you two to part ways, but think about it, it might be better for the both of you.'

An orphanage. The thought had never occurred to Malee. Would they really be able to take good care of her? She supposed they probably would. Perhaps someday she might even be adopted by a good family. Maybe if her real parents were looking for her they'd think to look in an orphanage.

As the tuk-tuk progressed ever closer to Pattaya, Malee and El began to smell the salt air of the nearby ocean. Coconut palms, illuminated by the dim light of the passing tuk-tuk, began to flicker by. The breeze coming off the sea made it much cooler than it was in Bangkok and reminded Malee of the cool mountain nights back home.

The realization of what she was about to do bounced Malee's emotions between happy and sad. She was sad because she knew she was soon to lose a friend. Even though Lek was just a baby, she and Malee had been through so much together that Malee considered her to be her closest friend. Would she be able to visit her? Most likely not. It would probably be better if she stayed away in case Chalarm caught up with her. Yet, the thought of never seeing her again was unbearable.

At the same time, she was happy because she knew she would be doing her friend an enormous service. Lek needed stability in her life and a chance to grow up away from all the bad things that had dominated her life up to that point. She deserved to be happy and an orphanage might be just what she needed.

'Where is this place?' Malee asked.

'If what my friend told me is true, I don't think it's very far from here,' El replied. He looked in his rear view mirror and could see Malee's face in the soft yellow glow of the dome light. She was staring at Lek's closed eyes and the corners of her mouth were trying to force a smile. It just wouldn't come. 'Are you sure that's what you want to do?'

'I'm sure it will be the best thing I could do for the baby.'

It was a little after midnight when the tuk-tuk pulled up in front of the orphanage. Not wanting her to lose her identity, Malee scribbled Lek's name on a piece of paper and pinned it to her tattered top. She looked down at the sleeping baby in her arms and was overcome with emotion. Lek looked so peaceful, so at ease with her world.

With a deep sigh Malee gently eased out of the back of the tuk-tuk and quietly made her way over to the entrance. She laid Lek down in front of the main door, pounded as hard as she could and ran back to the tuk-tuk.

El and Malee waited in silence, just out of sight, as a light came on inside the building. When the front door creaked open, the light from inside flooded out to cover the doorstep. A woman came out, picked up Lek and strained her eyes into the darkness to try and see who had come knocking at that late hour. Seeing nothing, she walked back inside and closed the door behind her.

The women of the orphanage estimated Lek's age at arrival to be about one year. They took her picture and logged her into the files, stating:

> 'Baby girl, approximately one year old, left at the front door anonymously at a little past midnight on 12 April 1972. The child arrived undernourished, had the beginnings of a cold and was in need of a bath, but was otherwise healthy. She had the name Lek pinned to her clothes. Therefore, for the sake of record keeping, we will keep her name as Lek and assign her 12 April 1971 as her date of birth.'

Another baby girl was left at the youth home under similar circumstances barely a month after Lek arrived. Her condition was worse than Lek's and no name had been left with her. The women took her picture and logged her in as:

'Baby girl, approximately one year old, left anonymously at the front door at approximately 2 a.m. on 15 May 1972. The child arrived undernourished, had a large bruise on her right thigh and a small cut on her left arm and was in need of a bath. After consulting the monk at our temple we assigned her the name Sulee and 15 May 1971 as her date of birth.'

During the first year after their arrival, both girls were prone to illness and injury. Lek was colicky and seemed to constantly have a cold and Sulee, when she wasn't taken down with a fever, which was quite often, seemed to always find a way to bump, bruise or scratch her young body. Shortly after each girl's second assigned birthday, the women of the home decided they needed to try and do something about the condition of these youngsters. As is often done in Thailand, they referred to ancient beliefs as a way to help cure them of their bad luck.

The most accepted way to do this was to enlist the help of the abbot of the local temple. So, on 9 June, the women cleaned and pressed the girls' uniforms and prepared them for a trip to the temple. They chose 9 June because the number nine has always been considered to be quite lucky. This particular day was warm and humid, and although the sun was out and there were only a few wispy white clouds overhead, huge thunder clouds rising thousands of feet into the air sat on the horizon. It was the beginning of the rainy season and each day promised an afternoon thundershower.

The abbot of the temple was widely known to be a wise man and was much respected by the people of Pattaya. He also loved children. To him they were pure and innocent, not yet influenced by the immoralities of society. He gladly accepted the women's request for his wisdom to help cure the girls of their unfortunate propensity to ill health.

For Lek, he recommended she be spiritually adopted by the largest Buddha statue in the temple. If the statue accepted her, she should be brought back regularly to pray to it, offer it gifts and make merit.

For Sulee he recommended shaving her head leaving only a small tuft of hair called a juk. He said that only Sulee could choose the style of juk and she must wear it until she reached the age of eleven. If both recommendations were followed precisely, the abbot predicted no further problems with their health.

The women had heard of the methods he spoke of, both were well known as effective ways to handle this particular problem. After thanking the abbot and making a donation to the temple, they left with high hopes for the quick resolution of the girls' problems.

For Lek it was relatively easy. After wrapping sai sin around her hands, they placed her on the floor in front of the largest Buddha statue in the temple. She somehow seemed to pick up on the significance of the event and sat quietly staring at the huge Buddha with her big brown eyes. The women knelt down beside her, placed their palms together on the floor in front of them and rested their heads on their hands. In their humble, Buddhist manner they begged the statue to adopt Lek and protect her. After only a few minutes, they bowed three times touching their hands and heads to the floor, picked up Lek, gathered in Sulee and slowly backed away.

Once they got back to the orphanage, it was time for Sulee to choose her style of *juk*. Although the process was simple, it would profoundly affect her appearance for the next nine years. A *juk*, also known as a top knot, is one or two tufts of hair that are left on a child's head after it has otherwise been completely shaven. There are three styles of *juks*; the first a tuft of hair is left on the top of the head, the second a pigtail is left near the back of the head, and the third two tufts of hair are left, one on each side of the forehead.

Since it was up to Sulee to pick her style of juk, three clay dolls were made, one in each of the three different styles. All three dolls were placed in front of her and after a few minutes of reaching and pointing, she picked up the doll with the pigtail and started to play with it. Her choice had been made.

That afternoon she was taken to the local barber, where she sat screaming and crying as he shaved her head. He left a small pigtail near the back, a look she would adorn until her eleventh birthday.

Locals might argue whether it was merely a coincidence or the direct result of the ancient ritual. For whatever reason, over the next few years both children remained remarkably healthy.

CHAPTER 14

'It's too damned hot,' Nid thought on her way back from dropping off another longtime customer at the airport. She didn't much like days like this. They were always the same. The men would promise to write, send her money and, or return someday to take her away from what they termed her 'sad life'. She knew they meant well but it rarely happened. It was too easy for them to forget about her when they got back to their family and friends with their rich homes, big cars and relatively carefree lifestyles. The best she could hope for was to become a pleasant memory that would grow better over time.

Bill was the first to teach her that lesson. Bill taught her a lot of things. He was the first to take her to the Mueang Issan Club, something she could never thank him enough for doing. Over the past couple of years she'd been going back regularly and her ability to learn a few western songs made her a crowd favorite. The two she liked the most; 'The sky, the sky, the skize in lub wichew,' and the all time hit; 'Oh, sweepee, woona dan wimee' always brought a good round of applause. The Thai members of the audience loved her renditions because it vicariously allowed them to show off how international they had become. None of them seemed to pay any attention to the critical remarks from the foreigners in the crowd about her pronunciation.

Nid loved to sing and would go there every chance she got, even though she never received any money for it. The remuneration she received was always the same, an appreciative applause from the audience and a bottle of imported liquor from the management. Bill told her not to worry about it, 'She had to pay her dues,' he said, 'her real chance would come soon enough.' She hoped so; she harbored dreams of someday getting a paying job there.

Sometimes she really missed Bill. He always treated her well and paid her plenty of money. He also spent a lot of time with her and after he introduced her to the Mueang Issan club he would go with her often to watch her sing. He only 'butterflied' a couple of times after they'd met which only got her a little upset. After all, he was a man and she knew all men liked a little variety in their lives. Besides, they had a good thing going and she knew he would always come back.

That's why it was such a shock when he told her he had to go home to England because the company he worked for wasn't going to renew his contract. He said something about how his company's image was being hurt by his running around with the bar girls. She couldn't understand why that would have anything to do with his job, but she was just beginning to accept the fact that life was full of unexplainable changes.

Nonetheless, it was a tearful departure at the airport the day he left. Even Bill cried, something she'd never seen before. She was deeply moved over how much she seemed to mean to him despite what she did for a living. He promised her he would do everything he could possibly do to come back and see her some day, even if he had to use up his vacation time and pay for the trip himself.

When he boarded the plane headed for Heathrow Airport, it was the last time she ever saw him.

It was mid-March 1974, the height of the hot season. That year it wasn't nearly as awful as it had been for the past couple of years. It was still bad enough to bring an instant sweat to anyone who dared venture out. To add to the uncomfortable conditions, it hadn't rained in over a month. This put an overwhelming hardship on the water supply and the citizens of the area were asked to try and conserve the precious commodity. Robbed of the cooling effect of multiple daily baths or showers, the normally gracious dwellers of the dry and dusty city became somewhat disagreeable.

The snarled rush hour traffic that had continued well into the early evening finally began to let up, and Nid's taxi driver took advantage of every tiny opening. An hour and a half of horn blowing madness after they had left Don Mueang Airport, on a trip that should have taken twenty minutes at most, the taxi pulled up in front of the Petchburi Coffee Shop and let Nid out. Not much had changed since she left earlier in the day. A few more customers had arrived but it was still far from full. Payow and Nong were in their usual spot sipping whiskey and cola and analyzing prospective targets.

'Has anyone seen Pom?' Nid asked, taking a seat at their table and helping herself to a glass of their whiskey.

Payow dropped a couple of ice cubes into Nid's glass. 'I haven't seen her all day. She's probably home drinking herself into a coma.'

'Yeah, what's been the matter with her lately? She's been acting awfully strange,' Nong chipped in.

'I don't know, she's been depressed about something. I wish I could find out what it's all about. I hate to see anybody get like that,' Nid answered.

'Rumor has it she's been smoking a lot of opium during the day and taking amphetamines for work at night,' Nong said and shook her head. They all knew what a dangerous combination that could be.

'No wonder she's been acting like she has,' Nong speculated. 'Half the time she's more mellow than I've ever seen her and the other half she's cruel and almost sadistic. You never know which Pom is going to show up, or when for that matter.'

Nid had to agree with the women's analysis even though their talk was painful to hear. Despite Pom's rather obvious efforts to keep it from happening, she eventually lost her struggle to remain distant and the two had become best of friends. Since Nid still believed Lek was with Pom's mother in Korat, she made every effort to stay close so she wouldn't lose the only connection she had to her child. She loved to listen to the stories Pom would tell her about Lek's cheerful upbringing on the farm. Nid trusted Pom blindly and never questioned the fact that Pom never showed her any of the letters she was supposedly receiving from her mother. She also never hesitated to give her as much money as she could afford to send to Lek every month.

The closer she got to Nid, though, the more introverted Pom became. What she had done to Lek and therefore Nid, her only friend, was eating away at her. It was true what Payow and Nong were saying, Pom had become moody and would fall into bouts of deep depression. Pom was falling deeper and deeper into a nasty, hopeless predicament.

Even though Pom was a good-looking woman who attracted the attention of many foreign men, her drinking and depression always seemed to chase them away, usually after only one night. It created a bad situation because the more men she stayed with, the more depressed she became. And the more depressed she became, the more unstable her personality became, causing the men to spend less time with her.

They began to pay her less, too, and to make matters worse, Pom spent so much on booze and drugs she was constantly low on money and needed to go with more men in order to pay her bills and feed her habit.

CHAPTER 15

While the three women sat in the coffee shop debating the deteriorating condition of their friend, Pom sat in her room listening to the American music her favorite radio station played every night between 8 p.m. and 10 p.m. She was trying to keep her hands steady as she held a spoon over a candle just like the American G.I. had shown her last month.

Somehow she had broken the golden rule of her profession and had let her soul become weak. She didn't know how, when or why, but somehow, something had made a vortex into her inner soul. Maybe it was Lek coming back to haunt her. Pom had cheated her best friend, her only friend, and was now forced to live a life of lies. She spent every day with Nid and every time she saw her she could see how happy she was thinking her baby was safely growing up away from all this. It was becoming harder each day not to tell her that her happiness was based on false truths born from greed and fed by Pom's lying imagination.

She found a vein and slowly slid the needle into the side of her leg, gently plunging the warm liquid out of the syringe until it had been emptied of its contents. The G.I. taught her that, too. He said that by shooting up in her leg instead of her arm no one would suspect what she was doing. All the women who worked the same as she did had bruises on their legs; it was a side effect of their work. It proved to be an effective guise; not even Nid seemed to know.

'Fuck work!' Pom said to herself, 'Tonight I just want to sleep. Sleep a long, long time.'

She began to feel the effects of the drug reach her brain and her thoughts returned to the G.I. He was a good boy, a little crazy but then again so was she. He put up with her and was a good listener when she needed someone to talk to. He had a way of making her problems seem small compared to what was going on around her.

She remembered how he used to get high and talk about what he once did in Vietnam. He talked about the killing, what it was like to see children burn, mothers cry, entire villages wiped out. Sometimes he cried in her arms telling her about being face to face with a young boy pointing a gun at him, too scared to move, too scared to pull the trigger. He talked about the look on that young boy's face when his chest exploded from his bullet, the pain and confusion that dominated his last few fleeting moments of life.

The G.I. knew how to deal with it, though, and he showed Pom how to deal with her rotten life, too. Together they found the smack man who allowed them to lose themselves in his magic potion and escape from the horrors of reality. He was gone now, probably back out there someplace stealing time from people's lives. Mercifully putting an end to their misery.

'My life's not that bad, I've done well with it,' Pom said aloud whilst attempting a smile. Within seconds she was crying uncontrollably.

'I've done good! I'm good! Please?' She screamed so loud her neighbor knocked on the wall and yelled for her to shut up. Pom grabbed her bottle of Mekong whiskey and took a long drink. It went down like water and didn't even cause her to flinch. She walked over and kicked the wall hard, 'Fuck you!' she screamed back at her neighbor, then turned her radio up so as not to hear the response.

'What did they know about life? Not a thing about commitment, that's for sure. They want everything to be perfect. If the world is full of problems they close their eyes so they don't have to see it. And if a girl's got a problem she's doomed if she dares open up to tell some man about it. He'll drop her faster then lightning.

'And now the doctor tells me I'm pregnant. Huh!' Pom continued to mumble, 'Just what I need, another baby. Look at me, what kind of mother am I? Some example I'm setting. Screw your friends for money, sell your body for money and for what? Are you happy? Sure, I'm so happy I could just cry. I am crying. Why? What's there to cry about? Life's good. I've got my bottle of whiskey, the smack is alive in my blood, my room looks good. Too good.'

She staggered over and tore her clothes off the hangers and strew them around her room, laughing all the while. She took another large swig from her bottle, then attacked her bed in the same way she did her clothes. Exhausted, she flopped down in the middle of the mess and lit a cigarette.

Clomp, clomp, clomp. Someone was coming up the stairs. The noise of heeled shoes on wooden stairs was so loud in Pom's head she thought it was about to break her ear drums. Boom, boom, someone pounded on her door.

'It's open!' She screamed. Everything was loud, the radio, the knocking on the door, the clink of her bottle as she nervously tapped it against the wooden frame of her bed. A distorted looking Nid peaked her head through the door.

'What's going on in here? You look awful, are you okay?' Nid asked her disheveled looking friend. She needed to yell to be heard over the blaring radio. 'Why aren't you down at the coffee shop? I've got us a couple of hot one's lined up.' Nid had taken it upon herself to try and get Pom out of her downward spiral, but she feared it was a losing battle. It seemed the more she tried, the worse Pom's condition got.

'Nid? Is that you?'

'Of course it's me. Who do you think it is?'

'Nid. Wow, I don't know. What are you doing here?'

'I told you, I came to get you because I've got a couple of nice looking guys waiting for us in the coffee shop. But it looks to me as though you're in no condition to go out.'

'Nid, stay with me, talk to me. I need you right now. I have to talk to you.'

'Okay, but only for a minute. I don't want to keep them waiting too long. Payow and Nong are trying to move in already.'

'Fuck 'em, it's important I talk to you, right now. But you have to promise me one thing, that you won't hate me. Promise?'

'Pom, what are you talking about? Of course I won't hate you, you're my friend.'

'I know. You're the best friend I have and I don't ever want that to change. But I've been bad, very, very bad. Please don't hate me.'

'Pom, what could you possibly do to make me want to hate you?'

'I lied, Nid. And I've been lying too much. This is very hard for me because I drank too much, as you can probably tell. But I have to tell you tonight, I may never get another chance.'

'Pom, you're not making any sense. What are you trying to say?'

'Lek isn't with my mother in Korat. She never was. I lied to you. I never meant anyone any harm. I was stupid and I'm sorry.' Pom began sobbing.

'Calm down Pom.' Nid could feel anger and confusion well up inside her. 'Where is she?'

'I sold her, Nid. I sold her to a man who wanted to use her with another woman to beg money from strangers. He said he'd be good to her, feed her, give her clothes and a place to sleep. He promised me she would be better off than living alone while you were out. He promised me, Nid.'

'Who is this man and where is he?' Nid was a model of self-control. The story Pom was telling her was almost unbelievable. She didn't want to believe it, but why else would Pom be telling her this if it wasn't at least partly true.

'I think his name is Chalarm. He works in Patpong.'

'You think his name is Chalarm or is that really his name?' Nid's anger was now beginning to erode her self-control.

'Don't yell at me, Nid. I can't take it. His name is Chalarm. He's a cook. He works just outside the entrance to Patpong. He's big and fat and ugly, but he's a good cook and everyone goes to his place to eat. Everybody knows him.' Pom was cowering away from Nid who was now standing over her with her fists clenched.

'Pom, I thought I knew you. I thought we were friends. Friends don't do this kind of thing to each other. How could you do this? How could you face me every day and lie? Our whole friendship is a lie, isn't it? Isn't it?!'

'Nid, please don't hate me, you're all I've got now.'

Nid sighed deeply and took a step back, trying to decide what to do. 'Pom, I'm going to Patpong. I really hope you're making all this up but if you're not, how can I ever forgive you? If I can find Lek, and if she's okay, and if I can bring her home with me, then I'll come back here to talk with you about what we can do next. At the very least you owe me a lot of money. But if something's happened to her I'll promise you this, you'll wish you'd never met me.'

Nid stormed out of the room, leaving the crying Pom in an unsightly heap on the floor.

CHAPTER 16

Nid raced down the stairs, grabbed the first available tuk-tuk and went straight to Patpong. Strangely enough, in the couple years she had lived in Bangkok, this was the first time she'd ever been there. It didn't take her long to find Chalarm. Just like Pom had told her, everyone knew him. She only had to ask a couple of people for directions before she found herself standing in front of a food stall looking at the man Pom had described so well.

'Excuse me, is your name Chalarm?' she asked, once she got the courage up to interrupt his work.

'That's me,' he grumbled back at her. 'What would you like to order?'

'Oh, nothing, sir. I'd like to ask you a couple of questions.'

'You don't want to eat?' He grumbled again. 'Well I'm a busy man. If you don't want to eat, get out of here so I can work.'

'Pom sent me.'

'Who's Pom?' he stalled. Nid detected a faint look of recognition in his eyes.

'She works with me in a coffee shop over on Petchburi Road. She says she knows you and you know her.'

'I don't know anyone by the name of Pom,' he snapped. 'Now get out of here. I told you, I'm a busy man.'

'She said she sold a baby to you about a year ago. She said you wanted her for begging. Does that sound familiar?'

He stared at her a moment without saying anything. He seemed to be pondering what he should do or say.

'So?' he finally replied.

'The baby was mine and I'd like to see her if I could.' Nid was trying to be cautious, she didn't want him to think she had come to take her back in case he didn't want to give her up. Of course if she did see her, she planned to grab her and run.

'Look little lady, I have absolutely no idea what you're talking about. Do you see a baby around here? Does it look like I'm the kind of man that would want a baby hanging around?'

Nid looked at him and didn't know how to respond. He was right about that. He didn't look the type that would have anything to do with children. Maybe Pom was lying, she was very drunk or high, or both, and Nid couldn't prove anything. It was also obvious that even if Pom had been telling the truth, Nid was getting nowhere with Chalarm.

'Sorry to bother you,' Nid said and turned to leave.

'I hope you find your kid,' Chalarm replied, a little too obviously relieved for Nid's comfort.

All the way back to Pom's room Nid tried to figure out what was going on. Could this all be just a cruel hoax? Had the booze and drugs warped Pom's mind so much that she was now capable of telling such a wild story? Her gut feeling was that Pom had been telling the truth, though. She seemed too distraught to be lying. But then, if she had been telling the truth tonight, that would mean she had been lying for a couple of years.

She didn't trust that Chalarm character, either. There was something about him that she couldn't figure out. He was hiding something, she knew that, but could he be that black-hearted to buy a baby? She had seen a lot of low deeds, but she had never seen one that low. And how could he stay so cool while he lied to her face? Then again, if all this was really happening, Pom had been doing it for a long time.

After the tuk-tuk dropped her off in front of Pom's place, Nid became obsessed with the fact that no matter what was going on, Pom had questions to answer. She didn't know whether to beat her or baby her, but she had to get Pom to help her find out what was going on. Nid bounded up the flight of stairs two steps at a time, ran down to Pom's room, flung open the door and gasped in horror at the macabre scene in front of her.

Pom was lying in a pool of her own blood, her vacant eyes stared into empty space. Her index finger and thumb were still squeezing the razor blade that she had used to carve deep, jagged gashes in her small, frail wrists. The blood had stopped flowing out of her wounds for her heart had none left to pump.

Nid ran over and checked for signs of life. She cried uncontrollably for a few minutes before her grief gave way to fear. 'I've got to get out of here. I've got to go home and try to figure out what to do.' She was in a blind panic.

She got up to go and got halfway out the door before she noticed Pom's blood had stained her clothes. She knew she couldn't go out in the street looking like that, so she went back inside and wiped her hands on the clothes that had been strewn about. She then dug around and found an unstained jacket off to one side of all the mess and put it on. On her way back through the door, she stopped and turned to look at her friend.

Nid ran all the way back to her room without stopping or slowing down. She was driven by fear, fear of life and fear of death. Bad things had happened to her pretty much all her life but never had so much come crashing down on her all at once. She entered the bottom floor of her building so fast she bounced off the wall as she made the turn toward the stairs. It didn't even slow her down, though, she just ricocheted off and bounded up the stairs.

When she reached her locked door, it felt like it took forever to find her keys and unlock it. Once she managed to get inside, she slammed the door shut and leaned against it as if someone might try to make their way through it. Completely out of breath, she stayed there a moment trying to regain her composure.

She wanted so very much to believe Pom was lying and that Lek was living with Pom's mother on their farm in Korat. How could she know for sure? And now that Pom was gone, how would she ever find out where in Korat her family's farm was? Think. She forced herself to clear her mind and think.

'Letters!' She yelled. Pom always talked about getting letters from her mother telling her how good Lek was doing and how much she loved her. If she could find those letters, that would be proof that Lek really was in Korat. Maybe she could track her down from the return address on one of them. Of course!

Nid quickly dressed, rolled her damaged clothes into a tight ball so that no one would be able to see the blood and started to make her way back to Pom's room. She walked slowly from her room on Petchburi over toward Pom's room on Nana Thai Road, about a kilometer or two away. The thought of going back into that room of death scared her and she was in no hurry to get there.

Just before she reached the little bridge over the *klong* that dissected Nana Thai Road into north and south, Nid veered off to find a rock. After a few minutes of hunting, she found one she thought might be a suitable ballast. With little effort, she tied her bloodstained clothes around it and returned to the path that would lead her over the bridge. Halfway across she stopped, made sure no one was looking and threw the item into the slowly moving waters below.

Pom's room was not far away from the *klong*, but Nid stopped just on the other side of the bridge to build up her courage to go back in. She took three deep breaths and just as she was exhaling the third, she began to hear the sound of police sirens rushing up behind her. The events of the night had made her so jumpy she bolted off the road and hid behind the railing of the bridge.

The siren got louder and sure enough, two police cars raced by her hiding spot and screeched to a halt in front of Pom's building. Two policemen got out of each car and went inside.

She waited in her hiding spot for a while on the off chance the police were there for some other reason. Fifteen minutes later when the coroner's car arrived she knew she had arrived too late.

'Stupid!' She called herself, 'Why didn't I think of the letters when I was there the first time? Now what am I going to do?'

She waited another minute or two to make sure no one saw her, then nonchalantly got up out of her hiding place and went back out onto the path by the road. She walked slowly across the bridge so as not to attract any unnecessary attention then picked up her pace as soon as the building was out of sight.

When she got back to her room she again sat on the edge of her bed and tried to figure out what was going on. The more she thought about it, the more convinced she became that she had been lucky to have taken her time going over to Pom's room. If she had been inside when the police arrived, who knows what might have happened? She wouldn't be here sitting on her bed, that's for sure. Most likely she would be down in the police station answering questions all night. They might even have put her in jail thinking she had something to do with it.

Anyway, maybe she could sneak back over there in a day or two to look around. She figured if she got caught she could tell them she was family or something. Right now, though, her adrenaline was running too high for her to sit around and do nothing. She had to try and figure out something else she could do to start sorting out this mess.

CHAPTER 17

With the option of finding the letters from Pom's mother temporarily on hold, Chalarm was her only lead, and even though he denied everything, she didn't trust him one bit. She made up her mind to go back to Patpong to try and see if her intuition about him was correct. She didn't know how she would do it, but she knew that this time she was going to have to change her tactics. Without a plan, she hopped in a tuk-tuk and headed to Patpong hoping she could figure out something along the way.

She arrived in Patpong and walked over to a spot where she could watch Chalarm unnoticed. Pom had been right, he did have a lot of people standing around ordering food from him. He kept busy cooking and did it with flare. To the locals he was grumpy, but to the foreigners he was pleasant and friendly. No doubt he was charging them double what he charged the locals, Nid thought.

Nid felt a soft tap on her shoulder. Startled, she whirled around to see who it was. A filthy and battered looking woman with a dirty, malnourished and half-naked baby in her arms extended her free hand and asked Nid for ten baht so she and her baby might eat. A flood of emotions rushed into her mind. It was the first shred of evidence that Pom's story might be true. She stared at the woman and child wondering if Lek was in a similar condition. That thought gave her an idea, maybe they worked in groups. She quickly looked around to see if Lek was nearby.

'Are there more of you?' Nid asked the woman.

'Ten baht, please, my baby is hungry and needs food,' the woman begged, ignoring her question.

'Okay, okay, here.' Nid handed her the money. 'Are there more of you around? I'm looking for my baby, I think she might be here somewhere.'

'There are many babies around here, but as far as I know they all have mothers already. Sorry.'

'Are you sure? I have reason to believe . . .'

'Thank you, I have to go now,' the woman interrupted her and began to walk away.

'Wait, I need your help,' Nid called after her but the woman didn't respond. 'Why won't you talk to me?' she asked as she followed along behind her. She finally gave up when the woman wouldn't acknowledge her questions. 'Something strange is going on around here.'

Nid returned to her position where she could watch Chalarm and try to come up with a way she could approach him. Fifteen minutes later she received her first stroke of luck. A red pickup truck full of policemen pulled up across the street and parked within sight of Chalarm's food stall. Nid took notice of it but didn't realize its significance right away.

The second important event took place a couple minutes later. She noticed the woman who had begged money from her making her way over toward Chalarm. He looked a little nervous as she walked behind the food stall and began to pull out money to hand to him. He quickly took it from her as he kept a wary eye on the police across the street. Without knowing for sure what she was getting herself into, Nid sprang from her hiding place to confront him again.

'Where's my baby?' She demanded to know.

'Get out of here, now's not the time,' Chalarm responded. He gave the police a nervous glance, one Nid was quick to notice.

'No, now is the time. If you don't tell me where she is I'll walk straight over and tell those policemen what I just saw.'

'I'm warning you, get out of here.' Chalarm was rolling the handle of a large knife over in his hand.

'Suit yourself,' Nid told him. She began to make her way toward the police.

'Hey you! Wait a minute, come here!' he called after her.

'Yes?' She turned to look at him.

'Come over here,' he demanded. 'We've got to talk.'

Nid walked back over to him but made sure to stay on the other side of his food stall and out of reach of him and his butcher knife. She could see that wasn't what he had in mind and needed to skillfully avoid his attempts to get closer. Frustrated, he seemed to give up.

'What is it you want, anyway?'

'Only my baby. If I get her back I will forget I ever saw you. If I don't, if she's hurt in any way, I promise you you'll wish you'd never met her. Or me.'

'Your stupid little threats amuse me. I don't think you know who you're dealing with here. Right now you've got me in a tight spot, though. Maybe you can refresh my memory. Who's your baby and why do you think I have her?'

Nid told him everything she knew about Pom, what she had told her and what had happened to her. The more she talked, the more recognition she could see emerging on Chalarm's face. By the time she was finished, a sinister smile had replaced his frown.

'The baby's name was Lek, wasn't it?' he asked her.

'Then you do know what I'm talking about.'

'Yes,' he finally admitted. 'But I'm afraid you've come too late. Over a year too late for that matter.'

'Why? What happened to my baby?!' Nid screamed at him.

'Calm down, it wasn't my fault. I was good to her, really. I paired her up with this tribal woman from up north who loved her as if she were her own. They made quite a pair, the two of them. Her name was Malee and she cared for that child better then you could have imagined. She always made sure she was well fed, kept her clean, too clean for begging. Just the same, the two of them brought in more money then any of my other employees. I hated to see them go.'

'Go where?' Nid was confused, she didn't know whether to hate this man for what he had done or love him for giving her hope of finding her baby.

'I wish I could tell you but I really don't know. If I did she would probably be back here working for me. She ran off with a tuk-tuk driver in the middle of the night over a year ago. I have no idea where they went.'

'What did she look like? I have to find this Malee and get my baby back.'

'Oh, she was about your height, maybe a little taller. She was heavier then you, though. I figure she was probably in her late twenties. She wore the costume of the Akha hill tribe, you know, thick, black clothes with all that embroidery on it. Her teeth were stained from chewing too much betel but her most identifiable feature was probably that big mole she had on the left side of her face down near her chin. She had a hair growing out of it that she never clipped, it must be pretty long by now.

'I hope you find your baby, I really do. And if you find Malee, just for good measure you can tell her that she caused me a lot of trouble. If I ever see her again, I'll kill her. I don't hold grudges, I get even. You should remember that, too, little girl, just in case you get any ideas after we finish this conversation.'

He began to wipe the blade of his knife on his apron up near his chest. He had a grin on his face and a steely look in his eyes. Nid returned his stare with an equally fierce glare, then backed away without saying a word and left.

Once she was back inside the safety of her room she found her cup, emptied it out the window as was her ritual and poured herself a large measure of whiskey. She took a big gulp then flopped down on her bed. Before long the events of the evening exploded in her mind and she began to cry. Maybe her lost friend Pom had the right idea. Why bother? Why put up with all the heartaches, all the pain and suffering? Maybe it would be better if she ended it now, started over with her new life. She could try to do better on the next plane of existence. It couldn't be any worse then this life, could it?

She tried to get her mind off suicide by thinking about Malee but it only seemed to make it worse. Who was this woman? Where had she gone? The more Nid thought about it, the more she realized there was very little, if any, hope in finding her. She had no friends to help her, only Chalarm knew for sure what she looked like and he wasn't about to help. Her only clue was vague at best. A tuk-tuk that raced off into the night. How could she ever hope to find an unknown tuk-tuk? There must be hundreds of them, maybe even thousands of them in Bangkok alone.

She poured herself another glass of whiskey and drained it in one effort, then poured another. The effects of the alcohol deepened her depression and made her think about what a lost cause she had turned out to be. She thought about Pom and how free she must be right now. No more lying, no more pain, no more bullshit. She wouldn't have to wake up tomorrow wondering if she would be able to get enough money to eat. She wouldn't have to go to bed with a stranger tonight. It seemed like a sure and easy way to get out of this mess.

Nid drained her third cup of whiskey and looked around her room. No, suicide wasn't for her. Either she was too afraid to try it or she was too brave to give up on this world so soon, she couldn't decide which. Plus, the good Buddha said that suffering is a part of life, and that you must fulfill whatever karma your past lives have left you with. Suicide would only mean that she would begin her next life with the same fate, or worse.

She was now a different person than she was a few hours ago. She was accustomed to change and could recognize it when it came. The few short eventful hours of that catastrophic evening had changed her life forever.

The good Buddha said that if one wants to get to the top of a mountain, just sitting at the foot thinking about it will not bring one there. It is by making the effort of climbing up the mountain, step by step, that one eventually reaches the summit.

Finding Malee with so little to go on would indeed be a huge mountain to climb. It might not be tomorrow, it might not even be this year, but she had to believe she would eventually find her and when she did, this Malee would lead her to her baby.

Nid told herself that all of her life up to this point had been meaningless. Until Lek was born she had only herself to look after and even after Lek was born she didn't realize how important it was to take care of her. She did a terrible thing by trusting Pom, but maybe, just maybe it wasn't too late. The past few hours had given Nid's life new meaning. She now had a mission: finding Lek.

CHAPTER 18

Nid had no idea how much having a meaningful mission would affect her life. In the shortterm, it meant that everything she did she could connect to finding Lek. Going with men was now only a way to get money to supply her search. She could now justify it in her mind as doing it for her missing daughter, not for her own personal gain.

She no longer needed to drink so much to escape the reality of her situation, either. Even that helped, for now her relationships became longer, more meaningful and better paying. She also found that everyone likes a good cause and soon had her customers helping in the search. Unfortunately, though, she never seemed to be able to turn up anything.

Singing at the Mueang Issan Club turned into a way to let go of her frustrations when she continually hit dead end after dead end. She sang with such passion that she became a crowd favorite and after a while, the management finally offered her a full-time, paying job. The pay wasn't much but it enabled her to work out of the coffee shop less and less. Eventually she managed to give up working there altogether.

Even though she was continually discouraged, she never allowed herself to give up her search. Every time she traveled by tuk-tuk, she asked the driver if he knew anything about a tribal woman named Malee who may have been traveling with a baby. Unfortunately, none of them knew anything about what she was talking about. As time wore on, she knew her chances of finding them were becoming minuscule at best.

Another tactic she used was to hang out in Patpong every chance she got and talk with anyone that would listen. She concentrated mostly on the tuk-tuk drivers, but didn't limit her search to them. Food vendors, souvenir peddlers, even the beggars were targets for her detective work. Day after day, month after month, she pressed on without success.

Finally, over two years after she had begun her search, she got a break. She thought by then she must have talked to every driver at least twice but evidently she had missed one. His name was Ponchu; he was in his late twenties and had a nervous twitch so that when she talked with him his head constantly jerked, never coming completely back to center until his chin nearly touched his left shoulder. It gave the appearance that he was trying to follow a slow, wobbly tennis match.

Nid had never seen him before; she would have remembered his distinguishing habit. She interrogated him with the finesse that had been polished from her years of practice. At first he acted as if he didn't know what she was talking about. He was well practiced in the closed mouth policy that dominated the area, but somehow she intuitively knew he was hiding something. Frustrated, she nonetheless pressed on, not willing to give up easily on a promising new target.

She continued to whittle away at his resolve and eventually broke down his defenses. To her complete relief, as soon as she got him to speak he didn't seem to want to stop. He told her he used to have a friend named El who drove a tuk-tuk around the Patpong area. He had been his best friend because he was the only person that didn't make fun of him. He also told her that he had left with a woman late one night because he thought they were in some kind of trouble. Ponchu didn't remember anything about a baby but when he thought about it he conceded that he could be wrong.

'This is a bad part of town, Miss Nid. People who talk have been known to disappear suddenly. You can't trust anybody, not even your own family. See that guy over there?'

He pointed to another tuk-tuk driver. 'His brother used to drive out of here, too. His brother said or did something to the wrong person and they got incredibly angry. He hid out at home and tried to let things cool off, but whoever it was that was mad at him knew that guy over there was his brother. Word has it they took him aside and held a gun to his head. They wanted to know where his brother was. He told them. Can you believe that? He turned on his own brother.

'Two weeks later the police found him floating in a *klong*. What a way to go. You know what? Now he works for the people who killed his brother and wears the murder like a badge of honor. Can you believe that?

'I may be simple minded but I think if it came down to protecting my family I would have made something up and got out of town in a hurry. I could never turn on my family or my friends, do you know what I'm trying to say here?'

'Look, I can understand your worry. I promise you I'm not in the mafia and I won't hurt you. I only want to find my daughter. Can you understand what I'm trying to say?'

'Yeah, I guess so. I kind of like you, too. You seem open and honest and I think I can trust you. It's not you I'm worried about, though. It's people like that guy over there that always seem to know everything that goes on around here. Look, he's even looking at us now. Shit, I'm a dead man already.'

'What have you got to lose, then?' Nid said unsympathetically but quickly changed her tone.

'Look, there's no way he or anybody else can have any idea what we're talking about. If it will make you feel any better, after you tell me where they went I'll go over and ask a bunch of other drivers, including him, and act as if you didn't tell me anything. I'm a desperate woman and I'm not afraid to do whatever it takes to find my daughter.'

'You've got a lot of nerve, Miss Nid. I've got to like that in a woman, in anybody for that matter. It's been a long time though, three or four years. What makes you think they're even still there? I know if I were running from those guys I don't think I'd stay in one spot for too long. You know what I mean?'

'It's a chance I've got to take, Ponchu. I have to find my daughter and right now you're the only lead I have.'

'Sad state of affairs, isn't it? When a simple minded tuk-tuk driver like me is all you have. This is against my better judgment, I don't know if I'm even remembering correctly, after all it's been a long time. I think he said he was going down to . . .' He hesitated for a moment as if he were having last minute second thoughts. 'Pattaya.' He finally spilled it out and looked as though the world had just been lifted off his shoulders. 'Remember, you didn't hear that from me.'

'Hear what?' Nid asked him to show that she understood his fears. He looked confused as if he didn't understand her game but before he could respond, she added, 'Thank you Ponchu. You won't regret it, I promise.'

The next morning Nid woke up with renewed enthusiasm. She reached into the tiny hole in the back of her stuffed elephant's head and found that she had managed to save up almost two thousand baht. She took out one thousand and replaced the rest, packed a few clothes in a bag and headed over to the southern bus terminal on Ekamai Road to catch the morning bus to Pattaya. She imagined gleefully that she could probably go down there, find Malee, get Lek and come home. The whole trip should only take a couple of days at most. She could then gratefully return to Bangkok with Lek all safe and sound, where the two of them could live together happily ever after.

During the three hour trip to Pattaya, Nid's mood bordered on ecstatic. She couldn't remember ever being that happy. As the bus gradually passed through the city limits and left the bustling Bangkok streets behind, the water soaked rice fields that crept ever so close to the winding road looked breathtakingly beautiful to her. Even the mud caked water buffaloes that munched lazily on the grass that grew on the mounds separating the rice paddies looked beautiful to her that morning. The breeze that blew through the open windows of the bus caressed her face like the hands of an experienced masseuse. She didn't even mind the little rain shower they passed through somewhere just south of Chonburi that caught them by surprise before they had a chance to pull up the windows. It soaked every passenger through to the bone. 'Let them complain,' Nid thought, she wasn't about to.

No, this was going to be a day to remember, the day that she was reunited with the love of her life, her one and only reason for being. Well, maybe not today, but surely within a couple of days, and this was the day that was bringing her closer to realizing that dream. When the bus finally ground to a halt in front of the tiny little station within sight of the beach, the conductor announced that all those passengers bound for Pattaya needed to depart. Nid sprang from her seat with vigor while the rest of the departing passengers stumbled out as if they had just been dragged through the depths of hell.

Her optimism was taken down just a little when she walked down to the beachfront, looked around and came to the realization that it wasn't going to be as easy as she had first hoped, especially since she'd never been there before. The town wasn't all that big but it was big enough so that it would be difficult to find someone she'd never met.

She started her quest by trying to get her bearings in the new town. To accomplish this she took a walk along the promenade that ran the length of Pattaya Beach. Looking around her she saw a handful of fishing boats that rocked idly in the indolent waters, Thai national flags flying proudly in the breeze above their poles. The delicate sound of light waves lapping the unspoiled beach, each one trying to go further inland then it's predecessor, had a soothing effect on her mind. Tall, curved coconut palms, top heavy with bountiful amounts of nearly ripened fruit rose up to shield the ground from the unrelenting sun. 'This would be a nice place to raise a child,' she thought to herself.

She noticed that there weren't any tuk-tuks operating on that road. Local public transportation seemed to consist of *songthaews*, small pickup trucks with two bench seats laid lengthwise in their beds with a makeshift roof to cover them. This discovery had a double effect on her thoughts about her search. The first thing that came to her mind was that it would be awfully difficult to find the tuk-tuk driver she was looking for if there weren't any tuk-tuks. But her second thought was more comforting. Maybe there were a few tuk-tuks in another part of town. If there were then maybe there weren't that many. This would narrow her search down before she even began.

She decided to start her search immediately, crossed the road, entered a gift shop and asked the proprietor if he knew where she might be able to find a tuk-tuk.

'You must have just come down from Bangkok,' he told her after he finished a chuckle. 'There aren't any tuk-tuks in Pattaya, at least not yet. If you want to get around town just wave down a passing *songthaew*. They can probably get you anywhere you need to go. Cheap, too.'

She nodded and smiled on her way out even though his news wasn't very encouraging. She had come too far and waited too long to get discouraged, though. The smartest thing for her to do at that point would be to find a room for at least that night, possibly for the next few days.

The first place she came upon was situated down a side street, a few buildings away from the beach. It was the sign that hung outside the front door that caught her eye. It announced the name of the place to be the Charoen Guest House and advertised rooms for rent. The price was right and after looking at one of the rooms she decided it would be a suitable spot to base her operations for the next day or two.

The room was even better than the one she rented in Bangkok. It was bigger, cleaner, quieter and even had its own bathroom, all for the same price. She felt rather decadent in her temporary new home; it gave her the feeling that she was moving up in the world. Her other room suddenly started to look claustrophobic and below the standards of a woman on the rise. Being an up and coming singer with aspirations of stardom, she needed to start living the part. She would have to look into finding a better spot when she and Lek returned to Bangkok.

It took her a week to figure out that it may have been too much to ask to find the proverbial needle in the haystack in such a short period of time. She had spent the first week asking *songthaew* drivers if they knew El, and shop owners and beggars if they knew Malee. Either her descriptions were inaccurate or she was asking the wrong people, for no one knew of either. She began to run low on money and knew she would need to make some kind of decision, soon.

On the last night of that first week Nid took another walk down the beachfront promenade and it filled her with the same quiet feelings as she had on the first day she arrived. She was becoming spoiled by the easier way of life in this ocean side community. Pattaya offered clean air, a more laid back lifestyle and this beautiful promenade to walk along, all making Bangkok seem like such a dirty and busy city to her now. She made a decision to stay, and found a job singing within a few days.

CHAPTER 19

When she returned to Bangkok, it felt more like a year than a week since Nid had been in her room on Petchburi Road. She had always considered living there as an acceptable way of life. Now as she looked at the peeling paint and barred windows and could hear the noisy traffic outside, she had trouble understanding how she could have lived there for so long. Her new room in Pattaya seemed like a palace in comparison.

That night she needed someone to talk to, someone to tell about the new direction her life was taking, so she walked down to the coffee shop to see if she could find someone she knew. The inseparable team of Payow and Nong were in their usual seating place just inside the front door.

'Nid! Hello, where have you been?' Payow greeted her. Nong looked at her and smiled before she quickly turned back to study the handful of foreign men scattered throughout the coffee shop.

'You'll never believe it. I landed a great new singing job down in Pattaya. I even found a beautiful room to stay in,' Nid told them excitedly.

'That's great, I'm happy for you. Kind of a slow night around here. Last week this place was packed with men. You should have seen Nong, she was in and out of here like a ping-pong ball. What a machine,' Payow said turning toward Nong. The two ignored the news of Nid's good fortune and became involved in small talk about their experiences with the foreign men from the previous week.

It was a subject that had long since grown old for Nid. She knew a lot about it but it was no longer the primary interest in her life. Seeing Payow and Nong's inability to get interested in anything else reminded her of how she must have been the same way not all that long ago. She could see her old self in the two women sitting across the table. She didn't like what she saw. It was such a stagnant lifestyle, the quick and easy money had a way of destroying a person's ability to dream for a better life.

The worst part was that they couldn't see what a hard life it was because they had never been shown what it was like to make it without sacrificing their dignity. To them it was easy to sleep all day, sell their bodies at night and pocket more money than ninety percent of the people in Thailand did who slaved day in and day out in dead-end jobs just to put food on the table.

It was then and there, sitting in the coffee shop on Petchburi Road, next to her former colleagues, that Nid made up her mind to do the best she could in her new job, take advantage of every opportunity they would give her to advance her standing and never let any of them down. She owed it to the manager for giving her a job, she owed it to the audience, she owed it to Lek to have a good life when she found her and she owed it to herself. She even thought she owed it to Payow and Nong to show them that a better life was possible even though she thought they'd neither understand nor appreciate what she was trying to show them.

Payow and Nong continued their small talk as Nid stared at them blankly, lost in her thoughts. Nong brought her out of it when she grabbed her arm to point out three men that had just entered the coffee shop.

'Three of them, three of us. Perfect set up, don't you think?' She asked Nid.

Nid looked over at the three men and thought about how a year ago she wouldn't have hesitated. 'No, you two go ahead. I'm not really up for it tonight.'

'What's the matter with you?' Payow protested. 'It's the first time I've seen them in here. Big payday, Nid, big because they don't know any better.'

'No, really, I'm sure you two can handle it by yourselves.' Nid thought about it and knew Payow was right, the poor suckers did look like they had just stepped off the plane. Usually it meant the women could get whatever price they asked for without too much protest from the men. Nid could definitely use the extra money to help her get set up in Pattaya. That evening, though, she could feel her life going through a transition and she couldn't bring herself to get back into the old trade. She wished them luck, threw the men a kiss for good measure and returned to her room alone.

The next day Nid spent all morning packing her belongings and cleaning her room. She picked out her best outfits for entertaining on stage and a small assortment of kick-around clothes to take with her, stuffed them along with some makeup, shampoo and her trusty stuffed elephant into the small knapsack Bill had given her so long ago, then threw everything else away. She wanted to make a clean break from Bangkok and didn't want to take anything with her that she wouldn't need in Pattaya.

She finally finished up in the early afternoon, took one last look around her room in case she had missed something, then grabbed her pack and locked the door behind her. The building had no reception area, just a desk behind which a sleepy guard sat to collect the rent once a month and put it in a lock box. On her way out, Nid handed him her keys and announced she wouldn't be back. He'd seen them come and go before and other than accepting her keys he hardly paid any attention to her.

By nightfall the trip south was behind her and she was sitting comfortably in her new room in Pattaya. She couldn't get over how good she felt about the move and how much it filled her with renewed hope. This clean and beautiful room would be a great place to work from to find Lek. Since she didn't need to report to work for the next couple of days, she was determined to use the extra time to continue her search.

By noon Monday she still hadn't uncovered anything even though she had spent nearly every waking minute walking around town talking to people. She asked questions of shop owners, *songthaew* drivers and street people. It was a disappointing weekend but she wouldn't allow herself to become discouraged, because she knew in her heart that in time something would turn up.

After grabbing a bite to eat, Nid walked over to the Malee Cafe, which had given her a job, to meet up with the band leader. She was a little early and didn't expect him to be there yet, which he wasn't, and other then a security guard she was the only one inside. It gave her a chance to have a look at the place during the daylight hours.

It was bigger than she had remembered when she had auditioned, with a least sixty tables, two full size bars and a kitchen out back. The stage was rather large, the back of it was crowded with a maze of equipment, wires and a P.A. system. She wondered how the members of the band could move around back there. The face of the stage was more open and was lined with colored lights that pointed up to the now empty space where the performers went about their business of entertaining the crowd.

The floor in front of the stage had been left void of tables and chairs to be the designated dance area for the customers. It was inlaid with beautiful red, white and orange tiles that came together in a nondescript artistic pattern. More colorful lights hung above, pointing downward toward the imaginary choreography below.

The band leader made his appearance around half past one, introduced himself as Narong and apologized for arriving late. He looked as though he had just woken up and seemed a bit put out that he had to be there at such an ungodly time of day. It didn't take him long to warm up to Nid, though, especially after he could see how polished she was.

He went over a few songs with her, told her where in the program she would be appearing and suggested the type of outfit she should wear for that night's performance. He then ended the meeting after only an hour by telling her it was going to be a pleasure working with her.

That first night was pretty indicative of the first few weeks and months of Nid's employment at the Malee Cafe. Even though the cast and crew were friendly and warm toward her, she had definitely gone from being the main attraction in the Mueang Issan Club to being just another one of the performers in the Malee Cafe.

She was also awestruck by the talent and professionalism of the people that surrounded her. When the big name performers arrived she became just as nervous around them as the rest of the public. It would take her a while to get accustomed to mingling with the elite. She was absolutely thrilled when movie stars and recording artists called her by her first name, talked to her and related to her on a personal as well as a professional level. She had come a long way from being just a little girl living on a farm upcountry to being a woman of standing in Pattaya. Lek was going to be very proud of her mother.

CHAPTER 20

Rattana Chokul was not a nice man. It seems that perhaps when he was born the doctor might have slapped him a little too hard and it knocked his conscience right out of him, for he had none.

The main thought that consumed him was how to make more money, and he didn't care who he hurt to get it. The problem was, he wasn't smart enough to figure out a way to make money legally, so he resorted to exploitation. And since he wasn't smart enough to exploit adults, he resorted to exploiting young children.

He could control young children with brute force and that made him feel good. Power was good, ultimate power was intoxicating, and he could assert total domination over the children he had in his camp. He was their god, and he made sure they knew it.

Adding children to his team, however, was becoming increasingly difficult. A new, what they called 'Catholic ministry', had recently been set up in Klong Toey. This Catholic minister made it his life's calling to care for the destitute children in the Klong Toey slum. Ending child exploitation was at the top of this minister's agenda, and that made taking children out of the slum to work on Rattana's team much more difficult—and expensive.

Rattana, therefore, began looking in other areas. The little girl he kidnapped from the train station ended up working out fine, but all the people that were around when he did it made it dangerous. The last thing he wanted was to get caught.

He had heard of orphanages in and around Bangkok, but the close call at the train station made him nervous, so he instead looked a bit further afield. He learned that there was an orphanage in Pattaya, so over the past week he had made a few trips down from Bangkok to stake out the area.

He usually sat in his car by the side of a dirt road that he found to be a regular route for youngsters walking from the local orphanage to school, and back again. He had his eye on a couple of young girls. They couldn't be more than five years old. Perfect for his scheme. What's more, they often separated from the rest of the children on their walk back to the orphanage. There were no adults on this back road, either.

Throughout her life, Lek had always been in the wrong place at the wrong time. On that day Sulee and her were walking home from school when Sulee stopped and sat down by the side of the road, put her elbows on her knees, her hands on her cheeks and began a worthy pout. Her dress was getting dirty, but she didn't care.

She was well into her silent tantrum when she heard a muffled whimper. Maybe Lek fell down and needed her help. Well, this time she'd just have to wait. When she heard a car door slam, curiosity got the better of her and she turned to look.

Sulee wasn't quite sure of what she was looking at. A strange man was looking in her direction. She couldn't see Lek anywhere. The man took a couple steps toward her, then seemed to be spooked by something off to his left. He turned away, went back to the car and got in.

As the car sputtered and eventually began to move, Sulee could see Lek looking out the back window, terrified. Sulee sprang to her feet and began to give chase, but the car was too fast and Sulee could not keep up. As the car rounded a corner and disappeared from sight, Sulee dropped to her knees, put her bald head in her hands and wept.

Several times Rattana yelled at Lek to 'get down!' Lek dutifully obeyed this strange man. She had no idea what had just happened, or what would happen next. She didn't dare speak, for every time she managed to squeak out a sound, the strange man driving the car would yell at her to shut up. Lek lay quietly across the back seat, not knowing where she was going, or why.

A young mind has a short attention span, and eventually the persistent hum of the rickety chariot as it progressed consistently northward had a settling effect on Lek. As she became braver and managed to look out the side window without being detected, the memory of her last glimpse of Sulee gradually faded away and was replaced by scenes of the Thai countryside. She had been too young to have any recollection of it, but she had traveled this road once before.

She watched as the coconut palms became fewer and she could see men and women with wide brimmed straw hats, standing knee deep in the rain soaked rice paddies harvesting their crops. Further along, an old man leaned on a stick that he used to tend his sleepy herd of water buffalo. It was the last thing she remembered seeing before laying back down and dozing off.

'Where are we?' she asked when she woke up. They had been traveling for almost three hours and the rice paddies had given way to buildings and crowded streets.

Without saying a word, Rattana pulled the car to a stop, got out, reached in the back and grabbed Lek, nearly dragging her into the house. Once inside, a middle aged woman gave them both a sinister look. 'Another one already?' she said.

An argument ensued during which time Rattana's grip on Lek's arm kept getting tighter until she cried out in pain.

Finally the woman retreated, barking obscenities as she disappeared into the house.

Rattana followed, still with a death grip on Lek's arm. Lek heard Rattana call the woman Siriporn, and the woman call him Rattana. For what it was worth, she now knew their names.

A dozen children ranging from Lek's age to about twelve years old were scattered about the inside of the house, lying on the floor. Rattana tossed Lek towards them, then followed Siriporn into another room.

It was late afternoon yet most of the children were still sleeping. Those who were awake looked as though they just woke up. The latter gave Lek's arrival only a quick glance with uninterested eyes before returning to whatever it was they were doing before she came in.

'Is this another orphanage?' Lek asked, confused at the sight in front of her.

'Go to sleep,' one of the children replied, pointing towards an open space on the floor.

Lek didn't know what to think as she took a panoramic view of the inside of the house. The ground floor was one big open room broken up only by a sentry of wooden support posts down the middle. Straw mats and pillows were randomly strewn about and had a child occupying each one.

One back corner was designated as the kitchen area and consisted of a gas burner, an assortment of pots and pans, some cupboards, a counter, a sink and a large icebox. The area was similar to, but smaller than what Lek remembered of the kitchen at the orphanage in Pattaya.

Next to the kitchen was the bathroom. It had been clumsily constructed out of corrugated steel. The toilet was nothing more than a hole in the floor near the back. The only other thing inside was a large earthenware *klong* jar filled with water for bathing.

Occupying the other back corner of the downstairs was an assortment of candy, gum and cigarettes piled unceremoniously into a large heap. When she spied this, Lek's spirits picked up.

With Rattana and Siriporn out of sight and the rest of the children seemingly not paying attention to her, Lek stealthily made her way over to the pile. Just as she was about to grab a piece of candy, one of the other children grabbed her arm.

'That's not for you,' the little girl said. 'We sell that candy. It's our job. Everyone in our family works and you will, too.'

'I'm too young to work,' Lek protested. Her spirits sank again. If she was going to have to live here and look at that candy everyday without getting any, well ...

'My name is Dow,' the girl said. 'Who are you?'

'I'm Lek,' she replied.

'Well, Lek, don't worry. You're not too young. Foreigners just love pretty little girls like you. They will buy lots of candy from you.'

'Foreigners? I've never seen a foreigner.'

'No? Well you will tonight. I'll help you.'

'Tonight? I'll meet foreigners tonight? I can't stay up too late, I have to go to school tomorrow.'

Dow chuckled, then replied, 'Oh, don't worry about school. We don't go to school here. Just think, you won't need to get up in the morning any more. You can sleep all day if you want. Won't you like that?'

'But I like school!' Lek protested.

'Uh huh, well, not any more,' Dow said, then laid down on her mat. 'I want to sleep,' she said, 'We have to go to work tonight.'

As Lek laid her head down on the mat she decided the orphanage in Pattaya was probably a better place to live. She allowed her thoughts to wander back to Sulee before she drifted into a troubled sleep.

CHAPTER 21

Lek awoke a little while later to the sounds of commotion. The older children were in the kitchen area cooking rice and chopping vegetables. The younger children were busy putting candy and cigarettes into small trays.

'Ah, you're awake,' Siriporn took notice of her. Siriporn looked rather bedraggled, but also seemed to be in a much better mood. 'I'm glad you got some sleep. How are you feeling?'

Lek rubbed her sleepy eyes and slowly picked herself up off her mat. 'Okay,' she said without much enthusiasm.

'Good. I'm going to have you working with Om tonight. She's in the kitchen, why don't you go say hello?'

Lek looked over toward the kitchen area and could see three or four older children busily preparing a meal.

She straightened out her hair and clothes and walked over to the oldest looking girl there.

'Are you Om?' she asked, tugging on the girl's shirt.

'What do you want?' Om replied without much empathy for the new girl.

'Siriporn told me to come see you.'

'Don't let her hear you call her that!' Om said sternly. 'To us her name is Mother. It's important for you to remember that; sometimes she can get really angry.'

'Well mother told me to come see you,' Lek said with an extra emphasis on the word mother.

'Why do I always have to take care of the new kids?' Om complained. 'Can't you see I'm busy? Why don't you go help the other shrimps?'

Lek stared at her a moment before she dejectedly shuffled over and began to watch the other children put candy, chewing gum, throat lozenges, cigarettes and cigarette lighters neatly into trays. 'What are you doing?' she said to no one in particular.

A girl only slightly older than her replied that they were getting ready for work. She explained that each tray had to have a little bit of everything in it and that each child was to carry around one of the trays that evening and try to sell its contents to anyone that would buy from them.

'Oh,' Lek said even though she didn't have any idea what the girl was talking about.

Trying not to let her ignorance show, Lek turned and found Dow. 'I've never worked before, is it hard?'

'Not too bad. I've been doing it a long time now and mother says I'm good, too. Mother will probably have you go with Om tonight. She always has the new kids go with her. I don't think Om likes it very much but she's really nice and helps a lot after she gets to know you. I was really scared when I first met her because she thought I was just a little shrimp. But now we're good friends. She doesn't tell anybody, but I know we are.'

Their conversation was interrupted by Om's announcement that dinner was ready. Lek perked up and was headed happily toward the kitchen when Dow held her back.

'Wait, it's not our turn,' she said as she began to explain the well ingrained pecking order. 'We have to stay out of the way until Om and Noy serve mother and father first. After that, it's the boy's turn, oldest to youngest, then it's the girl's turn. You and me are the youngest girls so we'll be last.'

When she finally filled her small bowl with rice and vegetables and sat down on her mat to eat, she noticed that no one was talking, not even the grown ups. No one even allowed their spoons to clank against their bowls. The downstairs of the house was now quiet except for soft chewing.

After the meal and cleanup were finished, the children solemnly collected trays and boxes of supplies from the pile in the corner, marched them outside and deposited them in a small pickup truck parked off to one side of the front yard. Rattana and Siriporn watched intently but offered no help.

When the children finished loading the truck with everything they would need for the night, they climbed into the back and situated themselves as best as they could on top of the cargo. The adults then drove their young flock to an area full of bars and nightclubs called Soi Cowboy.

Rattana hid the truck down a small alley just outside the Soi Cowboy area whereupon the children dutifully got out, grabbed one full tray each and hardly saying a word, marched off down the street. Om handed Lek a tray of candy and cigarettes, took one herself and led her by the hand into this adult playground.

Lek's first sight of this bold and brass area made her want to run and hide. Strange music blasted out of curtained doorways. Young women, wearing next to nothing, were hugging, pulling or teasing tall men with white skin. Neon lights flashed bright letters of a language Lek had never seen before.

The children fanned out without any perceived organization and merged into the bizarre happenings on the bustling street. Lek tried to watch and see where Dow went but quickly lost sight of her as Om took her by the hand and led her into the Our Home Bar.

'This is a fun place to work,' Om tried to sound happy. 'All you have to do is watch me and do what I do. It's easy, come on.'

The inside of the bar was crowded and smoky, and what Lek noticed most was how loud it was. Strange music in a foreign language played at a level that made ordinary conversation nearly impossible. The only way the patrons could communicate with each other was by either yelling or through body language. And there was plenty of body language.

Looking around, Lek could see several bikini clad girls clinging to shiny poles on the center stage as they wiggled their bodies to the beat of the strange music. Countless other scantily clad women were sitting on or around several foreigners who had taken up seats on the long couches that surrounded the stage. The girls who weren't with customers were either talking with the handful of barkeeps who were busy pouring libations or doing their nails and fixing their hair. It was an absolutely outlandish scene for Lek's young eyes to take in.

Nudging Lek to follow her, Om walked over, stood in front of one of the foreigners and patted him on the knee. He looked up from his playmate, smiled at Om and said something Lek didn't understand. He then pointed toward a pack of Krong Thip cigarettes in Om's tray.

'Ten baht,' Om announced without much enthusiasm.

It took a little effort for the foreigner to get untangled from the lady in his lap so that he could reach in his pocket and produce a crumpled ten baht note. Om nodded, took the money and handed him the cigarettes.

'See, it's easy,' she said to Lek as they moved on to the next foreigner.

Lek didn't think so. She had never had the need for money before and at five years old, she wasn't yet clear on the concept. Life was much simpler without it.

The next customer they approached happened to be a little more involved with one of the bikini clad women than the last customer. When Om put her hand on his knee, he stopped momentarily to look at her, gave her a disgusted look and waved her away. Om looked at Lek, shrugged it off and moved on.

The third customer they approached looked past Om toward Lek and said something she didn't understand. 'He said you're pretty,' Om told her. 'Go on, show him your tray.'

Lek looked at him with wide brown eyes and lifted her tray. He reached out and took a pack of gum, held it up in front of her and smiled. With a puzzled look, Lek turned to Om for help.

'Five baht,' Om announced.

The foreigner reached over and handed ten baht to Lek saying something that caused Om to smile. 'He said keep it,' she translated. Still confused, Lek cautiously took the money and gave the man a *wai*.

Om and Lek spent the rest of the evening going from bar to bar and foreigner to foreigner, occasionally meeting up with some of the other children to exchange stories and compare earnings. At a little before midnight, all the children gathered around Om and Lek and handed their money to Om. It was their way of covering for each other, for if all the money was given to their parents in one lump sum, no one would be able to tell if one of the children was having an off night and not selling much.

Mentally and physically exhausted, Lek thought maybe this would be the end of the evening's work, especially since they were all heading back toward the pickup truck. But instead of getting into the truck as she had hoped, the children refilled their trays and marched back into Soi Cowboy.

It wasn't until 4 a.m. that they finally returned home. Lek was so tired she fell asleep in the truck and one of the older children had to carry her into the house.

CHAPTER 22

It was nearly afternoon before Lek finally awoke. As she opened her sleepy eyes and looked around she had trouble remembering where she was. The rest of the children were still asleep, all except for Dow who was just waking up, too.

'I'm hungry,' Lek told the weary looking Dow.

'You'll have to wait, supper is the only meal in this house,' Dow said indifferently as she wiped her sleepy eyes.

'But I'm hungry,' Lek complained.

'Didn't you eat last night?'

'I ate here but that was last night before we went out. Om ate some chicken a foreigner gave her but I wasn't hungry then. Now I'm hungry. Can't I have some breakfast?'

'Like I told you, they only feed us once a day. What you have to do is get foreigners to buy you food when you're out there working. If you're lucky you can bring some home with you, like this.' Dow reached into her pocket and produced some dried beef, stuck a chunk in her mouth and happily began to chew.

Lek's desperate look finally grabbed her attention, causing her to stop chewing and look down at the food in her hands. When she looked back up at Lek, she cracked a smile and handed her new companion about half her remaining stash. Lek appreciatively devoured her friends offering.

'I guess you were hungry,' Dow exclaimed.

'Yes, thank you very much,' Lek answered, 'Are you my sister now?'

'Kind of, I guess.'

'Did you live in an orphanage like me?'

'What's that?'

'It's a place where kids without parents live.'

'No, I have parents. They live on a farm in Buriram.'

'How come you're here, then?'

'Well, we don't have much money so my parents sent me to Bangkok to stay with my aunt and uncle. When I got off the train Rattana saw me alone and told me he was going to be my new daddy. I asked him where my auntie and uncle were and he told me I would see them later.' Dow moved closer to Lek so that no one else could hear her, even though no one was yet awake to intercept their conversation. 'I think he lied,' she said with a stern look on her face.

Lek started to giggle. It was her way of agreeing with Dow's synopsis. As the two began to revel in their private joke, their laughter woke up the older Noy.

'Hey!' she said sternly. She didn't appreciate being woken up so early in the day. When Lek and Dow quieted down, she rolled over and tried to go back to sleep.

'What about you, where are your parents?' Dow asked.

'I don't know. The women where I used to live told me I was left there when I was really young.'

'How old are you now?'

'Five, I think,' Lek answered.

'I'm six,' Dow said. 'My parents told me I had a younger sister who was taken away when she was a baby. We kind of look the same, I wonder if we really are sisters.'

'Yeah, I wonder if we are,' Lek said excitedly. For the first time in her young life she had what she considered to be a realistic hope of having come from a real family. 'We're sisters,

I have a real live sister. Tell me about your family, I mean our family.'

'Well, we have two older sisters and two older brothers. They all work with mom and dad on the farm in Buriram. Maybe someday we can go there together.'

'Yeah, let's go there someday,' Lek said dreamingly.

As time progressed slowly forward, the children's nights were consumed by work, their days by sleep. Dow had long since taken over from Om as Lek's guide and companion and the two had bonded a friendship that was the envy of the other children. Their inseparability gave them security and a happiness that allowed them to cope with the intolerable conditions of their lives.

They also kept alive their hopes of someday returning to Buriram, which made each day exciting and hopeful for them, even though it was monotonous and hopeless for the other children.

Although the children didn't work together as a group, their paths did cross quite often. With increasing frequency, though, Om would not be around for hours at a time.

'Have you seen Om?' became a common greeting.

None of the children dared tell Rattana or Siriporn and when Om was confronted with her disappearing acts by any of the children, she would shrug it off and tell them to mind their own business.

After three or four months of her mysterious vacancies, one night Om didn't show up at the truck at the appointed departure time. The rest of the children loaded into the back of the truck as usual, while Rattana and Siriporn sat inside the cab and waited for her.

Rumors ran rampant among the children as to what may have happened to her. The consensus was that she had made a break for freedom, although no one could agree on where she would have gone.

Thirty minutes of waiting passed before Rattana and Siriporn became involved in a heated conversation. In the middle of the debate, a disgusted Rattana got out of the truck and walked toward Soi Cowboy. At the same time, Siriporn got out of the truck and asked the others if they knew of Om's whereabouts. The children answered honestly that they didn't know. Siriporn didn't believe them and promised stern action if Om didn't return.

Another thirty minutes passed before Rattana returned alone. He motioned Siriporn to get back inside and without saying anything to anyone else, he climbed behind the wheel and drove them home. Although they didn't know for sure, the children all agreed that Om had successfully made her escape.

CHAPTER 23

12 April 1978 was the ninth anniversary of Lek's 'rebirth' at the orphanage in Pattaya and the only birthday she knew. Rattana and Siriporn didn't care. There was no money in it for them, so they ignored each child's birthday.

Dow remembered. Dow would never let something like a birthday slide by unnoticed. She knew exactly what Lek wanted, too. Being the princess of stash, she even had a little extra money to get Lek a present. She wanted it to be a surprise, though, so after their arrival in Soi Cowboy that night she acted like it was just another night at work, the same as any of the other nights during the past few years.

Lek had become accustomed to playing down her birthday and although she was a little hurt that even her sister Dow didn't remember, she put it in the back of her mind and went about her business, too proud to make mention of it.

She did notice Dow was acting a little strange, though. Instead of their usual aimless meandering, Dow seemed to be guiding her around as if she had something planned. Lek was just about convinced it was only her imagination when Dow steered her toward their favorite little bijouterie shop next to the My Darling Bar. There, sitting in the window as it had done for almost a year, was the little silver mood ring that the girls had dreamed about someday having. The old man who ran the shop was sitting on his stool in front chewing betel nuts as he had for as long as the girls could remember.

'How much for the ring?' Dow asked him.

'What are you doing?' Lek asked surprised, 'You know we can't get that!'

The old man spat, looked over at the ring and said, 'one hundred twenty five baht,' then looked away. He'd been here a long time and knew these two youngsters were just dreaming. No need to put much effort into this wasted business.

'How about one hundred baht? Can you sell it for a hundred baht?' Dow asked. Lek couldn't believe how bold her sister was being, but she kind of enjoyed pretending to be a big spender.

'Where you gonna get a hundred baht?' The old man's demeanor frightened Lek a little but didn't seem to faze Dow. 'I know you haven't got a hundred baht, go back to selling candy.'

'If I had a hundred baht, would you sell it to me?' Dow persisted.

'Sure, if you had a hundred baht I'd sell it to you. But where you gonna get a hundred baht?'

Dow looked at Lek with a sly grin, reached inside her skirt and produced five twenty baht notes. Lek's eyes nearly popped out of her head.

'Where did you get that?' she exclaimed.

'Never mind,' Dow whispered as she handed the old man the one hundred baht.

He looked at them as if they had indeed just gotten one over on him, slowly shook his head and began to crack a smile 'I'm not going to ask,' he said as he took the money and walked inside. He returned a minute later with the coveted ring and handed it to Dow.

'Happy Birthday!' Dow said excitedly as she gave it to Lek.

'You remembered!' Lek screamed and gave Dow a big hug. 'You remembered! I thought everyone forgot. Thank you, thank you so much!'

The transaction had completely absorbed Dow and Lek's attention. They were so lost in the happiness of the moment they didn't notice that all the other illegal merchants, the child slaves, beggars, hawkers and candy sellers like themselves, had disappeared into hiding. They hadn't heard the 'red truck' announcement that was made through the grapevine, signaling the arrival of the police.

As the two young girls turned to leave the shop they bumped straight into two of Bangkok's finest. Lek's mood ring almost instantly turned black.

'Ah, what have we here?' said one officer to the other.

'Looks like we got us a couple of pretty little rats,' the other replied. 'Come with us little girls. We have some things to talk about.'

The officers took the two girls over to the infamous red police truck which was parked just out of sight to one side of the red light district. A handful of other officers stood around and didn't seem to take notice of their arrival.

'Where are your friends?' one of the officers queried.

'We have no friends,' Lek replied. Both girls knew not to betray their family.

'No friends, huh? What about your parents?'

'No parents, either,' Dow spoke, 'We ran away to try and make money for our family in Buriram.'

'Buriram, eh? Where did you get this candy and those cigarettes, then?'

'We found it,' Dow lied.

'Well I guess we better give them back to their rightful owners,' one of the officers said as he confiscated their trays. 'Do you have any money?'

Because of Dow's birthday surprise, the two girls hadn't worked much that night and only had about fifty baht between them. They quickly handed it over.

'That's all you have?' one of the officers asked as he split it with his partner and pocketed it.

Lek and Dow stood in front of the police and stared, too frightened to speak. One of the officers chuckled, turned to the other and said something about getting more later. The other just smiled and shook his head. Without giving them any further instructions, they went over to join the other officers leaving the two girls standing alone.

'Let's go,' Lek said, prompting the two to sneak away quietly even though the officers didn't seem to care whether they stayed or left.

Once they were out of sight they broke into a full run leaving many surprised faces in their wake as they weaved their way in and out of the crowd. They didn't stop running until they reached the truck where all the other children were already gathered.

Out of breath and both talking at the same time, they tried as best as they could to explain to Rattana and Siriporn what had just taken place. Rattana acted completely disgusted but Siriporn's cooler head prevailed. She told the two girls to sit in the cab and keep low, while she sent Gay out to scout around and directed the other children to restock their trays.

Gay returned fifteen minutes later and announced the police had just left.

'Okay kids, back to work,' Siriporn commanded. She turned to Rattana and told him, 'I'll stay here in case they return. You take Lek and Dow back to the house and come back by yourself as quickly as you can. We'll talk about what to do about this later.'

Rattana drove home and deposited the girls in the driveway, then sped off. He didn't say a word the entire way back leaving them worried about their fate. As they stood in the driveway looking at the dark house, they contemplated whether they should run away or go inside. Since they had nowhere else to go, they opted to go inside.

'Tell me about our farm in Buriram again,' Lek said to Dow once they were safely inside. They found some matches and managed to light a candle which they placed on the floor beside their straw mats. It cast a soft yellow glow that didn't seem to fill up all the corners of the room. The two small girls sitting near the candle cast large shadows that flickered against the wooden walls.

'I remember we had a big house that stood up on stilts to keep the flood waters away. There were a couple of places in the floor that would creak when we stepped on them. Us kids would each stand on a creak and try to make songs by stepping down or jumping one at a time until *Mae* would come in and yell at us. "Someday you're going to fall right through!" she'd say and we'd all run off and laugh.

'Our house wasn't very far from the Buriram train station. Every day we could hear the "toot, toot" of the trains leaving for Korat or Surin. My brother, uh, our brother and I would pretend we were engineers and chug around outside. We both want to work on the train when we grow up.'

'It sounds so wonderful. Let's go there soon,' Lek spoke with desperation in her voice.

'That would be great, but it's going to be difficult without any money,' Dow confessed.

'I know, but if anybody can get money, you can. And if we start planning now, I think we can do it pretty soon. What do you think?'

'Well, maybe. I'll need your help, though. Don't worry, I'll teach you all my secrets. If you do the same as me, no one will ever know.'

'Yeah, the two of us. We can do it.'

'Yeah, I just hope we don't get in too much trouble for tonight.'

'Me, too,' Lek said as she blew out the candle. The two girls talked and giggled themselves to sleep in the thick darkness that engulfed the almost vacant house.

'Happy birthday,' was the last thing Dow said before she fell asleep.

'Thanks sister.'

CHAPTER 24

Lek was the first to awake in the morning. She didn't remember hearing the others come back from work but they were all there sleeping peacefully. Hunger began to get the better of her and since none of the others were yet stirring she decided to look around the kitchen for something to eat.

Finding nothing suitable, she spied the pile of candy. Another look produced no open eyes so she stealthily grabbed an orange sucker, slid into the bathroom and as quietly as she could, removed the wrapper. Just as she put the candy in her mouth the door flew open and nearly caused her to jump into the *klong* jar.

'See, you're learning already,' Dow said with a pseudo accusatory look on her face. 'Got any more?'

'I think I peed my pants,' Lek said as she clasped one hand to her pants and the other to her chest to try and keep her heart from pounding through it.

'Ah, you're both awake, good,' Siriporn said. This time both girls nearly jumped into the *klong* jar. Lek swallowed the candy whole, almost getting it stuck in her throat.

Siriporn smiled, she enjoyed her successful sneak attack. 'Come into the kitchen, let's talk about last night.'

'Here it comes,' Dow whispered to Lek, who rolled her eyes and nodded her agreement.

Much to their surprise, though, the cross examination was conducted in a friendly and reassuring manner. Siriporn just wanted to know what had happened, what they had told the police and how they got away.

With all questions answered satisfactorily, she told them they should probably stay away from Soi Cowboy for a while. She said that she and Rattana had been talking about trying out the Patpong area and decided that this was as good a time as any. Starting that night, the two girls along with Gay and Tip would be working there instead of Soi Cowboy.

Relieved that they didn't get into as much trouble as they thought they would, Lek and Dow returned to their mats to try and find something to do that would keep their minds busy and off their hunger.

As evening fell, the selected four loaded up the small car Rattana and Siriporn had used to pick up Lek in Pattaya. It usually sat idle except for an occasional trip to the market and took a little coaxing to start.

The plan was to have Rattana continue to drive the truck and most of the children to Soi Cowboy as usual. Siriporn would drive the car the much longer distance to the new destination of Patpong.

Along the new route, Lek and Dow, plus two others, Gay and Tip, sat staring out the window at the crowded metropolis as Siriporn kept busy navigating the tangled streets. When they arrived at their destination and the busy traffic finally allowed her to pull up next to the beginning of Soi Patpong I, Siriporn let the children out near some food stalls and told them to meet her there around midnight. She also told them that any problems that might arise before then they would have to handle by themselves. They were on their own until she had a chance to scout out a suitable rendezvous point where she could park the car.

The first thing the kids noticed as they walked down Soi Patpong I was how much bigger and busier it was than Soi

Cowboy. They all thought Soi Cowboy was bustling but it now paled in comparison.

Patpong seemed to have a hundred bars and thousands of tourists crammed into the bulging area. So many carts clogged the streets selling clothes, jewellery and souvenirs that it was difficult to walk between them.

They also noticed other children selling candy, women with babies begging money and Thai men instead of women standing outside the bars yelling things to the tourists. They all looked at each other in amazement, then set out to explore their new surroundings.

Lek and Dow split off from Gay and Tip and walked up to the first bar they came to, the King's Castle Bar. Since they didn't get any resistance from the doormen when they peered through the curtained doorway, they boldly stepped inside.

It was about three times bigger than My Darling Bar, the largest bar in Soi Cowboy. At least a hundred girls worked inside. Twenty or thirty of them danced on the long, wide stage while the rest shared space with the hundred or so foreigners smoking, drinking, talking and fondling.

'Look, Lek, look!' Dow screamed and pointed at the stage.

'It can't be! Is that Om?' Lek asked, astonished.

Sure enough, Om was one of the girls on stage dancing to the music. Clad only in a skimpy bikini, to Lek and Dow she looked so much older than she was the last time they saw her. It didn't seem possible, but somehow she had grown up.

As if she knew she was being watched, she began to pass her bored look around the bar. When she spotted Lek and Dow, a look of vague recognition preceded a big, surprised grin. She pointed at them and winked, then continued her dancing with a little more vigor and enthusiasm. She injected some suggestive maneuvers causing Lek and Dow to giggle with embarrassment.

'I can't believe that it's really her,' Lek said, as she and Dow turned away from the stage and began to pester the tourists. To their surprise, business was quite good.

When Om's set was finished she climbed down off the stage, walked over and grabbed the girls and took them to a seat in a corner away from the crowd. 'What are you shrimps doing here?' she asked, obviously happy to see them.

'Never mind that, what are you doing here?' Dow answered.

'I've been working here for a couple years now. Don't tell Siriporn,' Om replied, saying Siriporn with mock defiance. 'I really miss you two, how have you been?'

'We're okay now. There was a little trouble when you first left but nothing we couldn't handle. Now, you know, every day is the same,' Dow said.

'What about you? We all wondered what happened because you just kind of disappeared. We thought maybe you escaped, but where did you go?' Lek inquired of her long lost mentor.

'That was such a long time ago. There was a man who used to come Soi Cowboy every night and take me to get something to eat. We'd talk for hours. He'd tell me how beautiful I was and how I was wasting my time selling candy. He said I could get good money if I went to work in Patpong. He was really nice so finally I decided, why not?

'After that it was easy. As soon as I said yes, he got us a tuk-tuk and we were in Patpong in no time. He took me into a place down the street from here where there are a lot of really young girls working. At first I was kind of shy but it really wasn't that bad. We just took our clothes off and danced around on stage naked. The customers were really fun, too. They'd buy us sodas and things, tell us jokes, play games.'

'Do you go outside with foreigners?' Dow asked shyly.

'I do now. Look, they buy me gold necklaces, rings and earrings. I make a lot of money and I even have my own room down off Silom.'

'Isn't it disgusting?' Lek felt sorry for her old friend.

'No, not at all. I learned a long time ago that each of us are two people—our body and our soul. I can sell my body but no one can ever touch my soul. If my body can make me money and buy me things then it would be a waste not to use it.

'In the meantime, I go to the temple as often as I can and pray to Buddha to keep my soul unharmed. Buddha taught me that no matter how much pleasure nor how much pain I get from going with a customer, my soul will always belong to me and my Buddha.'

At that moment an older women began to yell for Om over the din of the bustling bar. When Om pinpointed her location she saw that the woman was flapping her hand, palm down, indicating she wished for Om to come over. 'I gotta go shrimps, *mamasan* calls,' she said. 'See you later.'

Lek and Dow watched as she made her way through the crowded bar and was given by *mamasan* to a smiling foreign customer. Almost immediately, she jumped in the man's lap and gave him a big kiss on the cheek, leaving large red lipstick marks on his face.

Slightly embarrassed for their old friend and not wishing to see any more, Lek and Dow left the bar. As they headed for the next establishment, their heads were filled with wonderment about their former sister.

Their first night in Patpong progressed onward with the children wandering around from bar to bar taking in their new work place, stopping occasionally to let it all sink in. They mostly stayed together, but occasionally they split up to cover more ground. It was after one of these occasions that Lek found Dow with an American G.I. in tow.

'Are you hungry?' Dow asked her.

'Yeah, a little. Who's that?' Lek asked back.

'He's an American. He speaks Thai fairly well and said he wants to give me some food because I look hungry.' Dow gave

Lek a little raise of her eyebrows. 'He told me about a man around the corner who cooks good Thai food. He says it's not too far from here and when I asked him if I could bring my sister along, he said "sure." So, let's go.'

Lek looked at the G.I. rather suspiciously because for some reason she didn't quite trust him. 'I don't know, Dow. We've still got a lot of work to do.'

'Come on, Lek. He just wants to buy us something to eat.'

The G.I. could see Lek was uncomfortable with him so he tried his best to tell her in accented but understandable Thai, 'Look, I know all about what you do. I know if I buy something from you the money doesn't go to you but to your boss and sometimes bosses don't feed their children too well. I only want to help, but it's up to you. If you're hungry there's a man over there everybody calls Chalarm who is a pretty good cook. What do you say?'

Lek was still a little apprehensive but Dow didn't seem to be very concerned. Besides, she was getting hungry. She blew off her mistrust as just being a part of her suspicious nature and assented to go.

'Great,' Dow said. 'Let's go.'

The three made their way over to a group of food carts just outside the entrance to Patpong. 'Over here,' the G.I. announced as they approached a cart filled with anything the girls could have wished to eat. It was attended by a grisly looking older man who couldn't seem to stop looking at Lek.

After they had ordered their meals and as the older man was preparing them, curiosity got the better of him. 'Do I know you from somewhere?' he asked Lek.

'I don't think so, this is my first time here,' Lek replied a little confused.

'It's just that you look vaguely familiar,' he replied, but he still couldn't place her. 'I'm not good with names but I don't usually forget a face and I'm sure I've seen yours somewhere before.'

'I don't think I've ever seen you before,' Lek told Chalarm.

'No? Well, it must be my imagination,' he replied, but he just couldn't shake that strange and unexplainable feeling of déjà vu. He made Lek nervous by continually looking over at her as they ate.

They were just finishing the meal when Dow spotted Siriporn not too far away looking down the busy road. Gay and Tip were already with her, obviously she was looking for Lek and Dow.

Dow crammed some of the leftover beef and pork into her skirt and urged Lek to do the same. They then thanked the G.I. and the older man, with the latter still unable to figure out why he thought he knew Lek.

'That guy gives me the creeps,' Lek said about Chalarm as she and Dow ran over to meet the rest of their crew.

Siriporn informed them that she had found a suitable rendezvous point just around the corner and out of sight of suspecting eyes. She led them over to their new base of operations and counted the money as the children refilled their trays. The first few hours of business had been good.

CHAPTER 25

As days turned into weeks and weeks into months, the seasons changed but the work stayed the same. Out of the crew of four who worked Patpong, Tip, being the only boy, mostly kept to himself while Gay had joined up with Lek and Dow forming a close-knit trio. The three worked and dreamed together, always planning to someday make their escape to Buriram.

Left relatively unattended every night, they explored Patpong to its fullest and discovered hiding places that no one else knew about. Their plan was to stash away small amounts of money every chance they got, with the hope of saving enough to afford transportation out of town.

After a couple of years of this small-time embezzlement they had what they considered to be enough money to take flight. Lek and Dow were anxious and ready to go, but Gay's hesitancy continually held them back. She constantly complained about how they didn't have enough money or the time wasn't right. She could come up with any number of reasons not to go. Lek and Dow knew that she was just worried about the possible consequences of getting caught. Since she was part of the plan, they always listened to her.

Then one late afternoon just before dinner, Siriporn called a surprise meeting with Lek, Dow, Gay and Tip, the consequences of which would force the girls to play their hand.

'There's a new area in town called Nana Plaza,' she told them. 'It's closer than Patpong and Rattana and I think maybe it's new enough not to have too many others working there yet. Rattana and I have talked about it and decided it's time to move on. We want you to start working in Nana Plaza tonight.'

'Tonight!' Lek said with a little too much panic in her voice causing Dow to nudge her arm. All three girls knew that if they were to start in Nana Plaza that night there would be no way they could get back to Patpong to pick up their hidden money. It would effectively quell two years of well laid plans.

'Sure, why not? Tonight is as good a night as any.' Siriporn replied.

'It's just that we had something lined up for tonight,' Dow said. She was trying to think of something, anything that would postpone the move.

'Something special? What might that be?' Siriporn asked, her interest peaked.

'We can't tell you, it's a surprise.' Dow was doing her best to think quickly but nothing was coming to mind. She was trying hard not to let it show.

'It's a surprise for you,' Lek chipped in.

'For me?' Siriporn said, ignorantly flattered. It was her birthday next week but she didn't know any of the children knew about it. 'Hmm, tell you what. I'll talk it over with Rattana and see what we can do.'

Dow looked over at Lek and Gay, their spur of the moment plan was working. For, unknown to them, there were many factors working in their favor. Among them, Siriporn had long ago become lost in the illusion that these kids actually liked working for her, due in no small part to the bond that Lek, Dow and Gay had formed and the effect it had on the rest of the children. They had also become the informal leaders of the family and usually took care of any problems before they reached Siriporn.

In addition, other than at meal time or when he drove them to or from work, the children rarely had anything to do with Rattana. It was Siriporn they dealt with on a day-to-day basis and it was fairly obvious that she ran the operation. With all this in mind. and spurred on by the children's promise of something special lined up for her, it didn't take long for Siriporn to convince Rattana to allow them one more night in Patpong.

Dinner that evening was quiet as usual but for Lek, Dow and Gay it was unbearably tense. Not one of the three dared look at each other for fear of giving away their plot. For the rest of the family it was just another night, business as usual. When dinner was finished, the children cleaned and put away the dishes, then loaded up the vehicles as they had done a thousand times before.

'Maybe we'll have a short night tonight,' Siriporn announced, wishing to give the kids a break. She hoped to speed up the delivery of her surprise. 'These kids really have come a long way in the past few years,' she thought to herself.

Tip just shrugged off the suggestion; to him it was just another night. It didn't much matter whether he worked until the sun rose or quit now, work was work and at ten years old, it was all he knew.

Lek, Gay and Dow, however, all looked at each other and felt added pressure to make their move sooner than they could have hoped. None of them made any verbal response to Siriporn's suggestion and feeling a bit put out, she didn't repeat it.

The walk into Patpong was short in time but long in thought. The girls still weren't free to talk about their plan with Tip in tow. He, too, was curious about the surprise and when he asked to stick together with them to be part of it the girls gave him a quick and firm no. Feeling rejected, he ran ahead and disappeared into the night.

'We haven't much time,' Dow announced after looking around to make sure both Siriporn and Tip were gone. 'Let's split up and get the money from our hiding places then meet back in front of the King's Castle Bar. Make sure to keep an eye out for mother and Tip.'

'Are we sure we want to do this, now?' Gay was so scared her whole body was shaking.

'It's now or never,' Lek told her. 'Don't worry, it'll be okay. Just think, in a couple of days this will all seem like a bad dream. We'll be free and living on a farm in Buriram with our new family. We can run around in the fields instead of sleeping all day. Ooo, I can't wait!'

Lek's euphoric synopsis seemed to settle Gay's nerves and gave all three girls a new bravado to attack their desperate task. With nervous giggles and a feeling of comradeship, they set out to assault the night. Within an hour they had all returned to the entrance of the King's Castle Bar.

'I've been thinking,' Gay said once they had all met up. 'Why don't we take the money and hide it in the new place. What did mother call it, Nana Plaza? Then we can have more time to plan. It just seems like we're rushing into this.'

'I have a better idea,' Dow replied brushing off Gay's hesitancy. 'Everybody give me the money for safe keeping. You know me, I can hide anything from anybody.'

'Good idea,' Lek answered. 'And if somehow we get split up or something happens later on, let's meet by the Playboy Bar at the back side of Patpong. Right now I think we should go inside and see if Om can help us.'

'Yeah, Om's pretty smart and knows a lot of people. She'd probably be happy to help us. She ran away herself, remember?' Gay was now back into the plan, forgetting for the moment about how nervous she was.

Lek and Gay handed their money over to Dow, who counted it out to be around four hundred baht. Not a lot, but enough for what they needed it for. She hid it away under her ragged skirt and tried to arrange it so the large lump it was making in her clothes wasn't so obvious as to attract attention. Still toting their trays, the three went inside the bar to search for Om.

'Hi squirts,' Om found them first. She was sitting with three or four other bar girls near the entrance. It was still early in the evening and not many customers had arrived yet, leaving many of the employees sitting around with nothing to do.

'Om, we're glad you're here,' Gay said in desperation.

'What's up with you tonight? You look like you just got caught with your skirts up around your ears.'

'We're running away and we need your help,' Dow blurted out not caring who could hear her.

'Running away? That's great, where are you going?'

'We're making a run for Buriram to see our family,' Lek replied.

'Buriram? You've got your work cut out for you going there. How are you planning to get there?'

'We thought maybe we could go by train,' Dow said questioningly. Suddenly their plan didn't seem so sure.

'Do you have any money?'

'Yeah, we saved up about four hundred baht,' Dow replied proudly.

'Well, that should just about get you there. What are you going to do after that?'

'We don't know. We can figure that part out once we get there. We have family who will be glad to see us, I'm sure,' Dow continued to speak for the crew.

'Why don't you stay here? I can probably get you jobs in the bar. You can make good money here and if you're smart and save it up over a year or two, you can take a bundle back with you. Your family will be really happy to see you then.'

'No way!' the three girls responded in unison.

'Besides, mother would find us for sure,' Lek added.

'No, I don't think so. Well, how can I help? You already seem pretty firm on what you're going to do.'

'We don't know how to get there,' Dow said. 'I mean, we've never been to the train station before.'

'That's the easy part,' Om replied. 'Just take a tuk-tuk. Any driver will know where it is. The hard part is what to do while you're waiting for the train to leave. I've been to Surin a couple of times on the same line that goes through Buriram and there's only a couple of trains per day. You've already missed the last one for today and the next one doesn't leave until a little before seven in the morning. By that time both Siriporn and Rattana will know you're missing and will no doubt be looking for you.'

The three looked at each other in mild panic, they hadn't thought of that. Gay returned to her state of paranoia and to make matters worse, Tip revealed that he had been standing behind them the whole time. None of the three intended runaways had seen him.

'It'll never work,' he announced, forcing a mild shriek from Gay.

'He's not with you?' Om asked in surprise. 'He's been standing there all along. I'm sorry, I would have said something if I knew.'

'Get out of here Tip! Pretend you never saw us and if you tell mother or father what we're doing, we will make your life miserable for as long as we have to stay together!' Dow threatened.

'Your secret is safe with me,' he replied. 'But don't say I didn't warn you.'

CHAPTER 26

'Om! Om! Aaaah, zere ees my little tilac.' A tall blonde foreigner came through the door and with a pronounced swagger, walked over and planted a big juicy kiss on Om's cheek. She pretended to enjoy it but when she looked at the girls she rolled her eyes in mock disgust.

'Sven, you animal,' she said to him. 'Why do you come in here drunk already?' She turned to the girls and spoke in Thai so he couldn't understand. 'Men from Sweden are always drunk. I don't understand why they're never sober. Never mind, Sven's a good man and he gives me lots of money.'

Tip, sensing that now would be a good time to make his exit, raised his hands to the girls as if to say, 'don't worry about me' and headed for the door. Gay started to tremble visibly again and all three girls began to realize they were about to lose their best ally to a drunken foreigner.

Ignoring most of what was going on around him, Sven began beckoning toward one of the locals. 'Come to here, come to here. I vant a picture of my little tilac and me.'

A man with an instant camera hanging from his neck came running over to reply to Sven's call. He was one of the many locals who made their living taking pictures of foreigners with their bar girls.

Sven put his arm around Om's back, reached all the way around under her shoulder and pulled down part of her bikini top revealing her left breast. She giggled and pretended it didn't bother her while Lek, Dow and Gay stared in disbelief.

Flash! There is nothing quite like the aftereffects of a flash going off in a dark room. Try as one might, for a few seconds it is impossible to see anything. When everyone's eyes finally began to focus again, Sven suddenly noticed Lek, Dow and Gay standing close by Om.

'Ah, zeese are your children, no?' he said, blinking his eyes.

Om looked at the girls, tilted her head and gave them a look that spoke, 'I can't believe he just said that!' She turned to him with a smile and said, 'Why, yes Sven. I had all three of them two or three months apart when I was five years old.'

Sven let out a huge guffaw, turned to the self-proclaimed photographer and announced he wanted another picture of his little tilac and her kids.

As Sven turned to face his entourage he had trouble focusing his eyes, blinking them so often that it gave the appearance that they were closed more than open. He blindly handed the picture of the girls to Gay, stuffed the picture of he and Om in his shirt pocket, then grabbed Om by the arm and commanded, 'let's go drink!'

'In a minute,' Om protested, but he had a firm grip on her arm and began to pull her away with such force she didn't have a choice except to follow.

'Come back at midnight. *Mamasan* goes to eat at Tip Top every night at midnight and I think maybe I can slip away for a little while then,' Om hollered as she was being dragged away.

'Midnight?' Lek said disappointed. 'What are we going to do until midnight?'

'Let's call it off,' Gay said. 'It's just too risky right now. Nothing seems to be going right. It feels like bad luck to me.'

'Nonsense,' Dow scolded. 'Everything is still going okay, we just have to kill a little time, that's all. Let's just act normal and wander around for a while.'

After about an hour of aimless wandering, Lek began to give away her candy, gum and cigarettes to the beggars. Seeing how much pleasure this little act of defiance gave her, Gay and Dow were soon caught up in the act. All three began racing around the streets, trying to be the first to find a previously unseen beggar to give part of their goods.

'Red truck! Red truck!' the signal went out. Caught up in their fun, the three girls had become separated and although Lek and Dow were able to find each other quickly, Gay was no where around.

'Where is she?' Lek asked once she and Gay had dropped their trays and ran for cover by their rendezvous point near the Playboy Bar.

'I don't know but I don't like it,' Dow replied.

They waited and waited just as they said they would but Gay never showed up. 'Let's go see if Om knows anything,' Dow suggested after fifteen minutes or so.

Trying to stay hidden from suspecting eyes, the two girls stealthily made their way over to the King's Castle Bar. Om was sitting on a bar stool, still tangled up with Sven and when she saw them come in, she urgently waved them over.

'The police are here, be careful!' she demanded with a motherly tone in her voice. 'Where's Gay?'

'We don't know, we were hoping you could tell us. We got separated down the street and can't find her.'

All of a sudden Om assumed a panicked expression. She quickly stood up and shoved Lek and Dow behind her, then reached up and put her arms around Sven's neck and pulled him down to kiss her. Sven was now so drunk he was a willing partner for anything and he stumbled around perfectly. His enormous body not only successfully hid Om, but also covered Lek and Dow from any view from the door.

'What's going on?' Lek asked her busy friend.

'Shush! And don't move,' she mumbled back, her lips momentarily breaking away from her amorous behemoth. 'Siriporn's at the door looking in here!'

'Oh, no!' Dow gasped. Her breath momentarily left her.

'Ooo, I like too much my little tilac.' Even though Sven didn't have any idea what was going on, he liked his role.

Om peeked around his shoulder. 'She's gone,' she announced as she roughly pushed Sven back onto his bar stool. 'Not now!' she scolded him as he tried for more. Hurt and confused, he returned to what he liked best anyway. His beer.

'I don't know why I didn't think of this before,' Om said. 'Take my keys and go to my room. It's not far from here, just go to the end of Patpong, take a left onto Suriwong, then take the third right. It's the third building on the right. My room is number 41 and it's on the fourth floor.

'I'll keep Sven here as long as I can and if Gay shows up I'll send her down there, too. Two other girls who work here live there with me, too, so if they come home before I do just tell them you're friends of mine. I'll be back as soon as I can. Be careful and hurry. Now go. Go!'

Lek and Dow shot over to the front door and looked out just in time to see Siriporn going into another bar. They hurried across to the other side of the street and ran all the way toward the end of Patpong. As they approached the Playboy Bar, Lek came to a sudden stop and stared in disbelief across the road. It took Dow a minute to see what she was looking at and when she finally did she let out a gasp of horror. There was Gay in tears, standing in front of two police officers.

With tears blurring their vision they ran and ran, dodging startled pedestrians, speeding cars, tuk-tuks and motorcycles until they were both out of breath. They walked the rest of the way to Om's apartment in silence, hand in hand.

Om had given them two keys, one for the padlock on the gate downstairs and one for the lock on the door of her room.

After a minute or two of figuring out which was which, they landed themselves safely inside.

A large bed, with a half-dozen or so pillows scattered among a handful of stuffed animals, took up most of the room. Near the door a small table with a rice cooker and a few dirty dishes acted as the makeshift kitchen. Nearby, a small assortment of dresses and shirts hung from two metal racks acting as the closet. Dirty clothes were strewn everywhere.

A large ceiling fan creaked to life once Lek found the switch to turn it on. Still without saying much, she and Dow plopped themselves on the bed with their legs hanging off opposite sides and their heads meeting in the middle, pointing in opposite directions.

How had their plans gone awry? It seemed so simple before, how had it become so complicated now? Even though they had a couple of years to get ready for this day, neither was prepared for what was now taking place.

Lost in their thoughts, they were only vaguely aware of the commotion that was going on around them. A drunken woman in the room next door was throwing bottles and glasses around, screaming at her husband or lover. The other residents of the fourth floor who were unfortunate enough to be home at that time were in the hallway trying to shut her up.

After about an hour of this turbulence, the woman was finally restrained allowing the others to return to the semi-quiet of their rooms. With the commotion over, Lek and Dow slipped into an uncomfortable sleep.

CHAPTER 27

They were awakened around 4 a.m. by a rattling, then a pounding on the door. Lek cautiously opened it finding a somewhat disheveled, perturbed Om on the other side.

'You two are impossible to wake up!' She claimed as she pushed her way into the room. 'Now I know why I didn't give you my keys in the first place. I had to climb over the gate downstairs. Did you notice how there's just a little opening at the top of it? It must have taken me fifteen minutes to get through it. Then, once I got up here I stood outside the door for ten minutes trying to wake you two up. I think a herd of elephants could walk through here and neither of you would know.'

'Sorry.' Lek and Dow looked at each other as if this was exactly what they needed to hear after the night they'd been having.

'By the way, where are my roommates? Didn't they come home last night?'

'We never saw anybody,' Dow answered.

'Well, they must have gone home with foreigners. Sven took me back to his hotel for a little while but I told him I couldn't spend the night. He wasn't too happy but he gave me some money anyway. Then I came home to find you two dead to the world.'

'Sorry,' Lek apologized again.

'Ah, never mind, it's no big deal. Hey, I've got lots to tell you. I saw Gay with Siriporn and Tip walking through Patpong. Siriporn looked angrier then I ever remember seeing her. She had Tip and Gay by the arms and was dragging them through the crowd as if no one else was there. Both Gay and Tip were bawling and Siriporn's face was beet-red. Wow, was she upset! I hate to tell you, but I think your secret's out.

'I imagine by now both Rattana and Siriporn are out looking for you. This makes things a little more complicated, but hey, I like challenges.' Om wasn't being very reassuring.

'Shit,' Dow said with submission. Lek gave her a funny look because even though Dow was crafty and streetwise, it was the first time Lek had ever heard her swear. Dow looked at Lek, rolled her eyes and shook her head as if to say, 'Oh, grow up.'

'What's up with you two? This is only a minor setback. Now it's getting exciting. We'll have to disguise you, of course. I think I have some old clothes that will probably fit you and after we cut your hair and apply a little makeup, no one will recognize you.'

'Cut our hair!' Lek protested. Both girls had long beautiful hair that reached the middle of their backs.

'Do you want to get out of here or not?' Om scolded as she reached behind one of the clothes racks and produced a medium-sized mirror.

'We can't turn back now,' Dow admitted to Lek. They both looked at each other and realized it was going way beyond what they had originally thought it would take to escape.

Om cleared the rice cooker and the dirty dishes off the table near the door and carefully steadied the mirror on it. Grabbing a pair of old scissors out of her makeup bag she looked over at the two girls to see who would be first. Not getting a volunteer, she took Lek by the arm and sat her on a stool in front of the mirror. After putting a towel around her neck, she clipped and cut until there was hardly any hair left.

Om did the same to Dow and then rummaged around her clothes pile and produced some boyish looking outfits. She decided against applying makeup, figuring it would be better to try and pass them off as a couple of young boys. As Lek and Dow changed, Om returned to the pile and found a couple of baseball caps. When the girls were finished, Om put the caps on their heads and pushed them up against one wall, then stood back and announced, 'There, you're ready. Even I hardly recognize you.'

'I feel kind of foolish,' Dow admitted.

'Nonsense. These are perfect disguises. Now all we have to do is get you two over to the train station, buy a couple of tickets and put you on the train. You're almost home free.'

'How are we going to do that?' Lek said with resignation.

'What is it with you two? You are about to go on what may be the biggest journey of your lives and you're acting as if someone were making you do this. Don't you have any faith in public transportation? There's a tuk-tuk on every street corner, even at this time of night. Come on, let's go!'

'She's right,' Lek confessed. Her sleepiness was wearing off and her passion was beginning to return.

'Yeah, let's go!' Dow immediately picked up on the new sense of excitement in the air.

'That's the spirit, it's about time!' Om exhorted as she led them out the door.

She had been right, there was a vacant tuk-tuk only a few steps away from the entrance to her building. To Lek and Dow's delight, she negotiated the fare with the driver for three passengers to the train station and for one to return. Om was now their driving force and their security blanket. Both girls had secretly hoped she would accompany them to the train station.

At that time in the morning, only a small part of Bangkok's populace was awake and an even smaller number had ventured out of their homes. The empty streets gave the half-awake tuk-tuk driver plenty of room to race around and he took advantage of nearly every inch. As he ran red lights and careened around corners at high speeds, his passengers hung on for dear life.

'What a great feeling!' Om announced in the midst of all the commotion. 'This is more excitement than I've had in a long time. It's almost just like when I escaped.'

'When we get to the station you two had better wait while I check out the situation,' Om said attributing the girls quietness to the tuk-tuk driver's recklessness. The wild ride didn't bother her, though; it was just another typical tuk-tuk ride through Bangkok.

Lek and Dow's nods of consent were lost in the turbulence as the final turn into the train station was made on only two of the tuk-tuk's three wheels. After it screeched to a halt out front, all three passengers got out with extra urgency.

'Stay here, I'll be right back,' Om said over her shoulder as she walked inside toward the waiting area.

'Was that meant for me or you?' The tuk-tuk driver asked Lek and Dow.

They looked at each other and shrugged. 'It must mean you,' Dow said without conviction.

The driver shrugged his reply then climbed into the back seat and put his feet up, content to take a rest from his tiring task.

A few minutes later Om returned. 'We have a little bit of a problem but don't worry, I have a plan.'

'What's up?' Lek asked. Problems were now becoming ordinary on this journey.

'Don't panic, okay? Rattana is inside with Tip and poor Tip looks like he's had a rough night. The two of them are sitting in the waiting area near where the ticket counter is.'

'Oh, no. What'll we do now?' Lek groaned. Dow let out a gasp and looked as if she was about to run.

'I said don't panic!' Om scolded. 'I told you I have a plan. I'm going to create a diversion and when I do you two will need to work fast. I don't know how long I can hold Rattana's attention so you need to buy your tickets and run over and get on that train as quickly as possible. Don't stop for anything because we'll probably only have one shot at this. The ticket counter for Buriram is number four. The boarding gate is number four, too. Got that? Easy to remember, right?'

'Okay, but what are you going to do?' Lek wanted more details before they began.

'We haven't got enough time for me to spell it all out for you but I will tell you this. One of the main reasons I left when I did was because Rattana raped me.'

'How awful! I never knew,' Dow shook her head.

'Never mind all that now. I hate him more then anything else but I also think I know how to get to him, so get ready. When I make my move I want you to go straight to the ticket counter and buy your tickets. If there's a line, push your way to the front. Do whatever you have to do but do it fast because I don't want to be around that jerk for any longer than I have to.'

Om tucked in her blouse tightly to reveal her shapely young form and unbuttoned the top two buttons. Giving her two friends a quick wink of encouragement, she then walked away to complete her mission.

'Wait!' Lek screamed, almost loud enough to give them all away.

'What!' Om returned crossly. 'Are you trying to ruin everything?'

'I just wanted to say thank you. You've been a good friend. Without you we could never have done this. We'll never forget you,' Lek said as Dow looked on with watery eyes.

'Don't thank me yet,' Om replied. 'It's not over. Thank me when you're on that train but not until you're somewhere up around Korat. If you make it that far you should be safe. Come back and see me in a couple of years if you get a chance. Rattana and Siriporn will probably have forgotten about you by then.'

'We can only hope,' Dow replied with a sigh. She knew that if they made it out of Bangkok unscathed, the chances were pretty slim that they would ever return to see their friend.

'Yeah, well, I gotta go,' Om said and took a deep breath. She seemed to pick up on Dow's sentiment and tried to ignore it.

The girls peeked around the corner and watched as Om cautiously walked toward Rattana and Tip. When she approached the spot where they were seated, she began her ruse by acting surprised to see them.

As soon as Tip saw her he knew something was up, but Rattana didn't seem to recognize her. She leaned over and whispered something in Rattana's ear, making sure she did so in a way that he would notice her ample cleavage. He still looked a bit confused as she righted herself and began to walk away but a look of recognition quickly crossed his face.

Om only walked a few feet before she stopped and looked over her shoulder. She was no stranger to the game of handling men and knew exactly how to play Rattana. Sure enough, he got up to follow her.

As soon as his back was turned Lek and Dow rushed over and found counter number four. There was no line so they immediately placed their money on the counter and asked for two tickets to Buriram.

'What are you doing here?!' Tip lisped in desperation after he had snuck up behind them. He looked awful. He had a split lip and a bruised arm and his eyes were red and puffy. It was obvious he had been crying.

'Tip, what happened?!' Dow was aghast at the sight in front of her.

'Never mind. Mother and father are looking for you and they're incredibly angry. They think Gay and I know where you went and have been trying to get us to tell them. Don't worry, I told you your secret was safe with me and I meant it, but it hasn't been much fun trying to keep it.'

'Have you seen Gay?' Lek asked after taking the tickets from the counter.

'Yeah, she and Mother are at the bus station looking for you. Gay told me before we got split up that if I saw you to tell you to just go and forget about her. She said "good luck" and don't worry, she'll be okay.'

'Come with us, Tip. We have enough money for another ticket.'

'No, I can't. I just can't. Thanks, but, I don't know. Look, don't waste your time talking to me. Get out of here before father sees you. If he catches you we'll all be in big trouble.'

'Tip, you're a good brother and we love you. Take care of yourself!' Dow said. Tip was right, time was precious and they didn't have enough to waste arguing or trying to convince him to go.

A quick check of the waiting area showed them that Rattana was preoccupied with Om and was oblivious to what was going on only fifty feet away.

'Good luck, I hope to see you again,' Tip called out to them.

They rushed over to gate number four, passed through it without a problem and boarded the first available passenger car. Once they found a pair of unoccupied seats they sat down and strained their eyes out the window. The angle of the train didn't allow them a clear view of the waiting area and they could barely see Rattana and Om still having their conversation, which now seemed to be getting heated. After about five minutes that seemed like an eternity, the train began to pull away.

Keeping a watchful eye on Om, the last thing they saw of her was when she kicked Rattana in the groin and ran toward the waiting tuk-tuk. Rattana doubled over and dropped to his knees, seemingly too hurt to give chase.

CHAPTER 28

Rapid train number 31 leaving Bangkok bound for Ubon Ratchathani (via Buriram) was anything but rapid, for it stopped at every little village station along the way. The grueling journey, which was only a little over four hundred kilometers, would take almost eight hours to complete.

Lek and Dow each dealt with the monotony in their own way. Dow babbled away to anyone who would listen to her, while Lek sat lost in thought. This was going to be another moment of truth for her. All those years of dreaming were about to become either a reality or another cruel awakening.

She let her mind drift back to Pattaya and the image she had of the last time she saw Sulee. Lek wondered if she was happy now, if she had been adopted by a good family. She wondered what she must look like now with her hair grown back. She touched her head and realized that now she had very little of her own precious hair left.

Suddenly she became scared. What if this wasn't her family? What if this was all just a dream? The fear of being denied again rose up inside her. She looked over at Dow who was busy bothering another passenger seated near by.

Lek studied her for a moment and realized it really didn't matter. Dow was her best friend and no matter what happened in Buriram, she knew the two of them would try to stick together.

The train creaked to a stop at another little village station momentarily bringing Lek out of her deep thoughts. As was the case at each station along the way, a handful of people approached its open windows to sell the passengers cooked chicken pieces, beef or chicken satay, vegetables, fruit, rice or pastries. Along with the water and soft drinks sold by the conductors of the train, neither girl went hungry or thirsty. Indeed, Dow spent most of the trip with her mouth full of some tasty treat, at least when she wasn't talking to someone.

Once back underway, Lek took notice of the spectacular view the train windows offered of the trip through the countryside. Steep mountains and hillsides provided a backdrop to the rain soaked rice paddies divided up and squared off by mounds of earth that performed as paddy dikes to keep precious water from draining away. These occasionally gave way to fields of sugar cane and rows of tapioca with each small farm constantly competing for space with the jungle foliage. Occasionally, coconut palms, banyan trees and evergreens added variety.

Beautifully adorned Buddhist temples dotted the way. Every corner of their bright orange roofs reached toward the sky and their bright white walls glistened in the sun. Lek thought how Thailand must have the most beautiful places of worship in the world.

Wooden shacks with thatched roofs and small yards took up most of the rest of the available space and gave Lek an indication of how people lived outside the city. Almost every one of them had laundry strung up outside, two or three huge dirty orange clay *klong* jars filled with water, and half clothed young children playing along side scattered chickens and lazy dogs in the dirt yards.

A couple of hours before the end of their trip the two girls fell into an uncomfortable sleep on their rigid thrones. They had been awake for most of the previous night and even though they were excited about their journey, they could not fight off sleep any more.

At a little before three in the afternoon the conductor woke them up to let them know the next stop would be their departure point, Buriram.

As the train creaked to a slow halt in front of a small and rickety white building, a wooden sign with the words: 'Buriram, City of Pleasantries' painted on it confirmed their arrival. Amidst the confusion of people rushing to the open windows to sell their goods to the weary passengers, Lek and Dow disembarked with nothing but Om's clothes on their backs and a couple hundred baht in their pockets, each filled with their own optimism. Dow knew she was finally home. Lek hoped that she was too.

It took a little while for Dow to get her bearings. The last time she was here was that fateful morning her family put her on the train for Bangkok to stay with her aunt and uncle. It was over nine years ago when she was only the tender age of four.

She did remember her home was outside of town, yet somewhat near the tracks and she hoped that hadn't changed. With Lek right behind her, she began to walk up the only road that led north, away from the bustling little town and away from the station.

They hadn't gone far when things began to look familiar. About a kilometer up the dusty red road they took a left onto another dirt road leading into a small bamboo forest. A short distance further along it bent left and the forest opened up into a small farm.

An older woman chewing betel nuts sat on the front steps of a farmhouse pounding a wooden pestle into a stone mortar. A younger woman, slightly older then Dow, was busy feeding chickens.

'We're home,' Dow whispered. Her strong emotions wouldn't allow her any more volume for her voice. She grabbed

Lek by the arm and the two stood dumbstruck staring into the surrealistic picture in front of them.

'Can we help you?' a third woman said as she appeared in the doorway of the farmhouse. The old woman on the steps looked up and strained her eyes to see who had come calling at that hour of the day.

'*Mae?*' Dow said quietly to the older woman. Her voice still didn't have much projection. 'Is that you, *Mae?*'

'Oh my . . . !' the woman screamed as she jumped up from her perch. The stone vessel slipped to the ground and spilled its contents.

'Dow! It's Dow! She's come back!'

The chunky old woman came waddling over as fast as she could with her arms spread wide and tears streaming down her cheeks. Dow's two older sisters stood for a moment in disbelief, then joined their mother in pursuit of their long lost sister. The impact of the older woman nearly bowled over both Lek and Dow. Her hug was so tight it almost took the wind out of the frail girls. With the other two girls joining in the hug, all five women, both young and old, were overtaken with deep sobs.

Dow's mother couldn't stop saying, 'You're back, you're back! I didn't think I'd ever see you again!'

Off in the distance an old man and his son could see what looked like a struggle involving the women of their family. They immediately dropped what they were doing and came running to help, scythes in hand.

'Get out of here!' the old man bellowed, his scythe raised high above his head. 'Leave my family alone!'

All five women scurried back, cowering from this maniacal antagonist. Son took up a position on the right of his father, the two together were a force indeed.

'Wait, wait! It's Dow, she's come back!' the old woman screamed.

The old man bent his head forward to get a better look at the two young boys in front of him. First he looked at Lek, then at Dow, back to Lek, back to Dow. His scythe slowly dropped to his side as he stood concentrating on Dow. Her hair was short and she wore boys' clothes but slowly he began to see the resemblance of the daughter he had put on that train so long ago.

'Is that really you, daughter?' he said in disbelief.

'It's really me, *Por*,' she offered in return.

'Why do you look like a boy?' he asked.

Dow wiped the remaining tears from her eyes and explained that it was a long story, one which they had plenty of time to hear later. She was now back home with her family that she had waited too long to be with. And she had brought a surprise.

'This is a girl we call Lek. We don't know if that is her real name but it's the one she uses now. We both think she might be the sister we lost when I was too young to remember. Do you think maybe this could be your daughter, too? She looks like one of us.'

Por and *Mae* turned to each other in unison with a look that revealed they were wondering how to handle the situation. As Lek looked around at the others, their grave faces gave away the answer.

'We can talk about that later,' *Mae* said. 'Right now let's all go inside and find out what you have been doing all these years. Are you hungry?'

Dow looked at Lek and rolled her eyes to indicate that she was still stuffed from all the food she ate on the train. Lek returned her look with sad eyes. Even though Dow hadn't figured it out yet, Lek knew deep down that her long journey was about to be hit with another disappointment. Nonetheless, they had escaped a nasty situation and at least one of them was home.

At that moment, Dow's second and previously closest brother, Chatchai, came walking into the yard. He was carrying a tray with a few leftover pieces of chicken that he had been trying to sell to the passengers on the train.

'Chatchai, look! Dow's back!' Dow's oldest sister, Noot, shouted.

'That's Chatchai? He looks so big,' Dow marveled. He was a good-looking young man and both she and Lek had noticed him at the train station.

'Is that really you, Dow?' he asked as he came running over.

'It's really me,' Dow repeated. 'Was that you we saw working the trains just like we used to dream about when we were kids?'

'You're still kids,' *Por* interjected with a sly grin as he started for the front door.

'Yeah, well it's only part-time. Helps out the family budget, you know. I'm not driving the train, yet, but some day . . . ' Chatchai let his words fade out as he joined *Por* and the rest of the family in a procession toward the house.

'It's good to see you, I'm glad you're back,' he said as he leaned over and put his arm around her shoulder. 'Who's your friend?'

Dow threw him a sideways glance, no longer sure how to answer that question. 'She might be our sister,' she said tentatively.

'Yeah? Welcome home,' he said to Lek as he threw his arm around her, too. The gesture made Lek feel welcome even though she was a little embarrassed by the forwardness.

The entire family was now together at last. The entourage made its way up the steps into the small, wooden, stilted farmhouse. As they entered the living room area, Dow walked over to a particular spot and stepped cautiously onto a particular floorboard. Much to her delight it creaked.

'Look, it still works, just like I told you,' she said to Lek. Chatchai and Noot quickly took up positions at a couple of the other floor boards and stepped down to make them creak. Within seconds they were stepping down in order, trying to creak out an old Thai song. Lek laughed in delight as her friend's old story came to life.

'Stop that!' *Mae* said in mock anger. 'Someday all three of you will fall right through!'

Mae threw a look over to *Por* who shrugged in embarrassment for not having fixed the floor after all these years. The rest of the family roared their approval, Dow had indeed returned and she still remembered something that the rest of the family had long ago forgotten.

CHAPTER 29

'Nha, go over to the night market on Samatakan Road and get us some soft drinks?' *Por* said to Dow's second sister. As he handed her some money, Dow's oldest brother, Seua, offered to go along and help. The look *Mae* and *Por* gave him and each other confused Lek and Dow, although the others already seemed to know whatever secret it was that Seua was letting out.

'Get some beef, too. We haven't enough for supper tonight now that we have a couple more places to set at the table,' *Mae* added, then turned to Seua and said, 'You come back now, you hear me!'

Seua lit up a cigarette, cocked his head and gave *Mae* a sly grin that bordered on nasty. 'Don't you worry about me.'

After the two had left, the rest of the family sat in a semicircle on the floor, all of them eager to hear Dow and Lek's story. The next hour or two was spent spinning the web of train station and orphanage kidnappings, and oppressive living in Bangkok. Dow's family sat silent in awe and horror, occasionally gasping, continuously shaking their heads in disbelief.

When Nha returned from the market alone, *Por* grumbled about how he didn't know what he could do about Seua. It was becoming apparent to Lek and Dow that he had become somewhat of a problem for the family, but they didn't yet know what it was he was up to.

'What about Lek?' Dow inquired, 'Is she or is she not my little sister?'

Again *Mae* and *Por* looked at each other with sorry expressions. Lek felt her heart move up into her throat. She knew what was coming and didn't particularly want to hear the confirmation of her fears.

'Dow, this is going to be very difficult to tell you,' *Mae* began as she stared intensely into Dow's eyes. 'Minutes after you were born I gave birth to your twin sister, but she died.'

Dow was dumbstruck. She and Lek had grown up together and were sisters no matter what her mother was saying.

Mae turned to Lek and said, 'I'm very sorry that you got your hopes up, I really am. You seem like such a nice girl to have to live the life you've been given. I think it's better that you know now, though, so you won't have to live here with a false perception of who you are.'

Filled with mixed emotions, Lek didn't know what to say. She had suspected since the awkward moment in the yard that she wasn't part of this family, yet *Mae* had said one phrase that stuck in her mind and relieved some of the fear that was burning inside her. 'You said "live here", does that mean I can stay?' she asked with a cracking voice, trying to choke back the tears.

'Of course you can stay!' *Mae* and *Por* said in unison.

'You've brought back our daughter,' *Mae* continued. 'We owe you a lot for that. Besides, where would you go? Back to Bangkok?'

'No thanks,' Lek said emphatically. The thought of seeing Rattana and Siriporn again and what they would do to her made her shudder.

'Then it's settled,' *Por* announced. 'Now we can get on with the business of being a whole family again, with an extra addition, of course. The best way to start? Let's eat!'

'Oh, *Por*. You always think of your stomach,' *Mae* joked, and as she got up to gather more food, Dow and Lek hugged each other and began to cry. It was now all settled. All those years of living in hell were all now behind them. They were finally part of a real family.

'What's with them?' Chatchai wondered.

'Oh, never mind,' Noot said, wiping a tear from her eye.

For the rest of the afternoon time seemed to stand still. The reunited family was content to sit around the living room floor and eat, reminisce and catch up on each others' lives. While the rest of the world continued its busy schedule, this family was happy to let it happen without them.

A southbound train passed in the distance unnoticed. A soft breeze that blew across the golden rice fields did so unnoticed. Even the sun set without this family noticing it.

Not long after the sun set *Mae* and Nha prepared another meal. Lek was already full and Dow was absolutely stuffed, but both were learning that this is what you do at family reunions. *Por* was in his element and Chatchai remarked how he hadn't seen him laugh so much in years. 'Or eat so much either,' he added with a sly grin.

The last meal had a predictable effect on the family making each and every one of them sleepy. Neither Lek nor Dow wanted this day to end but they both knew there were many more to come and eventually the busy day caught up with them. At *Mae*'s urging, Noot and Nha prepared places in the girls' room for Lek and Dow to sleep. And as *Por* opened up a bottle of rice whiskey he had made the previous month and poured himself a glass, the four girls retired to their bedroom. Three of them stayed awake talking for a while but within minutes the fourth, Lek, was sound asleep.

CHAPTER 30

The roosters began crowing just after sunrise, waking Lek from her comfortable sleep. She hadn't slept that soundly in a long, long time and had absolutely no desire to end her bliss so soon. But after having grown up in the city, she wasn't used to farm noises and try as she might, she couldn't block them out. After twenty or thirty minutes of keeping her eyes tightly closed, she finally realized it was a losing battle and sat up to stretch.

In the diminishing darkness, Lek could see that the other girls were still asleep, so she quietly rose to go outside. On her way through the living room she tried to remember where all the squeaky floorboards were so as to avoid them, to no avail. As noisy as she thought she was being, it didn't seem to matter as the rest of the family had long ago become accustomed to all the early morning noises and none awoke.

Once outside, Lek stood in the middle of the courtyard and stretched again, reaching for the sky with as much effort as she could possibly muster. She took a deep breath and filled her lungs with clean, cool morning air. Unlike city air, the freshness of the farm air seemed to give her body new strength. She was going to like it here.

The farmhouse where she had spent the night was smaller than she had imagined, but was built up on stilts just like Dow had told her. Underneath, two water buffalo were tied to the stilts with ropes strung through their noses. They were so big that Lek couldn't help but imagine if they were scared or angered they could probably pull the house down. She made a mental note to try not to upset them.

The roosters started up their chorus again when the tip of the bright orange sun peeked through a small hole in the clouds. Lek followed her long, faint shadow over toward the chickens as they pecked the ground in search of left over meal. As Lek got closer, a rat scurried off behind the coop nearby. Her heart thumping, she decided she really didn't need to get that close a look at the chickens after all.

A small barn stood guarding the yard about fifty meters from the house and both it and the chicken coop looked as though they had been thrown together in haste. The old, unmatched wood they were made of was rotting away, creating large gaps in the walls and the thatched roofs that overhung their sides were in dire need of repair. The farmhouse was well made; Lek wondered why they had let the barn and chicken coop fall into such disrepair.

Lek made her way toward the back and the open fields behind, passing more chickens in a grassy area along the side of the barn. A short distance off to her left, a handful of papaya trees grew next to a medium sized vegetable garden. Beyond that, bordered by the bamboo forest, rows and rows of corn grew in different stages of development. Golden waves of rice made up the rest of the farm and stretched almost as far as Lek could see. They came to an end near the horizon which was blocked by patches of thick jungle and an occasional thatched roof.

This was Lek's new home. For as long as she could remember she dreamed of living in a place like this and she wanted to stay forever. Last night they told her she could and she decided then and there she would do whatever it took to keep them from changing their minds. Work in the fields, feed the chickens, clean the house, cook the meals, whatever they wanted her to do she would do it with a smile and a thank you.

Scruff, thump, groan. All of a sudden Lek's blissful thinking was interrupted by strange noises. She cautiously made her way back to the front of the barn to where the noises were coming from and peeked her head around the corner. What looked like a grown man was laying face down in the dirt just inside the wooden fence that marked the entrance to the farm. When he rolled over, Lek saw that it was Seua.

'Seua? Are you okay?' Lek said as she ran over to help him up.

'I'm okay! I'm okay!' he slurred and pushed her away.

His breath smelled strongly of whiskey and cigarettes. 'I can take care of myself.' He righted himself, took two stumbling steps, then fell down again.

'Let me help you,' Lek insisted.

'Yeah, okay, maybe, but sssshhhh, we don' wanna wake anybody up,' he slurred back at her.

'I don't know how we'll manage that one but we'll sure give it a try.'

Lek could see that Seua's eyes were bloodshot and unfocused. She doubted he knew who she was. His lip was split, his clothes torn and dirty and she guessed he had had a rough time getting that far by himself. She threw his arm around her shoulder, steadied herself, then without much help, she managed to get the two of them through the front door of the house.

Almost immediately, the door to *Por* and *Mae*'s room flew open. A very agitated *Por* stood in the doorway looking at them with burning eyes. He spoke with such bitterness it made Lek cringe.

'Put him down right there!' *Por* commanded and the way he spoke made Lek feel as if she had done something wrong. She carefully let Seua down to his knees and gradually released her support. Not knowing what she had done wrong nor what to do next, she slowly backed away. *Por* paid no more attention to her, though, his focus was on his oldest son.

'Drunk again. Look's like you've been in a fight, too. You and your no good friends have no responsibility whatsoever. When are you going to see you're killing yourself, huh?!'

'Shut up you old fool! What do you know, anyway? I don't need to hear this shit.'

'Why I ought to . . .' *Por*'s raised his hand and started toward him but *Mae* quickly stepped in between. *Por* flashed her a look of disgust but let it go.

'Ought to what, you old bastard? You want to fight me? You think you can hurt me, you old fart? Come on,' Seua said. As he tried to stand he lost his balance, fell to the floor and broke the whiskey bottle he had in his hand, cutting himself.

Por shook his head in disgust. 'We'll talk about this when you're sober. Right now, get out of my sight!'

The rest of the family was now awake and as most of the siblings stood watching the event unfold, Nha quietly walked over to Seua and started cleaning up the broken glass.

'Get out of your sight? You want me, your oldest son, to get out of your sight?' Seua slurred his response, paying no attention to Nha. Instead, he pointed to Lek and said, 'You let this sleazy vagabond stay here, no questions asked, and you want me to get out of your sight? You old twit.'

All eyes turned to Lek who was by now hiding in a corner, trembling, not sure of what was happening before her. Her early morning bliss of being part of a perfect family was taking an unexpected twist.

Dow gave her a confused shrug. It was all new to her, too, and she had no idea how to respond. She turned to Chatchai for help but he was busy looking back and forth between Seua and *Por* to see if he would be needed to step in before a fight ensued.

'Yeah, you!' Seua continued, looking at Lek. 'Do you think you can just move right in here like you own the place? What's your scam?'

Lek was both confused and petrified. Just minutes ago she had helped him into the house and if she hadn't, he would probably still be face down in the dirt.

Without saying a word, she rose to her feet, looked around at all the faces that were fixed upon her, then made a wide arc around Seua and ran outside.

'Lek, wait!' Chatchai called after her. The insensitivity of Seua's outburst and the effect he could see it had on Lek took precedence over whether or not *Por* would physically attack Seua. In fact, at this point he considered doing it himself. But when Lek didn't stop after he called to her, both he and Dow ran out the door in pursuit. On the way, Chatchai gave Seua a little nudge that caused him to grunt and fall over.

'Wait, Lek!' Chatchai called again. Lek stopped running and stood still with her head bowed and her eyes pointed straight down at her feet.

'He's drunk,' Chatchai continued once he caught up with her. 'He doesn't know what he's saying. None of us feel that way. As far as I'm concerned you're more than welcome here.'

'I don't care what anybody says, you're still my sister and you always will be,' Dow added after she caught up with them, too. 'I'm as shocked as you are about what Seua was doing.

'Hey, don't worry yourselves about all this,' Chatchai tried to sound reassuring as he addressed the both of them. 'Seua really isn't a bad guy. He's pretty likable when he's sober, but when he gets drunk, he's got a mean streak and a quick temper. Chances are he probably won't remember any of this when he wakes up anyway, so if I were you I wouldn't even mention it to him. I know it's not something you'll be able to forget easily but let *Mae* and *Por* handle it. After all, they've had plenty of practice.'

'Yeah, let them handle it. Besides, it's only the beginning of our first full day here. Let's not do anything foolish that we might regret later.' Dow said as she put her arm around Lek's shoulder.

Chatchai followed suit and put his arms around the both of them and the three stood huddled together with their heads down.

'I've got an idea,' Chatchai said. 'Let's work this morning's southbound together. It's fun, you'll love it.'

'Yeah, the three of us can do it just like we used to dream about,' Dow said enthusiastically.

Lek looked up at Dow and Chatchai and managed a smile. As painful as the Seua incident was, what was happening now showed her that being part of a family meant sticking together during crises.

'Great! Let's get moving,' Chatchai commanded. 'We've only got a couple of hours to get ready.'

Chatchai led the trio over to the barn where he had set up a little shop area just inside. It was complete with a workbench, a barbecue, cooking tools and primitive packaging material. For the next couple of hours the three prepared meals to sell at the station.

Following Chatchai's instructions, Lek and Dow helped him barbecue chicken, make green papaya salad, and cut up string beans and cabbage. None of the three went back into the house during this time and didn't know or seem to care how the Seua incident was resolved. The work they were doing kept them preoccupied and at least for the time being, each forgot about the morning's event.

Preparations complete, they put their wares on tin platters and made the short walk over to the train station where they joined about twenty of the local villagers who had gathered to sell food. At 11.15 a.m., the southbound train arrived full of weary and hungry passengers. It only stopped for about ten minutes and due to the short amount of time it was stopped at the station, none of the merchants were allowed to board. All transactions were done through the open windows and Chatchai, Lek and Dow had to work quickly to try and satisfy their customers.

With hungry passengers not yet fed and eager merchants wanting to maximize their sales, some transactions were made even as the train was set in motion and pulling away from the station. No one seemed to pay much attention to the inherent danger of running on uneven ground as they tried to keep pace with the accelerating train. The extra ten or fifteen baht was worth the effort.

The rush of the brief encounter left Lek, Dow and Chatchai in a state of excitement and as they met up among the mingling merchants and set off for home, the high they had achieved seemed to float them down the road. Singing and laughing as they went, Lek and Dow's new life made their awful past seem like a distant memory.

The morning and afternoon trains became a daily routine for the three young merchants. Up every morning at 7 a.m. to eat breakfast and prepare food, they usually finished a little after two in the afternoon when the last train left. This allowed them nearly a full afternoon to help with chores around the farm and since the money they made was shared with the rest of the family, *Por* and *Mae* were happy to let them continue.

Occasionally Chatchai was commandeered to work an entire day with *Por* in the fields, especially after Seua's binges, which always rendered him unable to work. Chatchai had been correct in his analysis of Seua, he was quite likable when he was sober, incorrigible with whiskey in his belly. Even though he went out with his friends almost every night, luckily for everyone he only drank to excess no more than once or twice a month.

With all this going on, life on the farm continued. Lek and Dow considered themselves to be true sisters, to the rest of the family Lek was a welcome friend. The two girls finally learned what it was like to live life as part of a real family. Daily routines that might have been boring were spiced up with the trials and tribulations of the individuals who performed them.

CHAPTER 31

What had started out as a short trip to Pattaya to find her daughter, turned into a seven-and-a-half-year singing career for Nid. Over that period of time she had continued her search of the town and the surrounding areas and although she never lost interest, she had explored so many options without ever receiving as much as a tiny clue she had begun to slow down her efforts over the past couple of years.

Nid had watched Pattaya grow from a small fishing community frequented by wealthy Bangkokonians getting away from the rat race of their daily lives to a much larger tourist resort. It had grown without the benefit of proper planning and was beginning to show the effects of its expansion without design. The unspoiled beaches that had attracted so many travelers began to show the early effects of pollution and the tiny roads that circumvented the town were too small to handle the influx of traffic.

All that time Nid had kept her room at the Charoen Guest House, even as larger and more expensive hotels cropped up around it. Her obsession with finding her daughter had kept her there because she knew deep down that Malee and her only hope of finding Lek was somewhere in that town, and the Charoen Guest House with its central location proved to be a good place to work out of when she conducted her search.

She also kept her job at the Malee Cafe. She viewed it more as a good job than a career, yet her durability paid off. As she watched many of the other entertainers come and go, her years of commitment enabled her to work her way up to being one of the top name regular performers.

The owner of the club left most of the day-to-day operations to his manager and never talked much with the regular employees other then to say hello, hire or fire them or hand them their pay packets. Being the boss, he liked to keep his distance to avoid being accused of playing favorites. Nid, however, had been there such a long time she knew most of the top name performers as well as he did. The stars always told him that it was only a matter of time before Nid was discovered by an agent or a record producer and become a star herself.

The owner owned a large beachfront compound in the neighboring town of Sriracha and two or three times a year he invited the biggest names in the entertainment business to party there. These parties had become legendary affairs among the professionals and lay people alike, and since most of them had come to know Nid so well, it was at their urging that the boss invited her to his New Year party.

The day of the party Nid was so excited she couldn't sit still. She tried on at least four different dresses before she was comfortable with one of them and her hands were so shaky she had to ask the receptionist downstairs to help her put on her makeup.

The older woman worked slowly and carefully and her soothing talk managed to calm Nid's nerves.

'You've been working there quite a while, dear, it's about time they involved you in some of their out of work activities.'

'You don't understand,' Nid protested. 'Only stars and big name producers will be there.'

'So, they're all people aren't they? You have to stop looking at them as if they were some kind of god. They're no different than you are. As a matter of fact you're one of them now. You've earned it, now take advantage of it.'

'I suppose you're right,' Nid confessed.

'Suppose nothing! I know I'm right. You'll probably come home from that party tonight with a recording contract in your pocket.'

'Let's not get carried away, it's only a party.'

'I know, but anything can happen, right? They wouldn't have invited you if they didn't think highly of you.'

The party was scheduled to begin at four in the afternoon and her boss had told her he would send a car to pick her up around half past three. At 3.30 p.m. sharp, the women's conversation was interrupted by the honk of a car horn. Nid's driver had arrived.

It was a rather short ride through the holiday traffic and thirty minutes later Nid could feel the tension build in her stomach as they pulled into the driveway that led to her employer's home. The driver parked the car, ran around to open her door, then led her through the vestibule between the garage and the main house into the back yard.

Nid silently gasped at the decadence of the spread in front of her. A large, perfectly manicured lawn sprawled all the way to the ocean's edge. It was protected from the diligent waves by a concrete wall high enough to do its job but low enough not to impede the view. Large canopies to protect the guests from the glaring sun were stretched over various parts of the garden. Rows of tables with white tablecloths, real silverware, imported china and crystal chalices were lined up under the canopies in the middle of the lawn while off to one side, a countless variety of Thai and foreign food was laid out. White jacketed servants stood ready to ladle out whatever food the guests might desire. Off to the other side a small stage had been set up and a local band was playing mellow dinner music.

Everyone was eating and drinking, laughing and joking, and all seemed to be having a good time as Nid went out and tried to mingle.

She did enjoy talking with Thailand's entertainment elite but had an underlying feeling that she just didn't belong. She knew that not one of them ever did or said anything to make her feel that way but she did just the same.

As the evening wore on, everyone started loosening up, due in no small part to the amount of alcohol being consumed. Everyone, that is, except Nid. She abstained from indulging with the rest of the partygoers in fear she would make a fool of herself in front such prestigious company. She opted instead to mingle around, keep a low profile and watch the others to see how they enjoyed themselves.

After a while, hunger got the better of her and she made her way over to try out some of the food. The spread was incredible. Anything she could possibly have wanted to eat was laid out somewhere along the long tables and there was such a variety, she had trouble making up her mind what she wanted.

A little embarrassed by her indecision, Nid continually cast tentative glances at the white-jacketed servers. Each one offered their service with mechanical politeness and each one seemed to be a carbon copy of the next. That was until Nid looked down the row and one of them caught her eye. It was the hairy mole on her chin that grabbed her attention.

Nid stood for a minute to study this particular woman and thought she was probably in her mid to late thirties. She had a look about her that Nid had seen before. It reminded her of the few migrant tribal women that passed through Pattaya selling handmade crafts. Although it would be an impossible fluke of chance if it were true, she did fit the description Chalarm had given her of Malee so long ago.

Realizing the impossibility of it, Nid nonetheless walked over and asked her what her name was. The woman looked up momentarily but quickly suppressed her eyes and whispered that she was not allowed to fraternize with the guests.

'Is it Malee, by any chance?' Nid pressed on.

'How did you know that?' she replied with a mildly confused look.

Nid's heart skipped a beat and tears began to well up in her eyes. 'You can't possibly know how long I've been looking for you.'

'Why would you be looking for me?' Malee's response was now one of complete confusion.

'Do the names Lek, El or Chalarm mean anything to you?' Nid asked.

'Why?' This time Malee took a step back. Had Chalarm somehow become important enough to have connections in the entertainment field? It had been almost twelve years, wasn't she safe yet?

'I'm Lek's mother,' Nid was getting so excited she had trouble containing her emotions. 'Lek was stolen from me when she was just a baby. A long time ago I was able to track her to Chalarm but when I finally found him he told me I'd come too late. He told me about you and what you did, described you to me and told me you loved her and took her with you when you escaped. Please tell me that was you and you know where my baby is.'

'That was almost twelve years ago, I don't think she's a baby anymore,' Malee replied, her relief clearly visible. She wasn't sure whether or not to believe this woman.

'Then it was you!' Nid screamed so loud a handful of nearby guests and servers turned to see what was going on.

'Look, I'm going to get in trouble if I talk with you now. Like I told you before, all of us are under strict orders not to fraternize with the guests. But yes, that was me. If you see the head waiter, ask him to give you the address of our home office. They'll know where to find me. We can get together tomorrow if you'd like.'

'No, I finally found you and I don't want to risk losing you. Meet me over by the corner of the house out of sight in fifteen minutes. I'll clear it with the maitre d' so that you won't get in any trouble. Okay?'

'If you can get the maitre d' to come over here and tell me to my face that it's okay, then I'll be glad to meet with you over there. This is a hard job to get and I don't want to do anything that will make me lose it. If the maitre d' says no, then I'll be happy to get together with you some other time.'

'Consider it done,' Nid told her. She forgot all about being hungry and left her plate of food in front of Malee when she set out to find Malee's boss.

'I'm sorry Miss Nid, but that's against our policy. We don't allow the servant's to mingle with the guests,' the maitre d' resisted.

'You know,' Nid replied, undeterred, 'it really wouldn't take much for me to rather casually mention to the owner how I feel a little sick, probably because of the bad smelling shrimp.

'I could also start a rumor to the same effect making sure it got back to the owner from some of the most influential people at this party. I can hear them talking to him now: "How could you have hired such inferior caterers?" By the way, isn't it your job to make sure everything is perfect at these gala events?'

'That it is,' he replied with a sigh of resignation. 'If it's that important to you then I'd be more then happy to grant such a trivial request to such an important and honored guest.' He rolled his eyes, shook his head and walked away.

As Nid walked over and stood beside the corner of the main house, she kept a wary eye on the maitre d' to make sure he made good on his obligation. He did walk over and stand in front of Malee but seemed to be talking to her for an awfully long time just to tell her it was okay to meet Nid over by the house. Malee stood at attention and looked him in the eyes the whole time with an expression that never changed from one of intense interest. When the maitre d' was finished, Malee nodded her head and turned to walk in Nid's direction.

'He told me to be careful because some crazy rock star wanted to talk with me behind the main house. It was all I could do to keep a straight face. Are you really a crazy rock star?'

'A little crazy maybe but I'm no rock star,' Nid replied and the two broke into a contained chuckle.

'Oh, you don't seem too crazy to me but you truly had me scared when you said Chalarm's name. Look, my hands are still shaking.'

'Why? I mean, I know he's an animal but he's a long way from here and you said yourself it's been, what, almost twelve years?' she said.

'That's what scared me. I thought it was all just a painful nightmare that finally ended years ago. Then along you come asking me if I'm Malee and do I know Chalarm? I tried so hard to forget it ever happened and suddenly it all came rushing back.'

'What did he do to you? And my baby, did he hurt her? If he did I'll kill him!'

'No, he was never able to touch Lek. I made sure of that even though at times it wasn't easy. I wish I could forget it but I'll always remember one night when I had Lek in my arms as he began to beat me. It was all I could do to keep her from getting hit or crashing to the floor but I managed to put her down, albeit roughly while he was punching and screaming at me. She wasn't hurt, just terribly frightened. She cried uncontrollably. When he was through using me for boxing practice he told me to shut her up or he'd start in on her. I hurt so much I could barely move but I did my best to cover her with my body and rock her until she quieted down.'

'That's despicable. Why would he do such a thing? He really is a low life dog!'

'He did it because he found out I was trying to leave and he wanted to show the others that escape was not a possibility as long as he was around. I couldn't give up, though. I had to get out of there. The living conditions were terrible and we were forced to beg for money from strangers to give him while he just sat back and cooked for his own enjoyment. I'm the daughter of a tribal leader. I knew I deserved better than that. And Lek, too. She was such a good baby, I loved her so much. There was no way I could leave her there so I took her with me when I finally got away.'

'Where is she now?'

'As far as I know she's in an orphanage here in Pattaya. I left her there on the very first night after I escaped from Bangkok. I wanted to keep her and raise her as my own but I had no home, no job, no money and no place to go. Pii El, the good-hearted man who risked his life to help us escape, suggested I take her there. I knew she would at least get well-fed and be taken care of, things I couldn't offer her at the time. I could offer her one thing though; a chance to keep her identity. Before I left I pinned her name on her shirt. I don't know if they kept it but we can hope they did.

'I wanted to go back and visit her but I figured it would be better if I stayed away and let her live her own life. Every now and again I still think about her. I hope she's doing well.'

'Of course! Why didn't I think of that in the first place? Malee, I love you, I truly do! I'm sorry for what you've been through. It took a lot of courage to do what you did and I have tremendous respect for you. Thank you Malee, thank you.'

'I only did what I had to do. It didn't take a lot of courage. Pii El is the true hero. He risked it all for a couple of strangers. He didn't have to but he did it anyway.'

'What happened to him?'

'I don't know. He took me to the Red Cross in Pattaya where a group of women had joined together to help women in need. And Pii El, well, he slept a couple of hours in his tuk-tuk outside the house where he dropped me off then rode away. I never saw him again. I sure hope he didn't try to go back to Bangkok, that bastard Chalarm has a lot of connections up there and I'd fear for Pii El's life if he tried to go back to work in Patpong. I think he had a brother that worked as a driver there, maybe he went to stay with him for a while. Who knows? I only hope he's living a good life somewhere. He deserves it.'

'I'm not sure, but I don't believe he went back to Bangkok. Before I came down here I must have talked to every tuk-tuk driver in the city and I never ran across him.' Nid tried to sound reassuring but wasn't sure she was convincing, as the story Ponchu had told her about the brother killer stuck to the back of her mind. She hoped there was no connection and wasn't about to mention it to Malee.

'Well, he'll always be a hero to me. Look, it's getting late and I really should get back to work. If you wouldn't mind too much, though, I would love to see Lek when you get her back. She must be a beautiful young woman by now. I live in Naklua and our office is on the other side of the town line in Pattaya. If it wouldn't be too much trouble, you can get the address from the head waiter.'

'I'll do better then that. I'll promise you that once I get her back I'll not only bring her to see you but somehow I'll get back at Chalarm.'

'Be careful! He's a dangerous man,' warned Malee.

'He'll never know who hit him. And when it's all over, I hope we can get together again, often. You're always welcome in my home.' Nid dug through her purse and found a pen and a piece of paper, wrote down her address and handed it to Malee.

'Thanks, I'd like that. But I'm only a food server for a catering company and you're a star. Don't you think it would be improper for us to get together?'

'Nonsense! You're a wonderful woman and I'm no star, that's for sure. I'd be insulted if you didn't allow us to see each other.'

'You've got a good heart, Miss Nid. Thanks. But I've really got to run before I'm not even a food server any more. Good luck, I hope you find her.'

'Thanks to you, I'm sure I will,' Nid called after her as she left to take her place behind the food tables.

CHAPTER 32

Nid sauntered over to try and join up with the party again but by now her heart just wasn't in it. She left shortly after but on the way back to Pattaya, Nid asked her driver if he would mind taking a short side trip over to the local orphanage.

He looked at his watch and saw that it was already 10 p.m. 'Why do you want to go there at this time of night? They're probably all asleep.'

'It's a long story,' she said, 'but I have reason to believe my daughter is there. I can't know for sure unless I go. Even if she isn't, they might know where she went. It's been a long time and I can only hope.'

The driver steered the car off Sukhumvit Highway into the grounds that made up the orphanage. It was incredibly dark as not a single light was on in the entire compound. The only illumination came from the headlights of the car as they swept the main building and came to rest on what appeared to be the entrance to the office.

'Here we are Miss Nid. I'll wait for you. Good luck.'

Nid acknowledged his encouragement as she got out of the car, then nervously walked up to the door and began to pound. A few seconds later a light shone in the window of a room not too far from the entrance. It was followed by a second light that lit up over Nid and, as the front door creaked slowly open, a sleepy looking older woman stuck her frizzy-haired head out to see who had come at that time of night.

'May I help you?' she said in a crackly voice.

'I hope so,' Nid replied, her excitement mounting. 'My name is Nid Sawang and I'd like to talk to you about a baby that was left here almost twelve years ago. I have reason to believe she was my daughter who was stolen from me. May I come in?'

'Of course dear, please. You'll have to excuse the way I look. I'm not used to being up at this hour. This is usually about the time when unwanted children are left on our doorstep, not when people come to claim them.' Mae Chii Siriluk shook her head trying to get the sleep out as she opened the door to allow Nid inside.

'Thank you,' Nid replied and followed her inside. The wooden floors looked old and worn. Somewhere deep inside the darkness Nid could hear a baby start to cry. Mae Chii Siriluk stopped for a minute to listen. The crying soon faded and she resumed her walk.

She opened another door and flicked on a light, revealing a small office inside. She motioned Nid to take a seat on one side of the desk as she waddled over to occupy the chair on the other side.

'You said twelve years ago?' Mae Chii Siriluk began. 'That's a long time. How old was she when she was left here?'

'I believe she must have been a little less than a year old at the time. I was told she was left in the middle of the night, maybe sometime in the spring. The woman who left her said she pinned the name Lek on her shirt.'

'That would make her somewhere around thirteen now, wouldn't it? I'm sorry if I'm a little slow, I'm still trying to wake up. Let me see. No, we don't have any thirteen-year-old girls named Lek. Are you sure it was here?'

'Yes, I'm fairly sure it was.' Nid tried to keep calm through the intense disappointment of the devastating news that Lek was no longer there. 'Do you keep records of the children that come and go through here? Maybe she was adopted.'

'Yes, we keep records. We don't usually allow the public to see them, though. If I do have a record of her being here, how can I be sure you're really her mother?'

'I guess you can't but I promise you I am. My only proof is my knowledge of her existence and when she may have arrived here. If you'd only be so kind as to look in your records maybe you will see that I'm telling the truth.'

Mae Chii Siriluk looked at Nid's face for a moment to see if she could pick up any sign of foul play. The desperation in Nid's eyes won her over and despite normal policy to the contrary, she lifted herself out of her chair and started to look through the filing cabinet near her desk. After a few minutes she pulled out two files.

'I see we had two girls about the same age left in the middle of the night back then. One was in April and one in May. Let's see, why don't we start in April?' Mae Chii Siriluk began to paw through the pages of the first file. 'It seems our April girl did indeed have a note with her that said Lek. Does that sound familiar?'

'Yes, that's her! Malee told me she didn't want her to lose her identity so she pinned her name to her shirt. That's wonderful! Where is she now?'

'Oh, yes, Lek,' Mae Chii Siriluk said, reading further into the file folder. 'Now I remember. How could I forget? I'm sorry. What's the best way for me to say this?'

Nid feared the worse.

Mae Chii Siriluk quietly contemplated a few moments. She rubbed her chin and cast her eyes towards the floor. 'Well . . . she was kidnapped . . .'

'What?'

'Kidnapped. On her way home from school. She was walking with her best friend Sulee. Evidently the two had a quarrel and Lek raced ahead. Otherwise they probably both would have been kidnapped and we would never have known what happened to them.

'It's all coming back to me now. Sulee was distraught. I don't think she ever recovered. All along she kept saying it was her fault, that if they hadn't been fighting it never would have happened. It didn't matter what we said, there was no comforting her. Eventually she ran off. We don't know where she went.

'After Lek was kidnapped, we called the police, but at the time the two girls were only five years old. Sulee could only remember that the car was light tan in color, and that a man got into it and drove away. She said she saw Lek looking out the back window before the car turned a corner and out of sight.'

Nid sat dumbfounded. Her first promising lead and it turned out to be this.

The nun let a few moments pass before beginning to speak again. 'I don't think the police put much effort into finding her. After all, she was an orphan.

'If it's any consolation, I do have a couple of pictures of her. I remember she was a very bright little girl who did very well in school. This is the picture we took the day after she was left here . . . and this one is a picture of her when she won first prize in the *wai khru* ceremony when she was about five years old.' The older woman's shaky hands passed the pictures over to Nid.

Nid nearly choked on the lump in her throat as she studied them. It was the first time she had seen Lek's likeness since the day Pom had taken her out of her room so long ago.

Despite the devastating news, the second picture caused Nid's eyes to well up with tears of joy. Healthy and fit, Lek looked so proud as she stood next to a bowl of flowers with her principal and teacher. What a beautiful little girl. 'May I keep these?' she asked.

'Yes, of course,' Mae Chii Siriluk replied.

A honking horn broke the moment.

'What could that be?' Mae Chii Siriluk asked, annoyed.

'I'm sorry, that's my driver. He must be getting impatient.'

'Well he'd better stop before he wakes the children,' she scolded, then started to get up to tell him off.

'Please, sit down. I'm sure he won't do it again if we hurry. He's gone out of his way to bring me here tonight and I don't want him to get in any trouble.'

Mae Chii Siriluk sat back down and cast Nid a sideways glance. After years of dealing with children, she had just the right look to leave no doubt in Nid's mind that if it happened again, it would be the end of their talk.

'I don't know if it will do any good, as it was such a long time ago, but you might try checking with the police,' Mae Chii Siriluk said. 'I'm afraid I can't offer you much more than that. I don't envy the task you have ahead of you, it might not be very pleasant.'

Another honk of the horn brought a quick end to their talk. As Nid rose to leave she thanked the elder woman for her cooperation and advice.

'Good luck Miss Nid, I wish you well. Come back and see me sometime to let me know how it all worked out. Do me a favor, come during the day and leave that obnoxious, horn-blowing driver of yours at home,' she joked with a grin.

'Thanks, I will,' Nid said as she rushed out the door and into the waiting car.

'What took you so long? My boss is going to kill me,' the driver snapped once Nid was inside. He spun around and raced out of the driveway and onto the main road.

'Sorry,' Nid replied sheepishly.

'Never mind,' the driver apologized, sensing that things didn't exactly go as Nid had planned. 'What did you find out?'

'She was kidnapped about seven years ago and I have no idea where she is,' Nid replied with very little hope.

'I'm sorry,' the driver said sincerely. 'That's terrible news. I suppose you will continue to look for her. I wish you all the luck in the world. I've only known you for a short time but I think you deserve it.'

'Thanks, you're very kind. Damn! If I'd only looked here when I first arrived in Pattaya we could be together by now. What a stupid fool I am.'

'Don't be hard on yourself. How could you have known?'

The driver pulled the car in front of the Charoen Guest House and as Nid disembarked, he wished her luck saying he would like to stick around and talk more with her about it, but he was already running way too late. Nid thanked him for all he'd done, then watched as he raced off down the street.

CHAPTER 33

Nid had a lot of trouble sleeping that night, only dozing on and off for an hour at a time. She was constantly having nightmares resulting from the picture *Mae* Chii Siriluk gave her that showed what Lek looked like when she first arrived at the orphanage. The dreams were so realistic Nid could feel the dirt on Lek's face and the hunger in her stomach. She could even hear her crying. Try as she did, though, she could never seem to reach quite far enough to save her.

At 5.30 a.m. she finally gave up trying to sleep. Getting out of bed, she dressed and walked out to the street and boarded a songthaew headed for the police station.

Nid knew it was way too early to be there, and the night clerk wasn't much help. When the shift change went through at around 7:30 a.m., Nid was passed around to a few officers before finally ending up at the desk of a young, low ranking policeman who had an air about him; he seemed to think he knew everything.

Once Nid explained her story, the officer just shook his head. 'Look,' he began, 'we're on a tight budget here. If you'd like to spend some time, and money, we might be able to ask around. I can't guarantee you anything, though. It was such a long time ago.'

Nid didn't even flinch. Maybe she was just overtired; what the officer was suggesting didn't even register with her. He took that as a sign of encouragement.

'The only children I ever deal with are those used in child labor scams around the tourist bars late at night. You know, selling candy and toys to the tourists. But those children are always illegal immigrants, either from Cambodia, Laos or Burma. Every once in a while, when the complaints start piling up, we go out and round them up, detain them, then deport them to their home countries. They always come right back, though, the first chance they get. Perhaps this Lek of yours is craftier than the rest. Perhaps she is better at hiding, but I doubt it. Sooner or later we catch them all, and so far anyway, I haven't caught anyone fitting the description you're giving me.'

Nid sat quiet and listened. She had seen the little children pestering tourists at night sometimes when she walked through Soi Marine Plaza on her way to Malee Cafe. She never thought to look for Lek.

'My guess is, if she was kidnapped here in Pattaya, the kidnapper probably would not want to use her here. My guess is that if she really was kidnapped here, they probably took her to some other touristy spot, like Bangkok, or Phuket, or maybe Chiang Mai,' the young officer postulated. 'And if I had to pick one of those locations, Bangkok is the closest, easiest to get to, and easiest to hide. If I were you, I'd look there first.'

Bangkok. Nid didn't cherish the thought of returning there. She considered what the officer was saying, and decided that maybe he was right. Only one way to find out.

Nid thanked the officer, gave him a *wai* and left the station. She was oblivious to the officer's reaction of her not giving him a monetary thanks.

Nid returned to her room, packed a few belongings and was on the next bus to Bangkok. By noon she was in a tuk-tuk heading across the big city toward the only police station she knew, over at Lumpini.

Nid wasn't able to sleep during the bumpy bus ride, and by this time, she was tired and discouraged. She didn't know whether anyone at the police station would be able to help her. She went inside anyway and asked around. After being directed here and there, around the building and in and out of a handful of offices for over an hour, Nid finally found someone willing to listen to her plight.

'Hello, my name is Officer Wichai,' he introduced himself. 'Please have a seat. What can I help you with today?'

'I'm looking for my daughter,' Nid began. She had already told her story to what seemed like everyone in the building and she was bordering on exhaustion.

'You've come to the right place,' Officer Wichai reassured her. And as Nid repeated her story yet one more time, the uniformed officer wrote down most of the details, including her home and work phone numbers.

'Is there any hope of finding her?' Nid pleaded. This time she was a bit more encouraged because he at least seemed to be listening.

'I'll have to be honest with you. The chances of finding her are slim at best. I'll have some of my people look into it and if we do turn up anything I'll be sure to contact you right away.'

Nid stared at the floor. The disappointment of the day's outing combined with the lack of sleep from the night before was almost too much. 'Thank you,' she managed to mumble. 'There is one more thing, though. Do you know of a man that works in Patpong by the name of Chalarm?'

Officer Wichai looked concerned. 'The cook?'

'Yes, the cook.' Nid went on to explain all about what Pom and Malee had told her about his operation, what he had done to Malee and how he fit into the whole picture of Nid's missing daughter.

'That's all very interesting,' he told her after he'd written down most of what she'd said. 'I'll make sure to hand this over to the right department so they can have a look into this matter. Thanks for the information.'

'Thank you for taking the time to listen to me. I just hope something happens soon. I miss my baby.'

'We'll do the best we can.'

Now even more discouraged than she was when she entered the police station, Nid picked up her tired body off the chair and quietly walked out to catch a tuk-tuk back to the bus station. Three dismal and lonely hours later she was back in her room getting ready for work. Her favorite American song, 'I'll Be There' by the Jackson 5 was stuck in her head and she vowed to herself that she would sing it again that night. She had enough knowledge of the English language now to understand every word. She sung it to herself when she was lonely and needed to express how she felt about her missing daughter. 'Whenever you need me, I'll be there.'

About a week and a half later as Nid was walking up to the Malee Cafe to go to work, she was greeted by Malee with a newspaper in her hand and a big smile on her face. Without saying a word, she handed the newspaper to Nid and pointed to a small article on the third page. It read:

A Patpong man was arrested yesterday for human rights violations, kidnapping and running an illegal scam on tourists. The Bangkok police converged on him after receiving an anonymous tip from a concerned citizen. The police have identified the man as Chalarm and are holding him without bail until a hearing can be arranged sometime tomorrow. No official details were given but it is believed he was using kidnapped children and deceived indigents to run a begging scam on unsuspecting tourists.

'That's great news!' Nid screamed at Malee.

'I know. I also think I know who the "concerned citizen" was. Am I right?'

'Shh, don't tell anybody,' Nid said. She then told Malee about Lek being kidnapped.

'I'm sorry about Lek. If there's anything I can do to help, please let me know. I really mean it.'

'Thanks, but you know, one battle at a time.'

CHAPTER 34

From the thirteenth to the seventeenth century, elephants played a large role in Thai folklore. Regarded as the supreme weapon of the time, sometimes single battles waged with elephants decided the outcome of larger conflicts. During that period, Thai royalty held them in great numbers, treated them with utmost respect and even gave many of them honorable names.

Born out of that era and continued ever since, a festival celebrating the importance of elephants in Thai history is held every year on the third weekend in November in Surin province. The locals there invite people from all over the country to take part in what is called the annual elephant roundup. During this time, many countrymen give their elephants a well-deserved holiday from working in the jungle and converge on the town, not only to honor the hard working pachyderms, but to show off their skills by competing in various contests as well. It is a festive occasion that allows everyone who takes part a temporary reprieve from the daily grind of making a living.

November was approaching fast. Although no one in Dow's family had ever been to the event, they had all heard about it. *Por* had always passed it over as an extraordinary expense and until now, everyone had agreed with him.

Chatchai was the first to have planted the seed. He had heard about the good times had at the festival every year from train passengers returning home and despite *Por*'s misgivings, had always dreamed of someday going himself. In his enthusiasm, he painted such a vivid picture of the fun that Lek and Dow were quick to join forces with him in support of the idea.

'So, when are you going to ask them?' Chatchai asked Lek and Dow as the inseparable trio returned from working the afternoon train.

'Us? You said you'd ask them,' Lek replied.

'Why do I always have to do the dirty work?'

'Because you're the oldest,' Dow reminded him.

'Besides, you're a boy. *Por* and *Mae* will listen to you, they like you better then us,' Lek chipped in.

'You know that's not true,' Chatchai disagreed.

'What's not true? That you're a boy or that they like you better?' Dow teased.

Chatchai mockingly chased after Dow with his fist raised as the three of them laughed off her wisecrack.

All three knew that if they had a favor to ask of their parents, Chatchai would be the one most likely to get it granted. None of them truly expected *Por* and *Mae* to agree to grant them a favor as big as the one they were about to ask but they had been thinking about it for a while and decided it would be worth trying.

They decided that if they couldn't convince *Por* or *Mae* to go, they would try to convince them to let the three teens go alone. Wishful thinking, maybe, but they had spent plenty of time preparing their case. They wanted to show how responsible they had been, how their train business had grown and how they had done it by themselves.

'I don't know,' was *Por*'s initial response, spoken with obvious hesitancy. 'I sure can't get away to go to any party and you kids are still too young to be out meandering around by yourselves.'

'Oh come on *Por*,' *Mae* broke form to stick up for the kids. 'Aren't you the one who's always telling me I don't give our children enough room to grow into individuals? Besides, they've shown us they can be responsible and it'll only be for a couple of days.'

'Yeah, we could leave on the afternoon train, spend two nights and come back on the morning train two days after we left. We'd only miss working a few trains and that won't kill the family budget, will it?' Chatchai pleaded the case.

'No, it won't,' *Por* conceded. 'But where will you stay for two nights?'

'We can get a cheap room in a hotel near the roundup.'

'You don't honestly believe I'm going to allow two girls and a boy to share a hotel room together unsupervised, do you? Do you think I'm crazy?'

'Come on, we're family. What could possibly happen?'

'I don't even want to think about what could happen,' *Por* resisted.

'You mean to tell me you don't trust your own children?' *Mae* piped in for their defense. 'I think we've raised them better than that.'

Por began to recognize he was outnumbered and fighting a losing battle. He finally bestowed upon them the closest he could come to his permission when he allowed that if it was okay with *Mae*, it would be okay with him.

During the remaining few days before their departure, the three would-be travelers worked hard to save up a little extra money for the journey. When the day finally arrived they had managed to put together a few hundred extra baht above what they normally contributed to the family budget. Confident that it would be plenty, they boarded the northeast bound rapid number 31 for the 45 minute ride to Surin at a little past three in the afternoon on 15 November.

The short ride through the countryside passed quickly and in no time they found themselves disembarking from the train and out on the streets of an unfamiliar town. Resembling three captive monkeys let out of their cage for the first time, the three teens bumbled and bumped their way around this little hamlet without a clue or a plan, giggling and laughing as they went.

Just the fact that they were there was enough to cause them to momentarily forget the particulars of their journey, but the sheer amount of elephants added even more confusion to their quest. They had expected there would be a lot, but had no idea there would be this many. The little town of Surin had become an ocean of grey with large pachyderms, babies and all sizes in between crowding the tiny streets. Each animal was attended by a man or a boy, lazily tapping them on their legs with a rod to direct them.

It was Dow who finally brought them around to their senses when she remembered that they should probably ask someone where the festivities would be taking place and where they might be able to get a cheap room for a couple of nights. Finding that room was remarkably easy given the amount of people that were in town and they managed to secure a place in a hotel not too far from the train station and just a few blocks from the main area of the festivities. It had a large bed and a modern Thai bathroom, and was well within their budget.

After checking in, they discovered that the water worked fine and all three took time to wash before heading out into the chaotic streets.

And chaotic they were. Engulfed in a carnival atmosphere, food vendors and craft booths lined the sidewalks and peeked out around the walls of elephants. Thai music played on makeshift stages on nearly every corner. And of course elephants, lots and lots of elephants meandered around the little streets making any other traffic next to impossible.

Dodging them as they walked, the three from Buriram tried their best to make their way to the main area.

'Why walk when we can ride?' Chatchai suggested when he found a homemade sign promising cheap elephant rides. After a couple minutes of bargaining, he managed to talk the handler into taking them to their destination for twenty baht.

Negotiations complete, the large elephant then responded to its master's command and bowed down to its knees. The three willing customers climbed up into a wooden seat strapped over its back and were soon underway.

Rocking back and forth with each step the elephant took, Lek, Dow and Chatchai slowly made their way to an open field just on the outskirts of the small town. The beast's master walked slowly along its side, gently tapping the elephant's shins with a switch.

The field was full of more elephants, some just munching on twigs and hay, others performing tricks to a delighted audience.

For the next couple of hours the kids strolled around the main field checking out the happenings, occasionally stopping to buy a bunch of bananas to supply the seemingly never ending hunger of the huge gray creatures. Lek didn't especially like the wet, slimy suction of the elephants trunks when they inhaled the food from her outstretched hand, but Dow and Chatchai enjoyed watching her pained expression so much when she did that it became somewhat of a joke. Every chance they got they bought more to coax her into feeding the giant animals. Lek managed to get used to it after a while but continued to pretend not to like it just to keep the joke going.

When evening fell, the three wanderers found themselves being cajoled into participating in an impromptu show. With a little too much pomp and circumstance, the master of ceremonies of this particular little sideshow had Lek, Dow and Chatchai lay down on the ground parallel to each other about two meters apart. At his command, a rather large elephant with a beautiful red sash draped over its back walked up and looked down at the three horizontal subjects. Again at its master's command, it stepped over them one at a time, stopping briefly between each.

Lek and Dow were too scared to look, but Chatchai played the brave warrior even though beads of sweat formed on his face and he couldn't stop his knees from shaking.

The crowd applauded politely when the performing elephant had completed its walk over the beguiled subjects and, figuring their work was done, the kids tried to leave. The M.C. wouldn't allow them to get up, though, and while they watched in a state of nervous amusement, the elephant turned around and made a second approach. At his master's command, it raised up onto its two hind legs and proceeded to navigate a course over the now squealing girls and the rigid but determined Chatchai.

This time the crowd roared its approval at the completion of the elephant's walk. Not wanting any more, the three kids immediately jumped up and rushed toward the sidelines before the master had a chance to dispute them. The M.C. had no intention of putting them through any more trickery, though. Instead, he heartily thanked them and urged the crowd to give them an ovation.

By now it was getting late for those used to keeping farm hours. So, amidst continued merrymaking, the Buriram three slowly and happily made their way back to the hotel room to retire for the night.

Once inside, the two girls pushed Chatchai aside and took command of the double-sized western-style bed. Its soft mattress and stuffed pillows promised a luxurious change from the woven mats on the floor that they were used to sleeping on. Chatchai could only look at the bed with yearning eyes as Dow wouldn't allow him near it.

The three teens slept late into the next morning, not bothering to get up until almost ten o'clock. Unfortunately for Lek and Dow, the soft bed turned out to be somewhat of a disappointment. Accustomed to sleeping on the floor, they had had a tough time getting comfortable and hadn't slept very well. Chatchai, on the other hand, had slept like a rock.

They joined the festivities once more, and watched an event that was organized for comic relief. About twenty five or thirty soldiers from the army base nearby took hold of one end of a rope. The other end was attached to a harness wrapped around the shoulders of a medium sized elephant. The public address system announced that they had chosen a smaller sized elephant to give the army a chance. This caused a chuckling murmur to waft through the crowd. When the announcer cried 'GO!' a tug of war ensued.

The elephant's trainer lightly tapped on the back of the elephant's legs as the small battalion pulled the rope with everything they had. The elephant took a couple of small steps back causing a rousing cheer of encouragement from the audience.

At just the right moment, when the confidence of the army was riding high, the trainer screamed '*By loei, by loei!*' and began to slap his elephant quite hard on its hindquarters with a switch. The elephant responded by digging in and pulling forward, causing its frustrated opponents to lurch forward in the direction of their foe. Most lost their balance, those who hung on were dragged through the dust until the trainer commanded his pulling pachyderm to stop. Again the crowd roared, this time with a mixture of laughs and cheers.

Lek, Dow and Chatchai were beside themselves in laughter. They'd never seen anything like it and were having the time of their lives. Sitting in the middle, Chatchai put his arms around both girls as they rocked in their rapture. When the commotion began to settle, Chatchai removed his arm from Dow's shoulder yet left his other arm around Lek, not catching the coy look she gave him.

It looked as though it would be a while before the next event, so the three agreed to explore more of the area. As they walked around petting and feeding the elephants, Chatchai would occasionally reach out to hold Lek's hand. He did it in such a matter-of-fact way that Lek was a bit confused over his intentions. Each time he did, though, she felt a rush of excitement.

Along the way they ran into a man with an instant camera, charging ten baht to have a picture taken next to his baby elephant. Thinking it might be a good idea to show the family back home, Chatchai talked Lek and Dow into having one made of the three of them together. With Chatchai in the middle and his arms around both girls, the entrepreneur snapped off a shot. For a moment it reminded both Lek and Dow of the last time they had their picture taken in one of the bars in Patpong. The circumstances were now so different that they were able to quickly wash away the unpleasant memory.

When it was over, the crowd began to thin out and the elephants were allowed to rest. Lek, Dow and Chatchai started to feel the effects of a full day on the move. They all agreed it would be in their best interest to return to their room to take a nap and regroup before going out for dinner.

The whole way back to their room, Chatchai kept a firm grip on Lek's hand and this time his forwardness didn't go unnoticed by Dow.

'What are you to up to?' she sang in a mocking way.

Chatchai held on tight as Lek tried to pull away from his grip. Now that his secret was out, he didn't care if the whole world knew and he wasn't about to be intimidated by his little sister.

'What's it look like?' he sang back in the same tone of voice.

Lek peered at Dow sheepishly and even though she felt the same way as Chatchai, she tried not to show it. After all, she still felt a little funny about being romantically inclined toward her sister's brother, even if they weren't actually related.

'I always thought that you two would get together someday,' Dow snickered, but the two young lovers ignored her and with Chatchai in the lead, walked ahead of her the rest of the way back to the room.

Not much was spoken as they entered the room and once inside, Lek broke out of Chatchai's grip to join Dow sprawled out on the bed. Before Chatchai had a chance to do anything else, Dow threw him a pillow and one of the blankets, again signaling that the bed was off limits. Lek tried to avoid looking at either of them and since she figured that Dow was probably the lesser of the two evils, she curled up in her direction.

Lek was the first to wake up. The last part of her dream, the only part she remembered, was of her and Chatchai running hand in hand down a dirt road toward the setting sun. Embarrassed, she quickly tried to forget it.

It was now after dark and hunger was becoming a driving force. The girls hadn't eaten since breakfast and were so hungry they would have eaten anywhere, but Chatchai wanted their last meal alone in Surin to be a special one. With Lek and Dow complaining about their hunger, the undaunted Chatchai pressed onward in search of just the right place. He knew exactly what he was looking for because Seua had told him there was at least one in every town.

Not more than 20 minutes passed in his hunt before he found what he was looking for. There, just on the outskirts of town, was a large restaurant that had no walls, only wooden posts holding up a big thatched roof. Under the roof in the center of the room were a dozen or so wooden tables surrounded by folding chairs. Set up towards the back was an open stage with a few instruments and a microphone. As they entered the area, a couple of musicians began warming up and tuning their instruments. It was just like the place Seua and Noot hung out in back in Buriram.

'Wow! How did you know about this place?' Dow marveled.

'I get around,' Chatchai replied with forced confidence.

'Yeah, right. When have you ever been here before?' Lek chided him.

Chatchai passed off her remark without comment as he led them to a seat near the stage. They were immediately converged upon by two waitresses bearing menus.

'Great, let's eat. I'm starved,' Dow commanded.

Money was getting low but they did have enough for one last little splurge, so they ordered a couple of plates of food and rice to share between them. As they waited for it to arrive, the band began to play and a young woman started to sing one of their favorite Issan songs. Lek and Dow knew the words and began to sing along, too shy to sing loud enough for anyone to hear them. Chatchai, meanwhile, reveled in the moment. Suddenly he felt as if he'd passed from being the child of his parents into being a man of his own.

As the evening wore on they indulged in the delicious local cuisine, listened to the music performed before them and allowed themselves to be swept up in the romance of the moment. A cool breeze filtered through the open restaurant and combined with the soft glow of the stage lights to create a truly romantic atmosphere. Lek and Chatchai again held hands, this time unafraid of who might see them. Lek gazed into Chatchai's eyes and watched the colorful explosions of the fireworks in the distance reflect off his pupils. 'Things haven't always gone so good for me in my life,' she said.

'But it's times like this that make it all worth it. I don't think I've ever felt the same way I feel right now. I wish I could take this feeling and somehow stick it in my pocket to bring out when I'm down or feeling bad.'

'You can,' Chatchai reassured her. 'But don't worry. If you stay with me, I promise you that things will never be as bad as they once were. You and me, together forever.'

'I love you, Chatchai.'

Dow sat quietly nearby as Lek and Chatchai huddled together, a perfect ending to a perfect day.

CHAPTER 35

The next morning came early for the three young travelers. Chatchai picked himself up off the floor, wiped his sleepy eyes, then walked over to the bed to wake the girls. Their little vacation had passed too quickly and it was now time to catch the morning train back to Buriram. Luckily they had purchased round-trip tickets before they left, for now they were out of money. Hungry as they were, breakfast would have to wait until they got back home.

The return trip went nearly as quickly as the trip up. This time it was Dow who sat quietly staring out the window. She felt a bit left out as Chatchai spun tales of his bravado and tried to impress Lek, who was already won over. Lek was somewhat bored with his rhetoric, but his hand clenched hers and that was all that mattered.

The train pulled into the Buriram station right on schedule at 10a.m. The three climbed down to the loading area with new hope and a refreshed feeling after having successfully completed a well-needed holiday. Underriding these feelings, though, was confusion as to their new roles resulting from what took place between Lek and Chatchai.

Dow was worried she would become the third wheel and feel out of place. Lek and Chatchai worried about whether or not they should tell *Por* and *Mae*, and if they didn't tell them, how they would hide it from them. That particular worry was laid to rest rather quickly, though. As the three walked away from the station, Chatchai continued to hold Lek's hand.

'What have you two been up to?' *Mae* demanded to know. None of the three had seen her standing there waiting for their arrival. She had come to greet them, not sneak up on them, and was shocked at what she had just witnessed.

'Umm,' was all that Chatchai could say as Lek pulled her hand away from his.

'I'm waiting,' *Mae* said sternly.

'Never mind, *Mae*,' Dow interjected on their behalf. 'I was there the whole time and I made sure nothing got out of hand.'

'I should hope not! And it never will either,' she said as she forcefully inserted herself between the two offending parties. 'We'll take this up with *Por* when we get back.'

The four marched home, Lek on one side, Dow and *Mae* in the middle and Chatchai on the other side. Dow continually peeked around at both Lek and Chatchai, but no one spoke until they reached the farm.

'Ah, the travelers are back,' *Por* greeted them cheerily. 'How was the trip?'

'We have to talk,' *Mae* said without allowing them to respond.

Por looked confused as the four marched by him into the house. As he turned to join the procession, he leaned over and whispered to Chatchai asking what was going on. Chatchai's only response was a sheepish look.

Once inside they all sat in a semi-circle on the living room floor as they had always done for family meetings. At *Mae*'s demand, Lek, Dow and Chatchai told them all about what had happened over the past couple of days. They disguised the romance issue as best as they could by filling in all the details of the rest of the trip but *Por* and *Mae* only heard what they wanted to hear, and what they heard was that something along romantic lines had taken place between Lek and Chatchai.

They both agreed that even though Lek was not really their daughter, she was still living under their roof and subject to their rule. They also decided both she and Chatchai were still too young to be romantically involved. Despite Chatchai's insistence that he was indeed old enough, 'after all, I'm seventeen years old!' they forbade them from any more physical contact and vowed to keep an eye on them. They made Dow promise to do the same.

As difficult as it was, over the next few weeks Lek and Chatchai adhered to the family rule. They continued to work together selling food to the passengers of the train. Surprise inspections by *Mae* made sure they didn't go astray. Dow was always around them, too. Her presence discouraged them from any relapse.

As the weeks wore on the vigilance upon them lessened and their teenage hormonal urges increased. Out of sight of everyone's watchful eyes, they spoke of maintaining their repressed love. They made a vow to each other that no matter how difficult it was, no matter what obstacles they might have to endure, they would stay together forever.

One lazy sunny afternoon after they completed working the train, *Mae* summoned Dow to help her feed the chickens. This left Lek and Chatchai alone to put away the trays and clean up the area. Having done so, Chatchai cornered Lek in front of the work bench.

'Come here,' he said coyly. 'We're alone at last.'

'Be careful,' Lek scolded him. 'Dow is right outside.'

'Never mind her, she's busy. Now it's just you and me.'

Chatchai pressed his body against Lek's, put his left hand on her ribs and leaned over to give her cheek a kiss. Getting only minor resistance, he slowly slid his hand upward until his thumb was just barely touching the bottom of her breast.

'What are you doing!?' Dow screamed as she slammed the door behind her.

Lek and Chatchai parted so quickly that Chatchai's leg caught the edge of the workbench and nearly knocked him over. Lek giggled in embarrassment, not knowing what else to do or say.

'You're lucky it was me that caught you, not *Por* or *Mae*,' Dow stated truthfully. She shook her head and smiled, amused at what she had just witnessed.

'Why aren't you out feeding the chickens?' Chatchai snapped, keeping his back turned.

'Lucky I'm not. Who knows what might have happened here if I hadn't come in when I did!'

Lek was happy to allow the two siblings fight it out without bringing her into it. She straightened herself and stood back, hoping somehow they wouldn't notice her.

Dow and Chatchai looked at each other crossly. Seeing that he was not going to be able to get any further with either of them, Chatchai left the barn in a huff to go help *Por* in the field.

The morning after the fight, Dow awoke early. She looked over at Lek sleeping next to her and felt sad. She realized that Lek had no family and was alone in the world. The feeling passed quickly when she thought about her and Chatchai. If the two of them did stay together, maybe someday they would get married. Lek would be able to make her own family and Dow would have Lek as her best friend forever.

She got herself out of bed and walked outside to view the beautiful sunrise. The sky was a gorgeous light blue without a cloud to be seen. It was the best she had ever witnessed. The roosters crowing added the perfect touch of nature to the already divine surroundings.

For the rest of the morning Dow was in an incredibly good mood and as she worked in the barn preparing for the first train of the day, she was almost giddy.

It drove Chatchai crazy. He thought she was just rubbing it in that she had caught them the day before and now had something to hold over him.

'What's with you?' he finally snapped at her.

'Never mind him,' Lek interceded. 'It's so good to see you so happy.' Dow's mood was contagious and soon had Lek feeling euphoric as well.

'She's making me crazy,' Chatchai complained after Dow had gone outside to pick some papayas, 'and so are you. I want to be alone with you so bad it hurts.'

'Calm yourself. We've got plenty of time for that,' Lek teased.

Later in the morning, as the 10 a.m. train was pulling away, Chatchai quickly made his way over to Lek. Before Dow had caught back up with them, he excitedly took her aside.

'I've got an idea,' he began, looking around to make sure no one was listening. 'This afternoon after the second train, let's sneak away over by the bamboo trees. We can tell Dow we're going into town for supplies. She'll believe us. We do need some cooking oil. It's a great excuse to be alone for a little while. Dow has to feed the chickens anyway so she won't want to come along. What do you say?'

'You're not going to try anything bad?' Lek asked.

'Of course not,' Chatchai responded indignantly. 'It's just that we never get a chance to be alone any more.'

'We're alone now,' Lek countered.

'No we're not, look at all these people.'

'There you are!' Dow said as she came running up to them. 'Chaiyo! I made two hundred baht this morning, the most ever.'

'That's great!' Lek said, putting Chatchai's conversation aside. Lek and Dow linked arms and ran ahead of him, laughing and joking as they went.

Discouraged, Chatchai walked behind. 'If we only could get rid of Dow somehow, just for a little while.'

When they got back to the farm, Chatchai went inside the house to hand over the money, while the two girls went into the barn to start preparing for the afternoon train.

'Lek, you're the best friend I could ever have,' Dow said suddenly.

'What do you mean, we're sisters.'

'No we're not. But that's okay. If you were my sister you wouldn't be able to have my brother as a boyfriend, right?'

'You mean you don't mind?'

'Nah, I thought about it this morning. I like having you as my best friend. Who knows? Maybe you and Chatchai will get married some day. Then I can have you as my best friend forever.'

'Dow, that's great! It's a little early to start talking about marriage, but whether that ever happens or not, you will always be my best friend.'

'I know, that's one of the reasons I'm in such a good mood today. By the way, what were you two trying to hide when I caught up with you this morning?'

'Chatchai said he wants to go into town to get some cooking oil after the afternoon train. He also said he wants me to go along so we can be alone for a while. I'm a bit worried about his intentions, though.'

'Ah, don't worry about it. He's my brother, he wouldn't do anything to be ashamed of.'

'You mean you don't mind if we go off together alone for a while?'

'Nah, I'll play along. I'll think of something to tell *Por* and *Mae*. You can count on me.'

The two girls immediately stopped talking when the barn door creaked open and Chatchai walked in. Seeing both girls staring at him with conspiratorial expressions just increased his paranoia. Without saying anything, he walked over and began to help with the preparations. When Lek and Dow looked at each other with sly grins, he caught their look and sighed.

'It's all set,' Lek whispered into his ear.

'What?' he said puzzled, looking between the two girls. Neither responded other than to smile at each other as they continued to shred papaya. Confused and outnumbered, Chatchai made no attempt to pursue the issue.

At 1.30p.m., they gathered the food they had prepared and made their way over to the train station. Along the way, Chatchai tried to tell Dow that he and Lek would be going into town for supplies after the train left.

'Okay, sure,' she responded in an exaggerated tone.

Lek looked at her and winked, then looked at Chatchai and shrugged her shoulders pretending she didn't know what was going on. Chatchai didn't know what to think. He let it rest hoping vainly that perhaps he had managed to fool Dow.

The three split up as they usually did, working different areas of the train to maximize sales. Business was brisk causing Lek to forget about her afternoon plans, but the 15-minute stop went quickly and soon Lek's thoughts returned to Chatchai and what he had planned for them.

Suddenly she heard a scream as the train pulled away and began to gain speed. She looked around to see where it had come from and saw people beginning to gather on the other side of the tracks. It wasn't until the tail of the train finally passed before she was able to see what they were looking at. It appeared as though Chatchai was on his knees, covered in blood.

'Dow, come quick, I think Chatchai is hurt!' she screamed as she ran in his direction.

'Dow! Dow! Chatchai's hurt!' she repeated. 'Dow! Where are you? Come quick!'

When she reached Chatchai, she knelt down beside him and tried to ascertain what was wrong. He had what looked like a large cut on the side of his head and he didn't respond to her questions. His face was ghostly white, his lips nasty blue, and he just stared into the distance. He was sitting back on his haunches with his knees pointing toward the tracks. Blood covered his face and clothes. His hands firmly gripped what looked like torn clothes and bloodied flesh.

'Dow! Where are you? Come here quick, something's wrong with Chatchai!' Lek yelled out again. Looking around to find her, she could see parts of someone's mutilated body strewn down the track. Without releasing his stare, Chatchai slowly turned his head toward Lek.

'Dow?' Lek asked softly. When he didn't respond, she let out a loud scream, 'NOOOOOOO!' before she slipped into unconsciousness.

CHAPTER 36

A few months had passed since the funeral, which itself had lasted three days, and Chatchai was still yet to speak. The trauma of the accident left deep psychological scars, and without the help of professional psychiatric care, no one was able to release him from his mental coma. Only he knew for sure what happened that day and his refusal to speak kept most of it a mystery.

Eyewitnesses provided sketchy details, but no one was overly sure of what they saw. The general consensus was that Chatchai and Dow had each been vying for the same open window of the train, each trying for the same customer to make one last sale. Evidently Chatchai either bumped into or pushed Dow out of his way causing her to lose her balance and fall.

Seeing what he'd done, Chatchai made a gallant attempt to save her, but it happened so quickly his sister never had a chance. Her momentum carried her onto the tracks and under the wheels.

When the caboose finally passed by, and the train faded into the distance, there wasn't much left of Dow's young body to cremate.

During the long months after the accident, Chatchai spent his days sitting on the front steps of the farmhouse, staring aimlessly into the plains in front of him. Only occasionally did he look down into the empty palms of his hands.

Nha had taken it upon herself to take care of him. She got him out of bed in the morning, bathed him when he needed it, dressed him, fed him, and led him out to his daily perch on the front steps of the farmhouse. And despite Lek's attempts to help, for some unknown reason, Nha wouldn't allow her to.

It broke Lek's heart. Not only would she never be able to bring back her best friend, she was extremely frustrated that she could do nothing to revive her secret love.

With no one to talk to, Lek tried to keep busy by continuing to work the trains alone. But in her mind she consistently heard Dow scream as they pulled away. The effect of those ghostly sounds made the memories of what happened excruciatingly painful. Lek worked less frequently and eventually stopped completely.

Without a job, Lek began to feel useless around the farm. The small menial chores she did were not enough to allow her to feel as if she was a valuable contributor to the family. What she wanted to do the most was take care of Chatchai, but Nha wouldn't allow that to happen.

What made matters worse was the inability of *Por* and *Mae* to look at her. Even now, a couple months after the funeral, they could only hold eye contact with her for a few seconds before they had to look away. To Lek it was as if they were saying that she was nothing more then a reminder of good luck gone bad.

She began to spend most of her time sitting alone in the bamboo forest. Amidst the quiet solitude of the lonely bamboo, she searched long and hard for some kind of answer to her predicament.

The voice in her mind kept telling her that perhaps it was time to move on. She continued to fight it because she didn't want to abandon her adopted family, especially now in this time of need. They had been too good to her to just run out on them.

She also remembered the pact she and Chatchai had made to stick together forever, no matter what happened. But her guardian spirit continued to whisper that this was no way for her to live.

It took another incident with Seua, and the family's reaction to it, for her to finally realize that the little voice inside her head wasn't lying.

It all started when once again Seua did his disappearing act after dinner. When he didn't return by the time the family was ready to bed down for the night, they all knew they were in for another one of his bouts with the bottle.

Sure enough, in the early hours of the morning, Seua returned home in a state of intoxication. This time it was a little different, however. Instead of his usual falling down drunkenness, he was able to enter the house quietly and under his own power.

With the entire household fast asleep upon his arrival, he quietly entered the room where Lek and Nha were lying peacefully, unaware of his existence, and made his way over to Lek's bed. It wasn't until he had Lek's *padung* mostly off and his hands groping her bare flesh that Lek finally came awake.

Groggy from sleep and confused over what was happening, Lek let out a muffled yelp and began trying to push him away. It only made Seua more determined and in the struggle, he managed to pin her to the bed and slide his pants to his knees.

Lek squirmed and fought him, but Seua was much stronger making Lek's a losing battle. Just a split moment before Seua was able to penetrate her, Nha came awake.

'Seua!' Nha cried out. 'What are you doing?'

Seua snapped his head around, raised his fist and made an ever so slight move toward his sister. The madness in his eyes was terrifying. But instead of going after Nha, Seua turned and struck Lek hard across the face.

Too scared to say anything else, Nha grabbed her *padung* for support and backed into the corner. She couldn't seem to get far enough away. With Seua's attention back on Lek, Nha was left to watch in silent horror the drama unfolding before her. Was what she could barely see in the dim light of the early morning really happening?

Drunk and unabashed, Seua remained towered over Lek with his genitals exposed, but made no further attempts to keep her pinned down. His eyes were wild and darting and even though he presented an image of complete madness, Lek could sense that with Nha awake, Seua wouldn't continue his sexual assault.

'What are you doing in my bed, you sleaze?' Seua half-yelled, half-slurred as he backed away from Lek.

'What are you talking about?' Lek grabbed her *padung*, covered her body and cowered away from him. The threat of physical abuse was still very real. Her lip split from his punch, she noticed the metallic taste of her own blood in her mouth. She looked to Nha for help but received no response.

Suddenly the light flicked on. *Por* stood in the doorway not believing what he was seeing. 'What are you doing in here, Seua? This is the girl's room.'

Seua gave Lek an angry look, then dejectedly pulled his pants up. Without looking at *Por*, he began his lie to redirect the blame. 'She dragged me in here. She must miss getting it from Chatchai and now wants me to fill in for him.'

'That's a lie!' Lek yelled in desperation. 'He tried to rape me!'

'Nha?' *Por* turned to his daughter. Surely she could set this all straight.

'I don't know *Por*, I was asleep,' Nha replied unconvincingly. She still wore a terrified look.

'What's going on here?' Lek was appalled. Just moments before she was engulfed in a violent nightmare. Now her honor was at stake and no one seemed to believe her. All eyes were upon her and all she could do was shake her head.

'Okay, enough. We'll settle this later,' *Por* said to diffuse the situation. Neither story was totally unbelievable, although he found it difficult to believe either one.

He walked over and grabbed Seua by the shoulder and directed him out of the door in front of him, then turned to Lek and said as calmly as he could, 'Try not to start anything. It's a difficult time for us right now.'

'I was asleep too,' Lek protested. She was now in tears. *Por*'s only response was a strange look before he closed the door behind him.

Lek slowly returned to a prone position on her bed. The terrifying incident was finally over. Or was it? As she laid in bed, staring at the ceiling, reliving the events over and over in her mind, she came to the realization that the repercussions were just beginning. Both Nha and *Por* had refused to believe her account of what had taken place. When it came down to it, they had both believed a drunk and lying Seua instead of an innocent and sober Lek. So that was what she was up against.

Lek realized she no longer belonged here with this family. With Dow gone and Chatchai incapacitated, she was nothing more then a strange visitor that had long overstayed her welcome. As painful as it might be, she had to listen to her guardian spirit and make plans to move on.

As the rest of the family awoke later in the morning and went about making preparations for another day on the farm, Lek stayed in bed until she was sure they were all outside doing their morning chores. She then quietly dressed and made her way out to Chatchai's usual perch on the front steps.

'Hello Chatchai, how are you today?' she asked. No response.

'It's me, Lek. I know you're in there. Why don't you answer me?' Again, no response.

'Never mind, if you can hear me I have some things I want to tell you. First, I love you. I know you know that but I want you to hear it from me. Do you remember when we said we would always stick together no matter what happened? I wish you would keep your end of the promise now because I need you. I really need you.'

Chatchai looked down at his hands.

'Yes, that's it, remember. It might be painful but you have to let it out, let it go. You can't keep it inside forever. Please let me help you.'

Chatchai returned his stare to the fields in front of him.

'Listen Chatchai, I love you. I always will. I think you know that but things are just too crazy around here right now. I can't stay here without your help and if you don't help me, I have no choice but to leave. Do you hear me?' Chatchai still didn't respond.

'Okay, okay. I know I said I'd never leave you but you leave me no choice. I have to go, Chatchai. I don't want to but what can I do? I will promise you this, someday I'll come back and take care of you for the rest of your life. I promise, okay?

'Chatchai, speak to me, please. I'll be on the morning train unless you can give me some kind of sign that you want me to stay.'

Chatchai never broke his stare. He apparently either didn't comprehend what Lek was saying or was unaware that she was even talking. Maybe he didn't even know that she was there. Lek's low heart sank further as she rose to go into the house, leaving him alone in his inner hell.

She entered her room and sat on the edge of her bed. A couple of feet from her, pinned to the wall, was the picture of her, Dow and Chatchai that they had taken when they were in Surin. She remembered how happy they all were when it was taken. They truly were on top of the world. How fast things seemed to change.

She reached under one of the floorboards near where Dow used to sleep and pulled out two hundred baht left over from the escape they had made from Bangkok. She then reached behind her pillow and produced the old mood ring Dow had given her for her birthday. It was scratched and bent and only fit on her little finger. She slid it on and remembered the day back in Soi Cowboy. Dow was such a special person in her life, she missed her terribly.

Finally, she wrapped a few of her clothes into a small bundle and with one last look around her room, she closed the door behind her.

Once again a feeling of great loss consumed her as she walked through the empty house and out the front door. As she passed Chatchai on the front steps she reached down and gave him a kiss on the cheek. Not saying anything to the rest of the family, she walked over to the train station, bought a ticket and boarded the ten o'clock southbound, number 932.

CHAPTER 37

Hardly paying any attention to the people seated around her, Lek kept her mind occupied staring out the train window watching the passing sights, occasionally trying to figure out what she would do when she got to wherever it was she was going.

Inside every hut, behind every working water buffalo, were people. People with lives. People with feelings. People with stories behind and in front of them. It was difficult to imagine each one lived in their own little world. Who were they? What were their stories?

They passed by the open window of the speeding train so very fast, much like the people in Lek's life. Lek couldn't afford to dwell on it though. What is past has passed, and although pain has a way of testing the resources of one's spirit, if dwelled upon, it can destroy that spirit.

No, Lek had to look forward to the new people, yet unknown, that would help shape her future.

'Beautiful, isn't it?' the young woman seated next to Lek said, offering her unsolicited evaluation of the passing Thai countryside.

'Yes it is,' Lek responded automatically, even though she hadn't actually noticed how beautiful it actually was. She smiled faintly, then returned to looking out the window.

'It's my first time outside of Ubon Ratchathani. I never knew this country was so big and beautiful. And you?'

Optimism. It was a refreshing change to listen to someone to whom the world was still an exciting, inviting, wonderful place. It was probably just what Lek needed at the time.

'No, I've traveled a bit before,' Lek understated.

'How lucky. Where have you been?'

'Here and there,' Lek replied. Right now she didn't much want to think about her past and wasn't enthused about rehashing painful old memories with a complete stranger, even if she was about Lek's age and full of enthusiasm.

'Oh.'

The young woman took the quick response as a put off. Yet when Lek continued to look at her, she felt compelled to say something. She began to fidget with the top button of her blouse. 'Where are you going now?'

'Korat, I guess,' Lek responded. At least that's what her ticket had written on it. She hadn't given much thought to whether or not she would stay or what she would do once she got there.

'Oh.' The young woman began to scratch her knee. 'Me too. Have you been there before?' The itch seemed to have found its way to her forehead.

'Actually I haven't.'

Lek began to notice the young woman's nervousness.

'My name's Lek, by the way. What's yours?'

'Toi.'

The informal introduction seemed to put her more at ease. The itch stopped. 'Do you have some sort of business in Korat? Or are you going there for a holiday?'

'I hope to find work there. Times are tough back on the farm,' Lek responded.

'I know exactly what you mean. I'm going to Korat for the same reason. My family back in Ubon sent me to work for my uncle. He's a manager for the bus company in Korat. If you'd like, I can introduce you to him. Maybe he has an extra opening for you. That is, if you're interested.'

'I sure am.'

Lek perked up. What an incredible stroke of good luck it would be if she could step off the train and into a job. She didn't even care what kind of work it would be as long as it paid something, anything, that might help her get started.

'I can't promise anything, but my uncle did say he was hiring conductors now. He also said there was a small room next to the terminal I could rent once I got there, but I don't have much money. If he did hire you, would you consider sharing the room with me, at least for a while? I sure could use help with the rent.'

'That would be wonderful.'

A job and a place to stay? That sounded too good to be true. And the more she thought about it, the more she realized it might be too much to ask. After all, if Lek had learned anything, it was that things didn't always go as planned. She caught herself beginning to scowl and quickly corrected her expression. Smiling at her new friend, she decided she had no choice but to follow it through. It was all she had.

'Great! Let's see what we can do once we get there. I'm so glad I met you,' Toi said with zeal.

'Me, too,' Lek agreed.

The low hum of the train's engines, the rhythmic clanking of the wheels on the track and the whoosh of the passing trees and countryside were completely ignored by the two new friends for the rest of the trip to Korat. They were so involved in talking and getting to know each other that they had shut out the rest of the world.

As they talked, the two young women had a way of building on each other's enthusiasm. Hasty dreams were put into words. Dreams of what they would do to the yet unseen room, what they would do with all the money they were sure to make and how great the life that lay just ahead of them would be in the yet unknown town of Korat.

As the train creaked to a halt at their final destination, the two disembarked, still talking, into the maze of tangled streets that made up the unfamiliar town of Korat. Only Toi had the slightest idea of where they were heading and even she had to stop several times to ask directions.

It took a couple of hours before they were finally able to locate the bus station, which, by the way, turned out to be only about one kilometer from the train station. Once there, they were easily able to locate the main office and Toi's uncle seated behind a small desk inside.

'Uncle Prasit?' Toi asked hesitantly. It had been a while since she had seen him and wasn't sure if she recognized him.

The man looked up from his work and studied the two girls that had just come in. His eyes settled on Toi and a faint glimmer of recognition spread across his face. 'Toi?'

'Yes, it's me. You remember.'

'You've grown. Look at you, the last time I saw you, you were just a child,' Prasit said as he leaned back in his chair. His easy smile eased the tension. 'How's your mother?'

'She's fine. Things on the farm aren't too good, though, but I think you already know that.'

'Yes, I've heard. It's been a bad year for farming all over the country.'

Standing somewhat in the back ground, Lek sensed that his sympathy was sincere.

'*Mae* said you might be looking to hire conductors,' Toi went straight to the matter at hand.

'As a matter of fact I am,' Prasit answered rather business like. 'We're short handed right now and can use all the help we can find. Who's your friend?'

'I'm sorry. This is Lek from Buriram. We met on the train. She's looking for work, too.'

Prasit nodded his head in acknowledgement. 'I don't suppose either of you have worked as conductors before.'

Lek and Toi looked at each other, knowing full well that neither of them had any experience. Both sheepishly shook their heads.

'Never mind. It's not that difficult if you don't mind putting a little effort into it. Have a seat and I'll explain it to you.'

As the two girls settled into a pair of chairs, Prasit pulled open a drawer of his desk and pulled out a tin tube filled with colored tickets and loose change. He also produced two pieces of paper filled with numbers.

'As conductors you will be responsible for collecting fares and handing out tickets to passengers on the bus. Some people will buy their tickets here at the office, others will get on the bus at different points along the route.

'For the people who buy their tickets here, you will just need to tear the tickets to invalidate them and make sure the passengers disembark at their scheduled destination. For the people who get on the bus along the route, you will need to find out where they are going and sell them a ticket. It's not that difficult, but you will need to study these rate sheets to know how much to charge. Any questions so far?'

Lek and Toi took the rate sheets and looked them over. Toi looked a little perplexed but Lek felt it wouldn't be all that much different than selling chicken to train passengers.

'When do we start?' Lek asked. Her eagerness produced another smile from Prasit.

'I could start you tomorrow if you think you're ready.'

'Wait a minute,' Toi broke in. 'What about pay? And working hours. And we don't even have a place to stay yet.'

'Well, we can pay you 50 baht a day. You will start about six in the morning and finish about six at night. For the time being we will ask you to work seven days a week, maybe a day off every other week or so. I realize it sounds a bit daunting but it really isn't that much different to the hours you put in on the farm. As far as a place to stay, I have a friend who rents rooms in a building on the other side of the parking lot from here. They aren't that expensive. Maybe the two of you could share one for a while.'

Lek and Toi looked at each other. How did he know what they had talked about on the train?

'Okay,' Toi said. 'Tomorrow it is.'

'Great,' Prasit responded. Pointing out the office window to an old run down building, he said, 'The rooms for rent are in there. Talk to Khun Somani and tell her I sent you. Get settled in and report back here at 5:45 tomorrow morning. Good luck and welcome aboard.'

As the girls got up to leave, the reality of what was happening began to sink in. They had done it. Within a few hours of arriving in Korat, they had both landed jobs. Thanking Prasit profusely, they left to try and find Somani and get settled into a room.

Somani turned out to be a wonderful older woman who greeted the girls with a warm smile and a subtle willingness to help. When she found out Toi's relation to Prasit and that the two girls had just landed jobs with the bus company, she agreed to take a two hundred and fifty baht down payment on the five hundred baht a month rent. Since neither girl had much money, they accepted the terms without hesitation.

The tiny room was barely big enough to hold the two western style single beds and makeshift closet inside. With no windows, a single tiny fluorescent lamp mounted hastily to one wall provided the only light.

At 5:30 a.m. the next morning, without even a thought for breakfast, the two sleepy young women made their way over to the bus terminal to report for their first day of work. The sun was just beginning to cast light on the day and the air was still thick with moisture.

'Good morning ladies,' Prasit greeted them, 'I trust you slept well.

'Toi, you will be working the number 5 in-town route. Lek, I have you working the Korat to Khon Kaen route. If you follow me I will introduce you to your drivers.' Both girls trudged along behind him as he led them to their respective buses.

After taking care of Toi, Prasit introduced Lek's driver as Soonton. He was a well-built man in his late forties, who wore khaki trousers and a buttoned shirt. He didn't say much more than hello to either of them before taking his leave to position himself behind the wheel of the bus.

'Never mind him,' Prasit apologized. 'He can be a little grumpy in the morning but he's a good man once you get to know him.'

Lek raised her eyebrows in acknowledgement. Forcing a smile, she then climbed aboard the dusty orange bus and took a seat behind Soonton.

Over the next few days Lek learned her job by trial and error. Soonton helped when asked, but rarely offered anything on his own. Stubborn as she was, Lek didn't ask often.

The bus she worked made two round trips to Khon Kaen every day. Each way was almost three hours. Aside from selling and collecting tickets, Lek also walked down the isle selling soft drinks, water and beer. The rest of the time she would sit down if there was a seat available or stand if there wasn't and pass the time looking out the window, bored.

CHAPTER 38

Nearly a year had gone by since Lek and Toi first stepped off the train in Korat. A year of hard work and nothing to show for it. They still lived together in the same little room, still worked the same bus routes and still had no money to speak of.

The first couple of months were especially difficult. The adjustment to the new job wasn't too hard to handle, but having no money was. If it weren't for the kind help of Prasit and Soonton, the two girls might have starved in the first month alone.

Neither Lek nor Toi had arrived in Korat with much money and after paying half a month's rent up front, they were left with only 100 baht each. With pay day coming only once a month at the end of the month, it didn't take long to figure out it was far from sufficient. By mid-month they were both out of money, this after eating only one meal per day. Each morning they went to work hungry, worked all day in that state, then only ate a little rice and maybe some vegetables in the evening.

When Prasit realized the situation he demanded they both eat their evening meal with his family. He also lent Toi a couple of hundred baht for her to eat during the day.

Soonton also chipped in. Cold and abrasive for the first couple of weeks, he gradually warmed up to Lek and began sharing his midday meal with her.

He certainly was different from anyone she'd ever met. He worked every day in his camouflaged army fatigue trousers and white buttoned shirt. A strange combination, Lek thought.

He also looked as though he always seemed to have ulterior motives for everything he did. He would go out of his way to help someone, but it always seemed to Lek as though he had some hidden reason for doing it. Even when sharing his lunch with her he would give her deep long looks as if he were trying to gauge how she accepted the meal.

Not that he ever did anything bad to her. On the contrary. He seemed to want to take her under his wing and protect her. He often talked about how dangerous it was for her, being a single girl living on her own. At least once a day for the entire year he had tried to talk her into learning self-defense techniques with him.

Often during break times, she would see him working out beside the bus, throwing kicks and punches at an imaginary foe.

Lek gratefully accepted his help with food, but turned down his offers of self-defense lessons. She remained casually friendly while working, but steered clear of him at all other times.

He didn't seem to mind. Apparently he was used to staying in the background. He also seemed to have a keen perception for people like himself. People, he thought, like Lek. No family history. No ties to anyone or anything but themselves.

That first year they spent together did wonders for him. Unknown to him, however, it was beginning to take its toll on Lek.

It wasn't Soonton that was the problem. It was the twelve hour days and seven day weeks. Toi had managed a day off now and again, but Lek had worked the past three months straight. Trying to think about it, she could only remember four or five days in the entire year that she didn't get up at 5:30

in the morning, board that orange bus and ride to and from Khon Kaen, twice.

The monotony started to wear on her. For the past couple of months it was as if all she could think about were the bad things that were happening. Nothing much, just the little things like dropping her change on the floor of the bus. Or forgetting to charge one of the passengers, or charging the wrong amount.

Lek began to yearn for the good old days in Buriram. She thought a lot about the old farm, about Chatchai and Dow. She often wished she had brought to Korat the picture of them together in Surin.

Then one day as she was returning home from work, the reason she left Buriram came hauntingly back to her. As she approached the entrance to her building, she noticed three scruffy looking men in their early to mid-twenties lingering nearby. They were a little closer to her entrance than she would have liked, but she didn't give the situation much thought. It wasn't uncommon for locals to loiter in the area. She would just hurry by them and within a few seconds she would be safely in her room.

The men had other ideas. Before she knew what was happening they grabbed her and forced her into the alley beside her building, out of sight.

'Get away from me! What do you want?' Lek yelled as she struggled to get away. She quickly froze when she felt a cold steel blade ever so lightly pressing against her neck.

Two of the men took up positions on either side of her, pinning her arms to the wall. The third stared her in the eyes as he added a little more pressure to the knife at her throat. A trickle of blood seeped out to stain the shiny blade.

Lek's heart pounded violently. Her breathing became short and irregular. What she was looking at wasn't real, wasn't human.

'If you're quiet, no one gets hurt,' the creature said in a soft, menacing way. He held her stare for a moment, then slowly began to slide the knife down the front of her shirt. One at a time, the buttons of her blouse offered no resistance to the razor-sharp blade.

He alternated his glance between her eyes and her torso as he gently slid the blade between her skin and her bra. One quick violent pull and Lek gasped as her breasts were laid bare.

'Oh, so nice,' he said as he gently caressed her nipples with his blade.

Lek stood frozen, staring her tormentor in the eye. This wasn't happening. Not again.

She wanted to close her eyes and pretend this was just a bad dream. But she couldn't. It wasn't a dream. It was all too real and she was helpless to do anything about it. All she could do was watch in horror as these animals violated her.

As the knife slowly slid down her torso toward her slacks, the two holding her arms lightened their grip to fondle her bare breasts. The knife wielder's attention was now directed solely toward how he would be able to get her pants off. Realizing it would be easier to undo her belt than cut through it, he put the knife sideways in his hand to free his fingers. It was the slightest of breaks, but the only one Lek had.

Summoning all the strength she had, Lek slammed her knee into his crotch. It was a direct hit eliciting a painful scream from her target.

The move took everyone by surprise, even Lek. The force of the kick caused Lek to fall to the ground, out of the other's grasp. The knife, too, fell to the ground and its holder collapsed to his knees. A confused moment of inactivity ensued before Lek came to her senses and scrambled out of their reach.

Without knowing it, Lek fled in the wrong direction. Her escape path had taken her toward the closed end of the alley, with no way out. As soon as she realized her mistake, she swore under her breath and spun around.

It was too late. By now the two unharmed rapists had spread out to cut off her escape. The third was still on the ground, writhing in pain.

'She's more feisty than you thought boss,' one of them said to the fallen man.

'Fuck you! Get her!' he fumed, causing the other two to chuckle.

'We can do that, boss,' the other said. 'But it looks like its going to take a more aggressive approach.' He reached down and picked up an old, nail-filled board that was lying in the alley. He turned it over in his hand, feeling how it fit nicely into his grip.

As the two began their approach, Lek readied herself for the impending battle. She knew there was no way she could win, but there was no way she would give up, either. They would have to kill her before she'd let those dirty bastards get their hands on her again.

It was a very real possibility that they would do just that, she thought. Never mind, maybe she would take one with her. She stood ready to fight to the end.

'Looks like you have gotten yourselves into a little more trouble then you can handle,' a voice came from behind them in the entrance to the alley. All heads turned to see where it came from.

'Soonton?' Lek whispered.

'Bugger off, old man!' the hoodlum on his knees said, as he grabbed for the knife.

'I don't think so,' Soonton responded steadily. He reached behind him and pulled out a handgun he had stuffed in his trousers.

'Is that supposed to scare us?' the wielder of the knife said with mock bravado.

'As a matter of fact it is.' Soonton clicked back the hammer. His expression remained calm but determined.

'There's three of us, boss. We can take him,' one of the others spoke out.

'Maybe you can, maybe you can't,' Soonton said calmly, keeping the gun trained on the man with the knife. 'I'm sure I'll get at least one or two of you. Who wants to be first? You?'

Still in pain from Lek's kick, the hood realized that the three of them would be no match for a handgun in experienced hands. The old man who stood pointing one in their direction was acting too calm to be an amateur.

'No, I don't think so. Let's get out of here, boys. There will be other days.'

'Smart decision,' Soonton said. 'You're not as dumb as you look.'

'Don't push your luck,' the leader said angrily. He motioned for his troops to follow him.

'Slowly!' Soonton said sternly. 'And the weapons. Leave them here.'

The leader shrugged his shoulders and shook his head. He began to walk away, ignoring Soonton's command.

'I'm not sure you realize what a .38 hollow tip does to the human body,' Soonton began. 'When it enters, it only makes a hole about a centimeter in diameter. It usually hits a bone on the way through causing it to flatten out. The velocity it travels keeps it moving on through, taking anything in its path with it. The result is, when it comes out the other side, it can be as much as ten times the size. It's not very pretty.'

The leader stood staring at Soonton, his head cocked to one side. He nonchalantly tossed the knife to his side. As it clanked to the ground, his mate tossed away the board he was holding. Without weapons, the three slowly made their way around Soonton and out of the alley.

'You won this time, old man, but we'll be back. You can count on it,' the leader said menacingly before disappearing around the corner.

'Are you okay?' Soonton turned to ask Lek once the three perpetrators were out of sight.

'I think so,' Lek replied as she tried to cover herself with her torn shirt. Holding her collar fast, blood began to seep over her knuckles.

'They cut you! Those bastards!'

'It's nothing,' Lek tried to sound sincere.

'Let me see,' Soonton demanded.

'No,' Lek blurted out forcefully. She quickly returned to being as calm as she could. 'I just want to go home.'

'Of course,' Soonton said as he put his arm around her. Lek shied away from his touch. 'You poor thing. I'm so sorry.'

'It wasn't your fault.'

Lek pushed away from him and began to trot toward her room.

'Maybe you should have a doctor look at that,' Soonton called after her. 'If there's anything I can do to help . . .'

Lek didn't respond. Within moments she had rounded the corner and was out of his sight.

CHAPTER 39

'Surprise!' Malee burst through Nid's door, carefully cradling a flat square box in her left arm.

'Malee! You scared me half to death. What are you doing here now? Why aren't you still at work?'

'It's June 11, your birthday!' Malee exclaimed as she walked over and set the box on the dressing table where Nid had been applying her makeup. She chuckled and wiped the smeared lipstick off Nid's cheek, obviously caused by her sudden entrance. 'I left a little early to make sure I caught you before you left. And here, I made this at work and snuck it out the back door.'

'How did you know it was my birthday? I didn't tell anybody,' Nid said, trying to hide how pleased she actually was that Malee had managed to find out.

'Don't be silly. We've been friends for a long time. Good friends know these things. Now open your present!'

Nid looked at her friend and smiled. A tear formed in her left eye. 'Oh, all right.' She carefully lifted the lid off the box. 'A cake! It's beautiful.'

'Apple raisin with cinnamon frosting. I made it from ingredients left over from a banquet we catered yesterday.'

'You shouldn't have. Won't you get in trouble?'

'Of course not. No one saw me do it. Besides, we would have thrown away most of the ingredients anyway. Now shut up and eat!' Malee said and laughed.

'Yes, let's eat.' Nid scurried around and produced a couple of plates and forks and a knife. She attacked the cake with excited vengeance, dishing out two large pieces.

'It's delicious.' Nid said with her first mouthful.

'Thanks, I made it myself,' Malee replied with mock arrogance. 'Too bad you don't have a man to share it with instead of me.'

'Oh, don't start that again.'

'Nid, you're 33 years old today, and you aren't getting any younger. Someone as beautiful and successful as you are should be able to pick and choose the men in your life. But you don't. You sit around here all day, either telephoning the police in Bangkok or waiting to hear from them about whether or not they have any leads on Lek. You have got to live your own life, too. It's not going to be any more difficult to find Lek if you have a man in your life. It may even be easier. He could help you find her. Take my advice: find a good man. I guarantee your outlook on life will be much better.'

'You talk about me, but what about you?'

'Never mind that. I'm already old and ugly. I lost all hope of finding a man a long time ago. But I'm at peace with that.'

'What do you mean "old and ugly"? You're a very good-looking woman,' Nid protested.

'No I'm not. I'm just an old tribal woman. It doesn't bother me. You know me, I'll be just as happy when I get back to my family in the hills of Mae Hong Son someday. But for you, life still holds a lot of promise.'

'Maybe . . . I don't know. I went with so many men when I was younger, as a job, I just can't look at them the same way as most women do. For me, men were just a source of income, a way to pay my bills and eat. After all I've been through, all the lean times when I sold my body just to survive, I can't bring myself to think of them as a way to express my love,' Nid said.

'That's very sad, Nid. I know you will change. I feel it in my heart. You will come around sooner or later, and when you do, you are in the perfect position to meet the right one. With the job you have now, you don't have to look at men as a way to survive and pay the bills. With all the movie and recording stars that pass through the Malee Cafe, it won't be long before you become a star yourself,' said Malee.

'Me, a star? I don't think so. That's just a fantasy that will never come true.'

'Nid! I feel like I'm pounding my head against the wall. I know you're not that stupid. I've seen you perform. You are every bit as good as anyone of the stars that come to sing at the Cafe. You told me yourself that the songs you've been writing are turning heads.'

'There's a big difference between performing a few original songs in a tiny little club, and making it to the big time,' Nid told her.

'That is where you are wrong. The Malee Cafe is no tiny little place. Some of the biggest names in the business pass through there, including record producers. It's only a matter of time before one of them wakes up and sees what a talent you are.'

'Malee, I'm so glad I met you. You always make me feel good whenever I talk to you. You have a way of making anything sound possible. I know some day you will make it back to your family in Mae Hong Son, and I will be very happy for you when you do, but I sure will hate to see you go.'

'Don't get too worried about it. It's not going to happen for quite a while. At least not until I can figure out a way to go back gracefully without upsetting my father over leaving Anan. Face it, you're stuck with me. Now let's have some more of that cake!'

CHAPTER 40

Sitting at a table in the corner of the Malee Cafe, Termsak Srisomson was quietly sipping a glass of whiskey, listening intently to the woman he'd come to see sing on the stage. Termsak assessed the talents of the person so many people had been talking about lately.

She was good, he decided. The two original songs she had sung during her set were performed with zeal and professionalism he'd rarely seen in club performers. When the set was finished, Termsak ordered another glass from the waitress, then sat back and waited as the manager led the woman over to his table. He stood to greet her when she arrived.

'Nid Sawang, I'd like you to meet a friend of mine,' the manager said as he stood proudly between the two.

'His name is Termsak. He's a record producer from Bangkok who came down to hear you sing.'

'Please, have a seat,' Termsak greeted her and waited for her to get settled in before he sat back down. The manager took up a position on the other side of the table.

Seeing a third glass, he motioned for the waitress to fill each one with ice, whiskey and soda water.

'Thank you,' Nid replied nervously. She was actually meeting a record producer. This was turning out to be her best birthday ever.

'You may not know this but your name has been popping up in a lot of conversations lately,' Termsak began. 'Word is out that a couple of your songs show a lot of promise,' Termsak continued. 'The other day my colleagues and I were discussing the possibilities of approaching you to try and buy the rights to your music. We wanted to add them to an upcoming album. After seeing you perform them, though, I have to admit that would be a colossal mistake.'

'Why?' Nid's heart sank. Her illusions of stardom quickly vanished.

'Why? Because you do them so well it would be a major injustice to you and to the public to allow someone else to take the credit.'

The manager, listening intently to the conversation, was now truly beaming. He knew he had a good thing with Nid, and it was he who had begun to contact people like Termsak to try and promote her. He had seen major performers come and go through his Cafe, but never before had he actually been the one to discover a new talent.

'Would you be at all interested in taking some time off to come up to Bangkok and do a little work in our studio? That is, if your manager here would allow you the time off.'

'Of course I would,' the manager broke in before Nid had a chance to say anything.

'If you're willing, I'd like you to try recording a song or two to see how it goes. I can't offer any guarantees, but if it works out maybe we can combine some of your songs with some standards and put together an album. If that works out, the next step would be to sign you to a contract. And if the album is successful, the royalties just might make you a wealthy woman.'

After taking a deep breath, Nid finally spoke her first real input into the conversation.

'Khun Termsak, I can tell you right now that I am interested. It's every singer's dream to record their work. Believe me, I've already thought about it quite a bit. Any more thought would be redundant.'

'I had a feeling you might say that,' Termsak said and nodded his agreement. 'Why don't you come in Tuesday around noon and we'll go from there.'

'Yes!' the manager said with excitement. 'Take all the time you need. We'll be happy to wait for you. And remember, you will always have a place here when you're done.'

'Thank you. Really, both of you. Thank you. Tuesday would be fine.'

'Great, we will be looking forward to seeing you then.'

Tuesday morning came quicker than Nid had anticipated. Not even the long, excited talks she had had with Malee during the week had prepared her for this moment. The bus ride to the capital was quick.

She almost turned around and headed back to Pattaya. It took all her courage to open the front door of the recording studio and climb the stairs. It must have been a full five minutes before she got up the nerve to open the door at the top.

'May I help you?' a woman seated behind a reception desk asked as Nid cautiously entered the room.

'I'm Nid Sawang. I believe Termsak Srisomson is expecting me.'

'Of course,' the woman replied. 'Have a seat and I will announce your arrival.' With that, the woman disappeared behind yet another door.

'Follow me, please. They are waiting for you in studio one,' she spoke pleasantly when she returned.

Nid followed her down a corridor flanked with several more doors. The receptionists opened one of them and smiled as she directed Nid inside.

'Right on time,' Termsak greeted her. 'I like punctuality.'

'Let me show you around and introduce you to the crew,' Termsak said. 'Then maybe we can get started. Are you ready to give it a try?'

'I'm as ready as I'll ever be,' Nid replied with a nervous smile.

'Great. Follow me.'

The first little room Termsak led her into, the mixing room he called it, was quite crowded with both people and equipment. He introduced her to at least ten people crammed inside, then began describing the machinery. The words he used were so foreign sounding, he might as well have been speaking ancient Sanskrit.

The middle area looked a little more familiar. Filled with musical equipment, the room contained four musicians, one each manning a guitar, a bass, a keyboard and a drum set. Termsak introduced them as the best studio band in all of Thailand.

The last room Termsak showed her wasn't much of a room at all. No bigger then a phone booth, a dim light hung from its ceiling and its walls were padded with bright red carpeting. Its scant furnishings consisted of a music stand, a microphone and stand, and a set of headphones. A small window looked out into the other two areas. 'At least it has a view,' Nid thought to herself.

'This,' Termsak informed her, 'is your new office.'

He handed her a small stack of papers containing the words and music from a couple of her songs. 'Why don't you pick one out for a practice run so we can check out the equipment? It'll give us an idea of how things might go.'

Nid accepted the stack and nodded. She was still too nervous to say anything intelligent, so she opted for silence.

'Adjust these so that they're comfortable,' Termsak said as he put the headphones over her ears. 'Take your time and warm up a little. When you're ready, speak into the mike and let us know what song it is you want to start with. In the meantime, if you need anything, don't hesitate to ask. The mike is live. We will be able to hear you.' He gave her a warm smile, then walked out and closed the door tightly behind him.

'Uh, excuse me,' she said timidly into the microphone and jumped back when her own voice blasted through her headphones.

'Sorry, we had your mike up too loud,' one of the technicians apologized. 'What can we do for you?'

'Why don't we do the Buriram number first?' Nid again spoke timidly. These were professionals and she felt strange making the decision where to start.

'Perfect choice,' Termsak's voice came through her headphones. 'First we need to check all the mikes. Let's start with you, Nid. Can you give us some a cappella?'

'Sure.' Nid cleared her throat and began to sing.

'Great, thank you very much,' a technician cut her off after allowing her to sing just a few lines of the song. 'Now let's try the instruments and the backup vocals.'

Nid had never been cut off in the middle of a song before and thought for sure she'd blown it already. She calmed down, though, when the technicians did the same to all the band members. She would learn soon enough that it was a normal part of getting started.

For the next six hours they did the song repeatedly. Sometimes Nid would sing together with the band playing, sometimes she'd sing with a recording of the band's music from one of the earlier tracks and sometimes the band would play with a recording of Nid's voice. By the end of the day she felt as if they would never get it right. 'That's enough for now,' Termsak finally announced.

'Great job everybody. Nid, I'd like to see you in my office. The rest of you, go ahead and pack it up.'

Exhausted, Nid solemnly removed her headphones and draped them over the music stand. 'He wants to see me in his office,' she thought to herself. 'Well, it was good while it lasted. I hope he lets me down easy. I hope he's quick about it, too. I might still have time to catch the last bus back to Pattaya.'

Termsak met her at the entrance to the mixing room and put his arm around her shoulder. 'You look exhausted. Come on, let's go get a cup of coffee. My treat.'

'Here it comes,' Nid thought.

The technicians in the mixing room were all busy at their stations. Only one of them looked up as Nid passed through the room. 'Good job Nid.'

'Thanks.'

Termsak led Nid down a hallway and into his office. He offered her a seat, then plopped down into his overstuffed chair on the other side of a large desk.

'I've never met anyone quite like you, Nid. Sure, you made a few normal rookie mistakes, but overall you were the best first timer I've ever had the pleasure to work with. I think you just might have a future here.'

Nid looked at him without saying a word. She was a bit stunned by his comments and didn't quite know how to react.

Termsak reached down and pulled open one of the drawers of his desk. He removed a rather official looking document and slid it across to Nid.

'This is a standard recording contract,' he told her. 'I'd like you to take it home with you tonight and look it over. Some of it is written in rather technical legal jargon, even I don't understand parts of it. It basically states that if you sign at the bottom, we will give you a bonus to get you started. Later on, we will pay you royalties from the sales of the album.

'In other words, given your performance today and your wonderful voice, we would very much like to record you. If you're willing, that is.'

Nid took the contract and gave it a cursory glance. Was this really happening? She let out a big sigh. Just one week ago, she was happily singing in the Malee Cafe. A small town girl who had thought she had made it as high as she was ever going to be. Now this man she had barely met was offering her a recording contract. A million things were going through her mind, not least of which was how proud Lek might be once they were reunited.

'That's wonderful news, Khun Termsak. I don't know what to say. I'm so tired I can't really think straight but I will look it over and get back to you in a couple of days.'

'A couple of days? The studio is booked; the band is here, we have the equipment all set up and ready to go. If you don't mind, we'd really like to get started tomorrow.'

'Tomorrow? I've got to go all the way back to Pattaya tonight. I'm not sure I can make it back tomorrow.'

'Why do you need to go back to Pattaya tonight? Don't you have a place to stay here in Bangkok?'

'No, I don't. I didn't know what to expect and I guess I didn't come very well prepared.'

'No problem, see the receptionist on your way out. I'll make sure she sets you up in a hotel, at our expense of course.'

'That would be too much to ask,' Nid quietly protested.

'Nonsense,' Termsak reassured her. 'It will be for our mutual convenience. We have a lot of work ahead of us.'

Termsak pressed the buzzer on his intercom. 'Phanee, I'm sending out Miss Nid. Find her a hotel room,' he said to his receptionist on the other end on the line.

'Thank you Termsak. I won't let you down,' Nid assured him.

'See you tomorrow,' he replied as his way of dismissing her.

Phanee not only booked her a room, she set her up in a beautiful suite just down the street from the studio. It was the most extravagant lodging Nid had ever seen.

Left alone in her mini palace, Nid sprawled out on her oversized bed and began to look over the stack of papers Termsak had given her. At the top of the stack was the recording contract. Termsak was right, it was a bunch of legal jargon. She didn't understand any of it. She looked around the room, found a pen in the desk by the window, signed the contract then tossed it aside. She would just have to trust them.

Laying back down on the bed, she glanced at her watch. Could it really be almost midnight already? Feeling a bit overwhelmed, she took out the picture of Lek she carried with her at all times and set it by her pillow. Thinking about all the work she had in front of her, she stared at the picture for a few minutes before she fell into a deep and comfortable sleep.

'That's a wrap,' Termsak finally announced after a short session in late September. They had finally recorded enough material to produce an album.

'I'm very pleased with the results,' Termsak added as almost an afterthought. 'Especially you, Nid. For a first timer you did exceptionally well. The studio executives have decided to give this album top priority. They seem to have high hopes for it. I have to agree with them. I know it's going to be a huge success, I can feel it.

'We are going to start by releasing a single within a few days and push for airtime. The album and CDs should start showing up in the stores in a couple of weeks or so. In the meantime, I'm working on setting up a deal where you will be backing up another band on a concert tour starting in mid-October. It would be the perfect way to promote this album. Nothing is definite yet but I think I can get you in.'

Nid was too exhausted to fully appreciate the impact of Termsak's speech. She did manage a weak smile. 'Thanks.'

'As for now, everyone go home, relax and take some well deserved time off. When the time comes, the studio will get in touch with each of you to give you details of the tour. Congratulations folks.'

During Termsak's speech, the atmosphere of the studio gradually turned from one of hard work and grim determination to one of exhausted celebration. Instruments and equipment were tossed aside unceremoniously as bottles of champagne appeared from the mixing room. Glasses were filled and emptied and talks of future plans were bandied about. After an hour or so of festive goodbyes, Nid quietly took her leave.

Over the next couple of weeks she remained in Pattaya, relaxing. The recording sessions had been long and grueling and now that they were over she felt drained but happy. She occasionally went over to the Malee Cafe to visit her former work mates and to do a cameo appearance on stage; for years it was something she watched other recording artists do.

In early October, Nid received a telephone call from Termsak. 'I haven't forgotten about you. Are you ready to get back to work?'

'Sure, why? What have you got?'

'Let's just say you should keep your schedule open for the rest of the month. We're pretty close to getting you into that concert tour. The group originally scheduled to be the backup band has been squabbling with the promoter over gate receipts. It doesn't look as though either side is going to give in. Even if they do, the promoter heard your demo and liked it. Chances are pretty good we're in.'

'That sounds great, Termsak. When will we know for sure?'

'Probably sometime next week. I have to admit, I'm a little nervous. I've never had things go this smoothly before. Something is bound to go wrong. Don't you worry about it, though. Just warm up those vocal cords. I'll call you back when I know for sure.' With that, Termsak hung up the phone.

Nid cradled the receiver and sat back on the edge of her bed. He said not to worry, but she did anyway. Nothing in her life had gone this easy before. She couldn't help but wonder what might happen to change the course she seemed so firmly on.

She wouldn't have to wait long to find out. A few days after her talk with Termsak, Nid received another phone call.

CHAPTER 41

'This is Officer Wichai with the Bangkok police. We thought you might like to know that we just arrested a husband and wife team named Rattana and Siriporn Chokul for breaking child labor laws. They are being held at the Central Police Investigation Headquarters just off Rama I Road, along with 14 children ranging in age from about five to fifteen years old. Rattana has confessed to several kidnappings, including at least one from the orphanage in Pattaya 10 to 15 years ago. Apparently the Chokul's used these children in a vending scam at various tourist-frequented nightspots around town. We don't know, but we think one of them might be your missing daughter. We'd appreciate it if you would come to the station and identify her.'

Nid nearly fainted. They found her! After all these years, they finally found her. 'Of course. I'll be there as soon as I can.'

The three-hour trip to the police station in Bangkok seemed like it took days. When her taxi finally pulled up in front of the station, Nid literally threw the driver some money and ran inside.

'I'm Nid Sawang,' she blurted out to the first uniformed person she saw. 'Officer Wichai called to tell me you have my daughter here. Where is she? Is she all right? Can I see her?' She was talking so fast the officer on duty at the front desk only caught half of what she was saying.

'Calm down,' the officer told her. 'Now what's this all about?'

Nid took a couple of deep breaths. 'I am Nid Sawang. I just received a phone call from Officer Wichai from missing persons. He told me that you just arrested Rattana and Siriporn Chokul. He said that my daughter was with them. Can I see her?'

'Hold on a minute,' the officer told her. He then picked up a phone and punched in a couple of numbers. After a short conversation, the officer hung up. 'Please take a seat. Officer Wichai will be right with you.'

Nid slowly retreated from the desk and merged with the bustling activity in the reception area. Finding a chair in the corner, she sat down and tried to collect her thoughts. It was all happening so fast. What would she say to her? How would she let her know that she had never given up hope of finding her? Would Lek be angry with her for not rescuing her much earlier than this? Would she ever forgive her for trusting Pom so many years ago?

Lost in her thoughts, Nid at first didn't hear her name being called. When it finally registered, she looked up to see a rather young uniformed officer searching the room. 'Yes. That's me,' she called after him.

'Ah, there you are. You might not remember me, I'm Officer Wichai. I'm glad you could make it so quickly.'

'You will never know how happy I am that you finally found her. I've been looking for years...'

'Well, we don't know that for sure, yet. We have a room full of children down the hall. We hope one of them is yours. If you will follow me, I'll take you there.'

Nid involuntarily swallowed. It hadn't occurred to her that Lek might not be among the children that had been found. Her excitement began to wane.

Officer Wichai eventually stopped in front of an unmarked door. Reaching for his keys, he unlocked it and swung it partway open. 'I'll wait for you out here. Good luck.'

Nid quietly stepped inside. Fourteen children, crammed into the tiny room, greeted her entrance with blank stares. Each one was dirty and underfed, and only one girl was old enough to be near the same age as Lek. She didn't look anything like what Nid would have predicted. Nonetheless, Nid asked her name.

'Gay,' she replied.

Nid managed a weak smile, then continued to look around the room. None of the children came close to the description Nid's mind had of Lek. 'Does the name Lek mean anything to you?' she asked Gay after her short surveillance.

Gay's face lit up. 'I used to have a friend named Lek. We worked together a long time ago.'

'What did she look like?' Nid pressed on.

'Here.' Gay reached in her pocket and produced an old Polaroid. 'This is us four or five years ago in Patpong. It was taken on the night she and Dow got away. That's her there.'

Nid took the Polaroid and sure enough, Lek was one of the girls in the picture. 'You said they got away. Do you know where they went?'

'Not really,' Gay responded with caution. The years of work she put in on the streets of Bangkok had taken away her innocence. She had learned long ago never to trust an adult stranger. 'Why do you ask?'

'I'm her mother and I have been looking for her for years.'

'You're her mother?' Gay replied unbelievingly. 'Is that your other daughter?' Gay pointed to Dow in the picture.

'No, I have only one daughter. Why?'

'Because Lek and Dow are sisters. At least they thought so. Are you sure you're her mother? Lek told us she came from an orphanage in Pattaya and when Dow told the story of how her family had lost a baby girl when Dow was young, they thought for sure they were sisters.'

The street hardened Gay slowly began to be replaced by the scared little girl that she actually was. 'They said they were going to Buriram to find their family. I was supposed to go too, but on the night they escaped I got caught by the police on my way to meet them. For me it was a terrible night. When the police finally let me go, mother and father beat me to try to get me to tell them where Lek and Dow had gone. I wouldn't tell them. I couldn't, we were family. I know either one of them would have done the same for me. I don't blame them for leaving without me, they had no choice. Everything happened so fast and it was going to be our only chance. They made it and I didn't, sometimes that's just the way things go.'

'You're a brave young woman, Gay.'

'No I'm not. If I was, I would have found a way to escape a long time ago, just like Lek and Dow. The problem was, I had nowhere to go. I don't remember ever having a real family. Rattana and Siriporn are the only mother and father I can ever remember having. They treated us terribly, but they are all we have. Do you know what will happen to us now?'

'I'm sorry, I don't. I only know that the police are trying very hard to find your real parents.' Nid looked up and noticed that all the children were listening intently to Nid's answer to Gay's question.

'Don't worry,' Gay said as she looked at the floor. Suddenly, as if a thought had just occurred to her, she looked up at Nid and a broad smile spread across her face. 'If you're looking for Lek, that must mean that our families are looking for us, too. Maybe there's hope yet.'

'Of course there's hope,' Nid followed her lead. 'Your parents are probably already on their way.'

'Yeah, did you hear that kids? Maybe our real parents are coming to get us. Thanks Khun Nid.' Gay left to sit with one of her friends.

When Nid reappeared in the hallway, Officer Wichai was busy talking with another policeman. Breaking off his conversation, he could tell immediately by the look on Nid's face that Lek was not in the room. 'Any luck?' he asked anyway, trying to sound encouraging.

'She's not there,' Nid said with a sigh. 'One of the girls told me that she escaped to Buriram a few years ago. She didn't know where in Buriram, but at least it's something to go on.'

'I guess you'll be off to Buriram then?' Wichai said as he began to escort Nid through the station toward the exit. 'Since Lek wasn't one of the children in that room, I don't suppose we will need you to testify against the Chokuls. Just in case, though, we'd appreciate it if you would keep us informed of your whereabouts.'

Although she hadn't yet made the conscious decision to go to Buriram, she admitted to herself that there was really no decision to make. If Lek was still in Buriram, Nid would have to go and get her.

'Hopefully I can make it there tonight,' she said.

CHAPTER 42

Nid returned directly to Pattaya to pick up a few clothes and prepare for the trip to Buriram. Along the way, she convinced the taxi driver to wait around to take her there that very evening.

Before they left, Nid made sure to call her manager to let him know what was going on.

'You're going where?' he asked incredulously.

'Buriram, to find my daughter. I don't really expect you to understand. This is something I have to do.'

'Can't it wait? The concert tour is scheduled to begin next week and we're so close to getting you in. Do you realize that you're on the verge of what I think could be a very successful singing career? This tour is a very important part of your career.'

'I know and I appreciate everything you've done for me. It's just that it would mean so much more if I could share it with my daughter.'

'Look, I'm sorry that I can't fully understand what you're going through because I've never been in that situation before. I can empathize with your plight, though. Tell you what, go up there, get her and come back as quickly as possible. No more then a couple of days, okay?'

'I promise I'll come back as soon as I find her. I'll call you as soon as I get word. Termsak, you've been wonderful. Thanks for understanding.'

'Don't push your luck,' was the last thing Termsak said before he hung up the phone.

Nid began to wonder if she was doing the right thing. Her career had reached a turning point and she didn't want to destroy her chances of success, yet she realized it would all mean nothing if she couldn't find Lek.

The ride to Buriram over some of the roughest and most unkempt roads Nid could ever remember took over eight hours. Half the time she wondered if the taxi driver knew where he was going. Indeed, more than once she awoke to find they had stopped and the driver was out of the car, asking a petrol station attendant directions.

The rickety taxi didn't arrive in the little village until after four in the morning. By the time they found a hotel, both Nid and the driver were completely drained.

Nid checked into the small hotel and bedded down to get some rest. She needed to build up her strength for what she knew might be a tiresome search ahead.

The trip must have taken more out of her than she realized for she didn't awake until the middle of the afternoon. Still tired and hungry, she showered, dressed, grabbed Lek's picture and headed out to get a bite to eat.

As she was eating in the little restaurant outside the hotel, Nid showed the picture of Lek, Dow and Gay to the waitress and asked her if she recognized any of them. The waitress shook her head no.

'Would you mind showing this picture to your co-workers and the customers for me? It's very important that I find these people.'

'I'd like to help you, but as you can see, I'm pretty busy right now. Feel free to show it around yourself, though.'

'Thanks, I'll do that.'

No one in the restaurant recognized any of them. Only a little discouraged, Nid took to the streets, walking around town showing the picture to everyone she could find. Nothing. Not even a hint of recognition from anyone. How could two young girls have gone unnoticed in such a small town? Had Gay remembered the right place?

Nid pressed on, refusing to give up. After a week of turning up nothing, she thought she had better call Termsak and let him know that it was taking a little longer than she had hoped.

'Where have you been? Why didn't you call sooner?'

Before Nid had a chance to answer, Termsak continued on his tirade. 'I've been going crazy waiting to hear from you. The first performance of the tour is tonight! I managed to get you in but I had to pull you out at the last minute. Do you realize what an embarrassment that caused me?'

'I'm sorry Termsak, but . . .'

'Sorry nothing! That was an extremely bad career move on your part, Nid. There's no telling where we can go from here. The promoter told me not to bother him with any more of my new prospects. We've been doing business together for a long time and this is the first time anything like this has ever happened. I've put a lot of time and effort into promoting you because I thought you deserved it. It's obvious to me now that you aren't anywhere near as committed as I thought you were.'

'Termsak, please . . .'

'I've got nothing more to say to you. Nothing else is lined up so you can take all the time off you want for all I care.' He then hung up the phone abruptly.

Nid looked at the receiver for a moment before replacing it in its cradle. Not only was she turning up a dead end in this little town, she may have ruined her career as well.

It was only a small comfort knowing that she had a good voice. At the very least she could go back to singing in clubs. That was all she ever had before. It was good enough then, it would have to be good enough now. She looked at her picture of Lek and decided that if she could only find her it would all be worth it.

The next day Nid decided would be her last day searching inside the town before she started to search the surrounding areas. In the middle of the afternoon she happened upon a farm supply shop and without much hope, went inside to ask the owner if he recognized anyone in the picture.

He looked at her a moment to try and figure out what she was up to. Satisfied she didn't mean him or anyone else any harm, he pointed to two men who were picking through some farm equipment. 'Show that picture to them. They might be able to help you.'

Nid looked over and saw that he had pointed to an older man and what looked to be his son. She studied them a moment before making her approach and noticed the teenage boy had a faraway look in his eyes. He didn't seem to be paying much attention to anything, much less his father's instructions.

'Excuse me sir. Sorry to bother you. Do you know any of the people in this picture?' Nid handed him the photo.

The older man took the photo and gave it an unbelieving glance. His mood quickly changed from one of peaceful bliss to concentrated anger. As he handed it back to her, his chest began to swell and Nid thought he would explode into rage.

'Why?' he asked sternly, taking half a step toward her.

Not knowing what was happening, Nid wanted to turn and run. Nonetheless, she held her ground. 'I'm this girl's mother. I've been looking for her for years. Do you know where she is?' she said in a shaky voice.

'Look lady, if you are who I think you are, you've got a lot of nerve coming up here after what you did. You stole our daughter away from us. You robbed us of having her around for almost her entire life. I'll never in my life be able to figure out how someone could be so cruel as to steal a child from the clutches of her family. I swear that as long as I live I will never,

never be able to forgive the likes of you. I'm a devout believer in my religion, but if you don't get out of here, now, I won't be held responsible for what I might do.'

'Wait! Wait, you've got the wrong idea. I'm not who you think I am. My daughter was stolen from me, too, and I'm just as angry as you are. I've been calling the police for years trying to find the people who kidnapped her. The police finally called me one day to let me know they had arrested a couple named Rattana and Siriporn Chokul for breaking child labor laws. They said they had 14 children with them and wanted me to come identify my daughter. But she wasn't there. This picture was given to me by one of the children in the police station in Bangkok. She told me that my daughter had run away with this other girl in the picture who she called Dow. She said she thought they had gone to Buriram together because they thought they were sisters. Does that make any sense to you?'

Por listened to her story and could see she was genuinely frightened. She also seemed to be telling the truth. He breathed a deep sigh and apologized for his rudeness.

'There is so much to tell you, I don't know where to begin. Dow and Lek just appeared one day, telling horror stories about their lives in Bangkok. We were shocked, not only at what they were saying, but that Dow had found her way home. After we lost her, we never expected to see her again. Then all of a sudden, there she was with this other girl she said was her sister.

'We brought Lek into our family and treated her as if she was one of our own. After a while, they started growing up and before long, Lek and my youngest son, Chatchai, began a kind of teenage romance.' *Por* motioned toward the silent boy. 'I tried to play the stern father figure, but I knew they had something special between them. Those were happy times for our family.

'Then the accident happened. We lost Dow.' *Por* went silent.

'How things changed,' he finally began again. 'We can only think that Chatchai somehow feels responsible for the accident. He hasn't spoken since it happened. We've tried everything, but we just can't seem to bring him back.'

'I'm sorry,' Nid said. 'You must be in deep pain.'

'Yes, well, life's not always fair. One day we had three happy and healthy children to go with the rest of our family. What seemed like the very next day, two were gone and my best son was lost in mental torture.'

'What happened to Lek?' Nid was almost afraid to ask.

'Without Dow and Chatchai, I think she began to feel like an outsider. One morning she packed her belongings and left.'

Nid's heart sank. 'Do you know where she went?'

'I'm sorry, I have no idea. She may have told Chatchai on her way out, but as you can see, he's not telling anyone.'

Nid looked at Chatchai and could see that there wasn't even a hint of awareness on the boy's face.

'When was the last time you saw her?' *Por* broke her thoughts.

'When she was six months old.'

'Six months? That's a long time ago. You sure are persistent. Tell you what, why don't you take this.' *Por* reached into Chatchai's pocket and pulled out an old picture. The action didn't seem to register on the boy's mind, he just stood and stared straight ahead. 'It's a photo the three had taken together a while back at the elephant roundup in Surin. I keep it with Chatchai to try and get a response from him. It doesn't work. Nothing seems to work. You might as well take it.'

Nid looked at the photo and sure enough, Lek was in it. 'Thank you, you are very kind. Are you sure you don't know where she went? She didn't ever mention any place she might want to go, anything at all?'

'Not to me she didn't.' *Por* tried to sound soothing. He could sympathize with her pain. 'As far as I know Bangkok is the only place where she knew her way around. Given the experience the girls had there I really doubt she'd go back. The only other thing she ever talked about was some day finding her family. Other than that I just don't know. I wish I could help you, believe me I know how you feel. We were lucky to get our daughter back, even if it was only for a short time.'

'I'm very sorry. They looked like they were very close in this picture.' Nid felt as if someone had just stuck a cleaver in her chest. She was so close yet so far away.

'They were inseparable. Suffering is a part of life, though. It serves to strengthen our belief in religion. You will find your daughter some day, and when you do, I hope you will find a way to let us know. We'd like to learn the good news,' he said.

Nid returned to her hotel room and began to cry. She couldn't understand why she was crying, not now. Maybe she was crying because of the unfairness of life. Talking with *Por* and seeing Chatchai's condition was a grim reminder of the reality of life.

It was so fragile and therefore so precious that every minute of it was borrowed time.

Por had his daughter returned to him only to lose her such a short time later. Nid didn't want the same thing to happen to her and Lek. How could she possibly know how to prevent it? She couldn't even find her.

Nid took out all the pictures she had of Lek and spread them across the hotel bed. She had one from when Lek was a baby, one when she was five years old, one when she was about twelve and now her newest one from a little more than a year ago when she was 15. The mosaic image before her was almost surreal. Nid was watching her daughter grow up through pictures.

Nid took solace in the fact that Lek looked so happy in all of them. Even that was a double-edged sword, for Lek seemed happy without her.

CHAPTER 43

The morning after her visit with *Por* and Chatchai, Nid called Termsak to let him know she had finished in Buriram and could return to Bangkok. She was hoping that somehow her faux pas with the concert tour had quietly blown over, and that just maybe she could resurrect her career.

'I'm sorry, Nid. Termsak isn't taking any calls right now,' Phanee, the receptionist, answered. She politely neglected to add that Nid was at the top of the list of people he wasn't taking calls from. 'Don't worry about it, Termsak is a bit eccentric. He gets this way sometimes, so don't take it personally. I'm sure he'll come around eventually. I think you should know that the concert tour turned out to be nothing but a bunch of problems. Your not being there was only one of them,' she said.

'I'm afraid that's not much of a comfort.'

'Listen, you're probably lucky not to have been involved. Termsak and the tour promoter are fighting, the owners of the venues are fighting with the bands, the bands are fighting with the promoters, every person who had anything to do with the tour is now at each other's throats,' said the receptionist.

'So, where do we go from here?'

'I don't really know. Termsak is still upset. Needless to say, he doesn't have anything for you right now, so you shouldn't feel the need to rush back to Bangkok. By the way, did you have any luck finding your daughter?'

'No, but I was close this time. It's frustrating. I seem to be messing up everything I do,' Nid said.

'Don't be too hard on yourself. You have a lot of talent, otherwise you wouldn't have made it this far. Give it time. There will be more chances for both your career and to find your daughter.'

'Thanks for the pep talk, I really needed it.'

'Good luck Nid. Keep in touch. Everything will come together soon enough.'

When Nid hung up the phone she was both encouraged and discouraged. Encouraged by Phanee's empathy and her perspective on the situation. Discouraged by Termsak's tantrum. She didn't quite know how to react to it all and came to the conclusion that the recording industry was beyond her comprehension.

Casually walking over and looking out her hotel window at the street below, the thought occurred to her that she had never been in this situation before.

Sure, she'd been alone in strange hotels in faraway places, but never before had she had money to spare and time to do as she wished. What would she do with this new found spare time?

Nid took out the photo that Dow's father had given her of the kids in Surin. They looked so happy. What a strange coincidence that this photo, the one that showed Lek at her best, was taken in Surin. The same town where Lek was born. The same town where Lek was conceived. Surin was where it all began.

It had been what, 16 or 17 years since she'd been there? Before now, she had never thought about going back. Why would she? She had other things that kept her from thinking about it. But now, for some reason, this photo stirred a desire to return. Was the brothel, her former prison, still there? Was

Somchai's farm still there? Did she really want to know? She wasn't sure, but she had no reason to stay in Buriram.

Nid began to pack her belongings. Where would she go? The choices were Pattaya and Surin. Still without her mind made up, she walked downstairs to check out of the hotel.

'Where might you be going on this fine day?' the desk clerk asked her.

'Surin, I guess. I thought I might go visit some old friends.'

'Surin, good choice. Lovely town this time of year. Might I suggest that if you hurry you might be able to catch the afternoon train? It's a nice short trip and it will give you a chance to see the countryside. Cheap, too.'

'That sounds like a good idea. Thanks.' So Surin it was.

The desk clerk had been right. The train ride turned out to be a pleasant 45- minute trip through the countryside in the central plains of Thailand. Could this have been the path that Lek, Dow and Chatchai had taken?

When Nid stepped off the train, she made her way out toward the streets of the little town, passing through a handful of vendors selling food to the passengers. Successfully making it through that obstacle, she was then greeted by a small army of pedicab drivers.

Not seeing any other taxi service available, she picked out an older man with a large toothless grin and an unfiltered cigarette dangling from his lips. He continually bobbed his head and upper body to show his gratitude that she had chosen him over the others.

He led her over to his prized pedicab, a rickety old three wheeler with a faded vinyl passenger seat. He politely helped Nid aboard where she was shielded from the sun by an old piece of canvas held up by fingers of rusty steel.

Nid gave him general directions to the area she wanted to see not wanting to reveal to him exactly what it was she was looking for.

His nonstop chatter along the way was interrupted only by his occasional coughing and hacking. It was slightly annoying, but he was full of information about the town and its history. Nid only half-listened to most of it. She was caught up in her own thoughts about what she was doing.

Nid was going back to the place where Lek was conceived. She couldn't know for sure who it was, actually it could have been any one of a number of men, but she thought she had an idea who it was.

She couldn't remember his name, she didn't even know if he had told her. She did remember the amulet attached to the gold chain around his neck. It was from Wat Phra Keow in Bangkok, the Temple of the Emerald Buddha.

He wasn't a regular customer, probably in town on business. He was a good-looking man with strong features. He obviously took care of himself. He didn't speak much. It was almost as if he didn't want to be there. Nid thought he had probably been put up to it by his business contacts in town.

His lovemaking was gentle, not the rough stuff that many of the others liked. Nid was still so young and scared—he seemed to sense that. He took his time and made the situation as comfortable as possible.

Nid couldn't know for sure that it was him, but of all the men she had been with during that particular time, he was the one she wanted it to be.

The pedicab driver continued to ramble on about this street and that house, and who used to live here and there, when suddenly, there it was.

Nid's stomach immediately cramped. The house had a fresh coat of yellow paint and a brand new pickup truck in the driveway, but it was unmistakably the same house. She could almost sense the girls peering out of the window upstairs.

'Stop here,' she almost shouted.

The pedicab driver slammed on his brakes. 'What is it? Is something wrong?' he asked, startled by the forcefulness of her demand. When she didn't answer, he turned to see what she was looking at.

'The Kamnan's son lives there. The Kamnan kind of "inherited" this house a couple of years ago and gave it to his son.' The pedicab driver stopped to gauge her response. Not understanding the look on her face, he continued on with his running commentary.

'The Kamnan is getting long in years and will be stepping down soon. Which means before long his son will be running this town.' He still didn't understand the look on Nid's face. Perhaps a change in strategy was in order.

'This house was vacant for four or five years before the Kamnan took it over. Before that it was a brothel. Back in those days, the prettiest girls in the whole province worked in there. Men would come from miles around for their services.' He could sense a faint bit of recognition. He was getting somewhere.

'The police had their hands in it, just like they do everything in this town. The problem was, the people who ran the place never took care of the girls. When the chief of police caught a venereal disease from one of them and passed it on to his wife, he shut the place down. No doubt at her urging. Can't say as I've never partaken in their services. Never could afford it even if I wanted to.'

'So they've closed the place down,' Nid thought to herself. 'I should have thought they would have by now.' It was a small consolation. Most likely they just moved on and opened up someplace else. They are probably still stealing young girls, children, from their homes and keeping them hostage, forcing them into a life of prostitution.

'Miss?' Nid looked up to see the pedicab driver staring at her. 'Will you be going in for a visit? I can wait for you here.'

'No thanks. Let's move on.'

'Where to?'

Nid thought for a moment. 'I need to find a car. Do you know where I might hire one?'

'What do you need a car for? I can take you anywhere you need to go,' the driver protested.

'I'm sure you could, but I need to get to a place quite a distance outside of town. It would be better for both of us if I hired faster transportation.'

'I do have an old friend who has a car. Sometimes when he's not busy he uses it as a taxi. Maybe you can talk him into taking you outside of town.'

'That sounds perfect. Where might I find him?'

'I'll take you there. Just sit back and enjoy the ride.'

The old driver coughed and wheezed as he peddled his precious cargo through the back streets and alleyways of Surin. He never seemed to tire of hearing himself talk, either. 'My friend is an old guy, just like me. I'm sure he'd probably be thrilled to drive you outside town. You can trust him, too, not like those crooks in town,' the driver said.

Before long they pulled into the dirt driveway of an old wooden house.

'Wait here,' the driver said as he dismounted and went inside. He emerged a few minutes later with a rather rotund man wearing a wide smile.

'I'm Tok,' the newcomer announced. 'My dear old friend tells me you want to hire my car.'

'Yes, I'd like to visit some friends outside of town. Are you available?'

'Of course I am. Get out of this rickety old thing, my chariot awaits you.' Tok paid no attention to the pedicab driver's insulted looks and verbal protests.

Nid could only shake her head and smile. Tok was laying it on pretty thick, especially since the chariot he had promised wasn't in much better shape than the pedicab. It was an exchange she needed to hear, though. The men's jovial attitudes helped release the tension she was feeling after having just come from the former brothel.

Nid was having a little trouble coming to grips with the feelings she was experiencing. She was relieved that she didn't have to confront the *mamasan*. She wasn't sure what she might have done if she did. It was a moot point, she thought. She was now moving on to a happier situation. She was going to visit the people who had saved her life.

What Nid didn't realize was that it would get worse before it got better. Along the way to Somchai's farm, Nid had vague recognitions of certain places where she went through her struggle to survive. She had begged for money on that street, slept behind that restaurant.

As Tok drove her further outside of town, the memories became a bit more blurred. There were fewer houses, fewer people to beg from. When she had reached this point the last time she was here, she was losing the battle.

The sun was getting low on the horizon when Tok finally turned down the long dirt path that led to Somchai's farm.

As they rounded one particular curve, Nid instructed Tok to stop the car. This was it. This was the place where she had given up hope. She was surprised that she recognized it, yet how could she forget?

Nid got out of the car and slowly walked over to the side of the path. This was it, all right. The years hadn't changed it much. With the rice paddies behind her, Nid quietly laid herself down and looked up at the sky.

Tok didn't say a word. He had no idea what Nid was up to, but he sensed it was something significant. Besides, he was paid to drive, and paid well, not to ask stupid questions.

Nid could feel the dampness of the ground seep into her clothes. It didn't matter. She put her hands to her belly. The pain came back, only this time it was a different pain. It was as if she had a hole in her belly, a gap that needed to be filled. It was a hole only a mother could feel. A mother who had lost her only child.

It was then she realized how far she'd actually come. It was then that she realized that she had been to the absolute depths, as low as anyone could ever get, and had fought her way back.

She didn't know how long she lay there before she allowed herself to get up. It was time to move on, time once again to begin the climb back to the top. It was time to visit the strangers who had given her a second chance.

CHAPTER 44

The sun had just set behind the bank of clouds that had been moving in from the west when Tok pulled the car into the small courtyard at Somchai's farm. The sky above was still bright, with a brilliant montage of pastel orange, red and pink colors reflecting off the wisps of clouds overhead.

As Tok turned off the engine, an older woman poked her head out the front door of the farmhouse to see what was going on. She looked like Soam, Nid thought, but was younger than Nid would have thought Soam to be.

'Can I help you?' the woman asked as Nid got out of the car.

'I'm looking for the Somchai farm. Is this it?' Nid answered.

'Yes, this is our farm,' the woman said as she approached the car. It was dusk and getting darker by the minute, making it difficult to see facial features.

'Does the Somchai family still live here?' Nid asked tentatively. She had a strange feeling she knew this woman, but couldn't quite place her.

'Nid? Nid Sawang?' the woman asked in disbelief, ignoring Nid's question.

'Yes,' Nid half asked in reply. 'You must be . . .'

'Wan,' she exclaimed, as if she found it hard to believe Nid didn't recognize her. 'I didn't expect to ever see you again. What brings you all the way out here?'

'I was just in the area and thought I might stop in to say hello. I hope I didn't catch you at a bad time.'

'Of course not.' Wan grabbed Nid's hands. 'It's so good to see you. You look great.'

'So do you,' Nid replied, although it wasn't entirely true. Where Nid had kept her youthful features over the years, Wan now looked old and tired. Most likely the result of many hard years of working on the farm. Her face was full of lines and the few teeth she had left were stained the tell tale blood red color from constantly chewing betel.

'It's so good to see you. Please, come inside. We have a lot to talk about,' Wan said as she led Nid toward the door. By then a couple of small heads had appeared in the doorway. As the two women got close, they scurried inside. 'My children,' Wan said almost apologetically. 'We have eight of them.'

'Eight?' Nid replied unbelievingly. 'You've been busy since the last time I saw you.' It was all too unreal.

Nid remembered Wan as a young farm girl, not unlike Nid once was. It was a bit of a shock to see her now.

'Like I said, we have a lot to catch up on.'

The tension was eased a bit when the women entered the farmhouse. At least the inside hadn't changed that much. The door still squeaked when it opened. The cooking stove was still in the same place she remembered from years before. The wood and charcoal were still piled in the same spot. Nid wouldn't have wanted it any other way.

The only things different about the inside of the house were its inhabitants. Eight dirty little faces stared curiously at Nid's arrival and a man Nid considered to be about her age sat at a table near the stove pouring rice whiskey into his glass.

'This is my husband Bonsoom,' Wan introduced him. Bonsoom smiled and nodded his head. He didn't know who she was, but she looked good. She had a way about her. Must be a city girl. Successful, too.

'Nice to meet you Bonsoom,' Nid said courteously.

He nodded his response before taking a taste of his newly poured cocktail.

'And these are our children,' Wan said, pointing to the huddled bunch. She introduced all of them but there were so many, by the time she was through Nid couldn't remember their names. The younger children sat still, staring at Nid as if they'd never seen such a strange being before. The older ones, after giving Nid a polite *wai*, took their introduction as a reason to be excused and set about milling around the house.

As Wan placed a mat on the floor, her eldest daughter brought Nid a glass of water, the Thai way of welcoming a friend into their home. And as Nid sat down with Wan taking a position beside her, a young girl came over and sat in Nid's lap.

'Go on back,' Wan scolded her.

'No, that's okay. I don't mind,' Nid told her. It had been a long time since she had the chance to hold a child. She squeezed her tightly and told her what a beautiful young girl she was. Although she didn't say anything, Nid could see the pride in Wan's face.

'So, tell me. What have you been doing all these years?' Wan was almost embarrassed to ask. The woman that sat before her was vastly different to the young girl she had once known. The girl that had left so many years ago was completely broke and dressed in barely more than rags. She now wore beautiful clothes and arrived with a car and driver. Wan could only surmise that Nid had gone back into prostitution. It was the only way a destitute farm girl could have survived and prospered on her own. Looking at her now, she must have been very good at her trade. 'Never mind,' Wan thought, she was happy to see her friend had done so well.

'It's a long story,' Nid said, shrugging off the question. Her response only served to confirm what Wan had been thinking.

Nid quickly changed the subject. 'Where are Somchai and Soam?'

'*Por* died about five years ago,' Wan began. 'We found him late one afternoon out in the rice paddies, right where everyone thought he'd probably want to go. His heart just finally gave out on him. He worked a hard life and smoked too many cigarettes I guess.

'Then just last year *Mae* got real sick with consumption. She hung on for about a month but everyone knew it was just a matter of time. "Death walking" is how our neighbor put it. On her last day she got out of bed and walked right out there where *Por* had died. She wouldn't let us stop her. We stood up here by the house and watched as she laid down in the same spot and joined *Por* in the next life. We were sad, very sad, but it was peaceful knowing that she was able to choose when and where it happened,' she said.

Nid held one hand to her mouth and stared at the floor. She kept her other arm wrapped tightly around Wan's daughter who had yet to leave her lap. When she was finally able to speak, her voice was scratchy. 'I'm very sorry to hear they're gone. They were both very good people.'

'It was difficult for a while, but life goes on. We mustn't dwell on things we can't change. But don't worry, we've handled it well. Bonsoom and I are keeping their legacy alive by keeping the farm in good running shape. It's not always easy but it has its rewards.'

'I'm sure they would have wanted it that way,' Nid said with sincerity. 'What about your brother, Thawanee? Where is he now?'

'Thawanee left a few years back. It pretty much broke *Por*'s heart to see him go. He wanted so much for Thawanee to take over the farm and keep the family line going. Thawanee had other ideas. Last I heard he was in Bangkok, but I don't know what he's doing down there. The rest of the family has moved on, too. We just weren't able to make enough money off the farm to feed everyone. Me, Bonsoom and the children are the only one's left,' she said.

A moment of silence passed between the two old friends. Nid could hear large, scattered drops ticking on the wooden roof above them as it began to rain. Large drops meant only one thing; it would be raining hard very soon.

'What about you?' Wan broke the tension. 'You still haven't told me what you have been doing over the years? I mean, look at you. And how about your girl? Was Lek her name? She must be a lovely young woman by now.'

'Like I told you, it's a long story,' Nid began to sputter. 'I'm going through a rather confusing time right now. I just seem to mess up everything I do. It's been that way all my life.'

'What do you mean? You look like you've done quite well for yourself,' said Wan.

'Yes and no. I mean, I became successful as a singer. I even recorded an album. I was supposed to go out on tour but I messed that up when I thought I could find Lek.'

'Find Lek? Why, where is she?'

'I don't know. She was stolen from me when she was still just a baby. I haven't had much luck trying to find her. I do know she's still alive, but I always seem to just miss catching up with her every time I get information as to where she is. Or was.'

'That's terrible. What happened?' Wan asked.

Wan listened intently as Nid explained Lek's abduction and all that Nid had been going through to try to find her. Realizing there was little or nothing she could do to help, Wan set about concentrating on the positive sides of Nid's story.

'Well at least you know she's alive. From the pictures you've shown me I can tell she's turning into a beautiful young lady, too. I'm sure it's just a matter of time before you two are reunited. After all, you've become a big singing star. How can Lek miss seeing you or hearing about you eventually.'

'I wish that were true,' Nid replied. 'But she doesn't know who I am. It wouldn't make a difference if I was the biggest star there ever was. Lek wouldn't, couldn't make the connection.'

'Bonsoom! Children! We have a celebrity in our house!' Wan called out, ignoring Nid's debate. Loss was a way of life in rural Thailand and although one never forgets loved ones lost, the sooner one moves on, the better off everyone is. Now success stories, they are rare occurrences. Having one sitting right here in her house, in living flesh, made Wan push the Lek story aside.

'No, really,' Nid quietly protested. 'I'm not really . . .'

'Nid's a singing star,' Wan kept talking to her family as if Nid wasn't even there.

'I knew there was something about you,' Bonsoom chipped in as he turned his chair to face her. He took a big gulp of his drink then smiled a wide, semi toothless grin. 'The minute you walked in I knew you were a movie star.'

'I'm not a movie star,' Nid protested again. The situation was beginning to spin out of control.

'Tell us what it's like to be a big star,' Wan's eldest girl said as the children gathered around. Nid guessed Wan's eldest daughter to be just a couple of years younger then Lek. Her eyes were wide and dreamy, obviously caused by her imagination running wild about what it must be like to be a star.

'First of all, I'm not really a star,' Nid said once she finally gained the floor. 'I've been singing in a club in Pattaya for the past few years. A producer heard me and thought it might be good if I recorded an album. So I did.'

'What was that like?' Wan's eldest wanted to know.

'It was hard work. We stayed cooped up in the studio, sometimes 12 or 14 hours a day. For months.' Nid paused, wanting nothing more than to change the subject. Lucky for her, she was saved by a loud knock on the door.

'Tok!' Nid said, only just then remembering her driver. It was now pouring outside and Tok had been sitting in his car all this time. 'I'm so sorry,' she said apologetically, once Wan's eldest had let him in.

'No problem Miss Nid. I was just wondering if you will be spending the night?' It was getting late, and the amount of rain coming down would make for a tiresome journey back into Surin.

'Of course she is,' Wan spoke out before Nid had a chance to respond. 'I even have a place for you if you'd like to stay.'

'That would be most kind of you.' The relief on Tok's face was evident.

'We couldn't possibly put you out.' Nid made a feeble attempt to turn her down. She wouldn't put up too much of a fight, though. She wasn't looking forward to the trip back into town, either.

'Nonsense. I'd be insulted if you didn't stay,' Wan replied, much to Nid's relief. 'Children, get out the sleeping mats for our guests, then it's off to bed for all of you.'

The children tried to protest at being sent off to bed so early. After all, it was a rare occurrence having strange guests in the house and they didn't want to miss a thing. But there were chores to be done early in the morning.

Bonsoom invited Tok to join him in a glass of rice whiskey and water, a gesture Tok was more than happy to oblige. As the two men sat around talking and drinking, Wan and Nid were once again left alone to rehash old times. It was then that Wan mentioned something that Nid hadn't thought about for years.

'What about your sister Nok? Did you ever hear from her again?'

'Nok? No, I've been so caught up with trying to find Lek I haven't thought much about her. I guess she's probably still living in America or whatever country that foreigner took her to.'

'How about the rest of your family? Have you been to see them?' asked Wan.

'No, this is the first time I've been up this way since I left. I guess I'm still shy over what my mother did, how she sold me. I don't know what I'd say if I saw her again.'

'Don't be silly, now that you're a successful recording artist you've got nothing to be ashamed of. I think you owe it to yourself to touch base with your roots. Aren't you just a little curious about what your family must be like now?'

'Not until you mentioned it. I suppose someday I should go back up there to see them,' said Nid.

'What about after you leave here? It's not that much further north considering how far you've come already. Another four or five hours up the road is within reach.'

'I don't think I'm ready yet. Besides, I really should be getting back to Pattaya soon. There might still be a chance to save my singing career. Maybe after I find Lek I'll take her up there so that we can share the experience together,' she added.

Wan sensed it was a subject Nid wasn't ready to discuss, so she moved on to other things. As the two men sat and drank whiskey and the children fell asleep, the two women sat and talked with each other for the rest of the evening.

When the hour grew late, they finally reached the point where they could talk no more. Just for old times sake, Wan set up a bed where Nid had stayed the last time she was a guest in their house.

Nid had forgotten just how quiet it could get in the rural farm lands. It was so quiet, in fact, that the silence was almost loud in itself. Being accustomed to the constant hum of life in the city, Nid had trouble falling asleep.

Before long, a cricket began to chirp a hypnotic rhythm. It allowed Nid to relax her mind and soon she became lost in thought about her family back in the tiny little village of Tha Thum nestled along the Mun River. What were they like now? Did her mother ever think of her? Her thoughts gradually turned into dreams as she fell fast asleep.

Nid awoke the next morning to the sounds of children going about their chores. She must have slept soundly, for Tok had already arisen and was out talking with Bonsoom next to the car. Wan had prepared breakfast and was sitting quietly by, waiting for Nid to wake up.

'Good morning,' she said once she saw Nid's eyes open. 'Are you hungry?'

'A little,' Nid replied sleepily.

'Good,' Wan replied as she set two breakfast plates down in front of Nid.

'I waited for you so that we could eat together.' Wan knew that Nid would be leaving soon and wanted to spend as much time with her as possible.

Not much was spoken between the two old friends as they ate their breakfast. It wasn't until the meal was almost finished when Nid suddenly seemed to remember something. She reached into her purse, pulled out a one hundred baht note and handed it to Wan.

'What's this for?' Wan looked confused.

'Don't you remember?' Nid replied.

'Remember what?'

'The morning I left we exchanged promises. You promised me you would stay here and live the life you were supposed to. You kept your promise and now I'm keeping mine.'

'But what was your promise?'

'You gave me a hundred baht to help me get started. That one hundred baht probably saved my life, and Lek's too. I don't think you'll ever know how much it meant to me. I promised I'd pay you back and it makes me very happy to be able to do so.'

'After all these years and you still remember a silly little gift of a hundred baht?'

'It wasn't silly to me, Wan. At the time it wasn't such a little gift, either,' she said.

Wan took the one hundred baht note and held it in her hand. She didn't want to take it, but she could see what it meant to her friend. The two women looked at each other a moment before embracing. The time was at hand, time for Nid to start the long journey back to Pattaya.

They walked outside to the awaiting car, arm in arm. As Tok started the engine, Nid and Wan exchanged addresses and promised to keep in touch. The two women embraced again and had more than a little difficulty separating.

Her eyes filled with tears, Nid had to pry herself away from her friend to get into the car.

On the way back to Surin, Tok sensed Nid's mood and her wish not to talk. Without his interruptions, Nid was able to stay lost in her thoughts. Her visit with Wan reassured her that she could go back. And if she could, then Lek could, too.

CHAPTER 45

'It's 10 p.m.,' Toi announced, annoyed.

'I know. Sorry to wake you,' Lek apologized. She tried to be quiet as she entered the room, but now that Toi was awake, Lek no longer needed to tiptoe around. Besides, within a few minutes she would be in bed herself. Hopefully, soon after that they would both be asleep.

'Don't tell me, let me guess. You've been over to Soonton's house again, right?' Toi said argumentatively as she wiped her eyes.

'Right.' Lek tried to sound cheery. She wasn't in the mood to get into a verbal battle with Toi. She was exhausted and just wanted to sleep.

'We have to talk,' Toi replied, not yet ready to let the subject rest. 'I know it's none of my business . . .'

'You're right, it isn't,' Lek interrupted.

'Lek, you've been over there almost every night for the past six months,' Toi pressed on. 'I don't think that it's a good idea.'

'Why not?'

'For one thing, he's three times your age. For another thing, well, I just don't trust him. The man is weird. And the people I see him with sometimes. They give me the creeps.'

'What are you trying to say, Toi?'

'I think he's involved in some sort of crooked activity. I don't have any proof, but the men I see him talking to now and then have got to be crooks. None of them are from around here and they come and go at the strangest times. They're always looking around, trying to make sure no one is watching and they always stop talking whenever anybody gets close enough to hear what they're saying. I'd hate to see you mixed up with them. It could be dangerous.'

'I agree that some of those people are not the pillars of society, but you can't always judge a person from the company he keeps. Soonton would never do anything to hurt me. It's just the opposite. Ever since those thugs trapped me in the alleyway last year, it seems like Soonton's new purpose in life is to make sure no harm comes to me.'

'If you ask me, I think those thugs are probably friends of his. They seem like the type of people he would know,' Toi responded, unconvinced.

'He does know who they are, but they are absolutely not his friends. He told me that they are the henchmen of a rather well-known drug dealer who operates north of here. He didn't say how he knew, and I didn't ask, but he also told me that he was aware of their comings and goings and would try his best to make sure he was around to protect me if and when they came back. In the meantime, he's been teaching me how to protect myself in case he can't be there.'

'Are you sleeping with him?' Toi blurted out the question. It had obviously been on her mind all along.

'Toi! I can't believe you asked that. Of course not. He's like a father to me.'

'Then what is it you do over there every night?'

'I told you, Soonton is teaching me how to protect myself. He set up a gym and a boxing ring outside his house. He also hung up a couple of punch bags and tied an old tyre to a tree to practice working with sticks. I've been exercising and learning different kinds of martial arts.' It was true that the exercise was developing muscles Lek didn't even know she had, which, in turn, was developing her self-confidence. 'It's great. You should try it.'

'Are you sure that's all you're doing? There's no funny business going on over there?'

'If that is what's really bothering you, I can assure you that there isn't. I told you, he's like a father to me.' Lek reached over and turned off the light, hoping Toi would take the hint.

Still unconvinced, Toi nonetheless let it rest. The alarm would be going off at five in the morning and they both had a full day of work ahead of them.

The next morning started out the same as most of the others had in Korat. It was early April and almost two years to the day after the girls had arrived. The alarm still rang out at 5 a.m. Lek and Toi still ate breakfast at the little cafe downstairs and then, sleepy eyed, walked over to their waiting buses.

What gave Lek her first hint that this day would be different was when she thought she caught a glimpse of the three men who had accosted her last year. Although she passed it off as unnecessary paranoia, she would have a word with Soonton about it just the same.

'They're here all right,' Soonton told her without elaborating.

'What are we going to do about it?' Lek asked excitedly. This time, Soonton's words weren't reassuring.

'We are not going to do anything,' Soonton replied, putting extra emphasis on 'we'. He reached down and turned the bus's ignition key, slowly bringing its huge engine to life. 'Let's go, we've got work to do.'

Lek was well accustomed to Soonton's demeanor, but this morning it seemed to have a little extra bite. Not wanting to make matters worse, Lek dismissed his response and went about her business of getting ready for the first load of passengers.

Business was slow during the morning, as it usually was in the middle of the week. The boredom that ensued allowed Lek extra time to stew about what Soonton had told her. Yet every time she tried to pursue the subject with him, he told her to forget about it.

He got worse at lunch time. Lek and Soonton usually ate together and Lek always looked forward to their half hour alone.

But today Soonton left her to eat by herself. Instead, he opted to take his break with three other men. Lek didn't know who they were, although she had seen them before. Bemused, Lek noticed they fit the description of the type of people Toi described in her argument last night.

Curious, Lek watched their exchange, trying to figure out what was going on. The conversation occasionally became heated, yet gave no clue as to what they were talking about. Lek thought she might have seen money changing hands, but wasn't sure.

She edged closer to try to hear what they were saying, without letting on she was eavesdropping. She kept her back to them, and did manage to hear, 'We have made sure he will be at the corner of . . .' Then silence. Lek slowly turned to look and found that all eyes were fixed upon her. Even though her heart skipped a beat, she remained calm and acted as though she didn't notice, then casually climbed up into the bus.

When their lunch break was just about over, Soonton broke off the conversation with his friends and joined Lek in the bus. 'Why don't you take the afternoon off,' he more or less commanded.

'You know I can't do that, Soonton. Toi's uncle would never let you go out there without a conductor and who could I get to fill in for me?'

Soonton looked tired. 'You're right, of course,' he said as he slowly shook his head and sighed. 'Just stay out of the way.'

'What do you mean, "stay out of the way"? What are you talking about?'

Soonton didn't respond. He didn't even look at her. Seemingly lost in thought, he fired up the bus and prepared to leave.

The way Soonton was acting, Lek thought better of trying to get him to tell her what he was up to.

It was barely 15 minutes later when it happened. Lek had finished taking tickets and was just settling into the seat behind Soonton when he suddenly swerved off the road. The bus ricocheted off a parked car and plowed into a small group of men who were standing on the sidewalk, then abruptly came to a halt against a cement wall.

They weren't traveling very fast when it happened, yet the impact was enough to send Soonton toward the windshield. The large steering wheel pressed hard into his stomach, keeping him from flying through the glass.

Lek was sent flying out of her seat. She somersaulted over the bar that separated the passengers from the driver and landed head down on the floor with the gear shift pressed into her back.

The passengers were slammed into the backs of the seats in front of them but most of the damage, luckily none serious, was done by flying debris. Books, groceries, handbags, everything that had been hastily stored in the racks overhead came raining down on top of them.

Within an instant, it was over. A moment of total silence followed. Lek thought for sure they were all dead.

Soonton was the first to act. He righted Lek, grabbed her by the shoulders and looked into her eyes. 'Are you okay?'

Lek wasn't sure. What she was sure of was that Soonton was scared. His eyes were wide, his hands were shaking and he looked as though he was in shock. She had never seen him that way. 'I'm okay. What about you?'

Soonton didn't respond to her question. Instead, he turned and made a quick survey of the passengers behind them. 'What a mess,' he muttered.

'Soonton, are you okay?' Lek repeated.

'Yes. Yes I am,' Soonton responded unconvincingly.

'Stay here and see if you can help them,' he said as he nodded his head toward the passengers. He then kicked open the smashed door beside him and climbed out.

A small crowd had already begun to gather as Soonton rounded the back of the bus. He stopped short when he saw what he had done. Two men were lying on the ground and it didn't take a doctor to see that one of them was dead. The other was injured, but it looked as though he'd make it. As he was being tended to by his friends, Soonton slowly made his way back behind the bus. Panicking, he turned and fled down a side street.

By the time the police arrived, the crowd of onlookers had grown rather large and included a couple of journalists, who were walking around taking pictures. By that time, Lek had managed to get everyone off the bus. Most had minor bumps, bruises and scrapes, but none of the injuries were serious. Lek was still tending to them when a couple of uniformed officers approached her.

'Do you work for the bus company?' one of them asked.

'Yes, I'm the conductor.'

'Can you tell us what happened?' he asked as he led her away from the crowd.

'I'm not sure. It happened so fast.'

'Try to remember. Take your time,' the cop asked.

'Well,' Lek sputtered, 'I was just sitting down when I thought I saw a motorcycle taxi cut us off. Soonton did a good job to avoid hitting him, but I guess he must have lost control.'

'Soonton, is that the bus driver's name?'

'Yes,' Lek responded tentatively.

'Do you know his surname?'

'No,' Lek again responded tentatively. Soonton was her friend and given the scene they had during lunch, Lek wasn't sure how much information she should give the police until she had a chance to talk to him.

'Do you know the person you ran over?'

'No,' Lek said, confused. How could she have known him. It was an accident.

'Are you sure you didn't know the man who was killed here today?' the officer pressed on. He didn't seem convinced.

'No, I didn't,' Lek said forcefully. 'Why?'

'I'll ask the questions,' the officer replied sternly. 'Now, where is Soonton?'

'I don't know.' And she didn't. The last time she saw him was when he got out of the bus.

'Look, I don't want to have to ask you again. Where is he?'

'I told you. I don't know.' This time Lek's response was more of a plea. It was all too confusing.

'We're not going to get anything out of her,' the other officer spoke for the first time.

Lek's interrogator stared her down. 'Don't leave town, we may want to ask you a few more questions. I trust the bus company will know where to find you?' he asked.

Lek nodded, afraid to say any more.

'Okay, let's go,' the second officer said as he took hold of his partner's arm and led him away.

As they turned and left, Lek started to follow them back toward the accident, but stopped when she finally took a look at the small group of men the bus had hit. One of them was definitely dead. Yet more disturbing to Lek, she recognized the injured man as one of the men who had accosted her. The two who were tending to him were also in the alleyway last year. Frightened by the sight, Lek turned away, quickly found a motorcycle taxi nearby and instructed the driver to take her back to the bus station.

Prasit was busy doing paperwork when she burst through his office door. 'What are you doing here?' he asked incredulously. 'Why aren't you at work?'

'There's been an accident,' Lek began.

As she told Prasit the story, she paced back and forth across his office. Her speech was quick and excited and left no chance for Prasit to interrupt with questions until she was through. When she was finished, Toi's flabbergasted uncle looked as though he was about to have a nervous breakdown.

'So you don't know where Soonton went?' he asked as he nervously rapped his fingers on the table.

'No. He just disappeared.'

'And the police think you know who was killed?'

'I don't know, maybe. But they sure didn't seem to believe me when I told them I didn't,' Lek said.

Prasit sat back in his chair and wiped his face. It seemed as though he was searching for something to say. 'Okay, I guess I'd better get out there and try to figure out what happened.

'You should probably stay put for the next couple of days until we can get this whole thing straightened out. Stay out of sight and don't talk to anyone, especially the press. The company doesn't need any bad publicity from this mess,' he said.

Lek nodded her head in consent, then dejectedly followed Prasit out the door. Despondent and with no place else to go, she walked over to her room and locked the door behind her.

CHAPTER 46

It wasn't until early the next afternoon, long after Toi had gone off to work, when hunger finally drove Lek out from the relative safety of her room. She timidly made her way down to the cafe and ordered some fried rice. Nervously waiting for her meal to arrive, Lek spied a newspaper that had been left vacant on the table next to her, probably by someone from the morning crowd.

A large picture dominated the front page. The picture, Lek quickly noticed, was of the accident from the day before. To make matters worse, she was in it.

The headlines above the accompanying article read: 'REPUTED DRUG LORD KILLED.' Shocked, Lek read on:

'Reputed opium drug lord Anan Witanuchi was killed instantly around noon yesterday by an out of control bus on the outskirts of Korat. Infamous for his drug running exploits from the northern area of Thailand known as the Golden Triangle, police had been tracking Anan through several northern and central villages. Although police are not releasing any details about his death, they did state that they have not ruled out foul play.

'Eyewitnesses to the accident revealed that it appeared as though the driver of the bus deliberately swerved to hit him. The driver fled the scene and was unavailable for comment.

'The conductor of the bus, whose name was not made available, also fled after brief questioning.

'The police stated that the conductor was currently
not a suspect and made no further comment on her possible
involvement. A city wide search is now being conducted
for both persons.'

The article continued with background information about
Anan's involvement in the opium trade with certain hill tribes
in the Golden Triangle, but Lek stopped reading when it sunk
in that she was getting tangled up in something she knew
nothing about. She lowered the newspaper and sat staring out
the front door.

She was so lost in her thoughts she didn't even notice when
Soonton opened the door and walked in. He saw her sitting
alone and hurried over to her table.

'I see you've read the paper.'

'Soonton? I didn't see you come in.' Lek was visibly startled.
Soonton looked bad. He had a large bump on his forehead, two
black eyes and walked crouched over as if he was in pain from
his stomach injuries.

'I know. You have to be more careful.' Soonton looked
over his shoulder toward the door. Satisfied that no one was
following him, he turned back to Lek. 'We've got to get out of
here, kid. There's a whole bunch of people looking for us.'

'What's going on, Soonton?'

'You really don't want to know. I'm sorry to have dragged
you into this. If I had known they would be after you, too, I
would never have . . .' he let his sentence trail off and turned
back toward looking out the door.

'Have what, Soonton? Tell me what's happening,' Lek
said.

'We don't have time for that now. All I can tell you is that
the police think you're involved. And if they think you're part
of this then Anan's men will think so, too. Both of our lives are

in danger and we have to leave. Now! I have a car waiting on the other side of the parking lot.'

'I can't just leave. I have a job. And . . .' Lek hesitated. She couldn't come up with any other reasons to stay. It was all so confusing. The newspaper said the police were looking for her. Soonton said Anan's men, whoever they were, were looking for her. Prasit told her to stay out of sight. The worst part was that she had no idea what was going on and would have no answers for any of them. Her intellect told her to stay, her instincts told her to run.

'We can't sit here and argue. This is the first place they will look for us. Let's go.' Soonton urged her.

'Where will we go?'

'I have some friends that will put us up for a couple of days until it calms down a little. After that, we can move on to another city and start over.'

Lek sat staring at Soonton. It seemed like a bad dream.

'Come on, we've got to get out of here!' Soonton growled. Realizing he was scaring her, Soonton steadied his voice.

'I took a big risk coming back here but I couldn't just leave you to deal with all this. But you must understand that it's imperative we leave before anyone finds us. We have no choice.'

'Okay, okay,' Lek solemnly gave in. 'I have to gather a few things first. Wait here and I'll be right back.'

'Don't take too long,' Soonton warned, 'and don't talk to anybody.'

Lek ran up to her room and gathered what few belongings she could fit into a small plastic bag. She was just sitting down to write Toi a quick goodbye note when a knock at the door caused her to freeze. Another knock was followed by a woman calling out her name. She didn't recognize the voice.

CHAPTER 47

After returning from the north, Nid Sawang, recording artist and budding celebrity that she was, was still receiving the silent treatment from Termsak. She occasionally heard one or more of her songs being played on the radio, which gave her hope that things might soon change, but when her first royalty cheque arrived, it came with no note, no letter, no portent of future prospects.

The amount of money she received from the royalty cheques over the next few months wasn't enough to make her rich, although each new cheque was slightly larger than the last. It meant she didn't need to go back singing full time at the Malee Cafe.

The irony of the situation wasn't lost on her. With extra free time and a growing bank account she could now do just about anything she wanted. Yet what she wanted to do most, to find Lek, she couldn't do because she had no clue as to her whereabouts. That all changed early one morning in April.

Lost in her dreams during a sound sleep, Nid was abruptly awakened by a loud knock on her door. The faint light of the early dawn that filtered through her window was barely enough to enable her to read her beside clock: 6:00 a.m.

Who would be calling on her at this early hour of the morning? Not overly enthused about finding out, Nid pawed around until she found her robe and stumbled toward the door.

No sooner had she opened it a crack, Malee burst through waving the morning newspaper.

'I'm free!' she exclaimed as she danced around the room, waving the newspaper above her head.

'What are you talking about?' Nid made an attempt to sound annoyed, but Malee's enthusiasm wouldn't allow it.

'It's Anan,' Malee said, finally calming down a bit. She handed the newspaper to Nid then plopped down on the edge of her bed. 'He's dead. I can't believe it, he's actually dead.'

'Ah, Anan's dead,' Nid said with mock understanding as she accepted the newspaper. Giving Malee a furtive look, she sat down beside her excited friend. 'Who is Anan?'

'Look at the paper,' Malee commanded, as if everyone should know who Anan was.

Nid gave Malee a sideways glance as she unfolded the paper to reveal the front page. The main headline read, 'REPUTED DRUG LORD KILLED'. Under it, a picture showed a group of people gathered around a bus accident in Korat, where a man who had been run over lay dead.

'Don't you see,' Malee said, exasperated, 'He's the man I told you about that gave me to Chalarm after my father gave me to him.'

'So, what does that mean, Malee?'

'It means,' Malee threw her hands in the air to show that she couldn't believe Nid didn't understand the significance of the event. 'Now that he's gone, there's no reason I can't go back to my family.'

'That's great, Malee. I'm very happy for you. But I have to admit I'm a little confused. Why did this person have to die in order for you to go back to see your family?'

It finally occurred to Malee that Nid truly didn't understand the ways of her people.

'Okay, I'll start from the beginning. My father gave me to Anan as a present for closing a business deal. It doesn't matter that Anan gave me to Chalarm; in my father's eyes, I was still the property of Anan. If I were to return to my village while Anan was still alive, I would have brought shame to my father and my family. I would have been an outcast. Most likely I would have been banned from my village forever. But now that Anan is dead, I can bring this newspaper as proof and return to my village, and my family, without bringing shame on anyone. Anan's death means that I am finally, truly free.'

It finally began to sink in. 'I never thought I would be happy about anyone's death,' Nid said quietly as she reached over and gave Malee a hug. For all the years she knew Malee, Nid never realized what torture her best friend must have been going through. All this time Nid thought that Malee was an emancipated woman, an escapee from the shackles that Anan and Chalarm had wrapped around her. She never knew that it was so much more than that. She never realized that their influence was so debilitating, that Anan's mere existence was enough to keep Malee from returning home.

'So,' Nid managed to gather her thoughts. 'When will you be leaving?'

'I don't know.' Malee sat staring at the floor. The reality of the situation was beginning to sink in for her as well. 'Ever since I left I've dreamt about the day I would be able to return home. But it's been a long, long time and I've made a place for myself here. It will take a while to get myself mentally prepared to return.'

'If there's anything I can do to help . . .' Nid let the sentence trail off. She was happy for Malee, but didn't relish the thought of losing her best friend. Unable to look at her, Nid absentmindedly stared at the picture on the front page of the newspaper.

'Thank you, Nid. I think you know how much you mean to me. You being here is all the help I need.'

'Wait a minute!' Nid gasped. 'Look at the picture,' she instructed as she handed Malee the newspaper.

As Malee looked at the gruesome sight that the crowd in the photo was staring at, Nid reached over and grabbed a photograph off the table by her bed. With the newspaper now in Malee's lap, Nid lined up her photo next to the picture in the newspaper. The likeness of one person in both pictures was identical.

'It's Lek!' Malee choked.

'It is!' Nid screamed.

'But . . .' Malee tried to speak but Nid cut her off.

'I'm going up there today. Right now in fact,' she said as she quickly rose from the bed and began to gather some clothes to put in her travel bag.

'Nid, wait a minute. I think maybe you should finish reading the article.'

'Why?' Nid said as she continued to pack.

'Because the article says that the conductor might be involved. And judging by the picture, Lek appears to be the conductor.'

'What?' Nid yelled, flabbergasted.

'Here, read for yourself.' Malee handed her the newspaper.

Nid began to read standing up, but as the words crossed in front of her eyes, she slowly sat back down on the edge of her bed. She read the story out loud.

'The conductor of the bus, whose name was not made available, also fled after brief questioning . . . A citywide search is now underway . . .'

'I'm sure it's all a misunderstanding,' Malee offered, hoping to ease the tension.

'Of course it is,' Nid responded defiantly. 'Lek wouldn't get herself involved in anything like that. I'm going up there to straighten it all out and bring her home with me where she belongs.'

'You sound like a mother,' Malee observed as Nid rose to finish her packing.

It didn't take long for Nid to gather all that she felt she would need for a quick trip to Korat. When she finished, she sat back down next to Malee. She was so excited she didn't even think to ask Malee to go with her. 'You will wait for me to return, won't you?' asked Nid.

'Of course I will,' Malee responded. 'I wouldn't think of leaving without saying goodbye.'

'Besides,' Nid added enthusiastically, 'you can't leave without seeing Lek. It just wouldn't be right. Not only did you free her from Chalarm, but it's because of you that I now know where she is.'

'It is strange how that worked out,' Malee pondered. She silently debated asking to go along, but decided against it. She still needed her job, at least until she could save enough money to return home.

'Miracles occur in strange ways. It's not our place to question them,' Nid said as she grabbed her bag and headed for the door.

'Good luck and hurry back,' Malee offered as her friend set out on her journey.

It took Nid nearly five hours to travel the bumpy roads and even though she started from Pattaya early in the morning, it wasn't until early in the afternoon before she arrived at the bus station in Korat. With the newspaper in hand, she rushed inside and found the person in charge.

'Do you know this girl?' Nid inquired, as she showed him the newspaper.

'Why?' Prasit wanted to know after he examined the picture on the front page.

'She's my daughter.'

'You're Lek's mother?' Prasit responded in astonishment. 'I didn't know she had a family. The way she talks, I assumed she was an orphan.'

'It's a long story,' Nid told him. Wanting only to find her as soon as she could, she didn't offer to elaborate.

'Do you have any proof?' Prasit started to sound leery.

Nid sighed. 'Only these,' she said as she produced the pictures she had gathered over the years.

Prasit studied the photos and seemed to be convinced.

'I'm sorry to have doubted you. Given what happened yesterday, I expect a lot of people to be looking for her. I thought you might have been with the press or something. Sure, I know Lek. She works for us on the Korat to Khon Kaen bus, at least she did until this accident yesterday. She shares a room with my niece in that building over there across the parking lot. It's on the third floor, room 3 A.'

'Do you think she is there now?' Nid couldn't contain her excitement.

'Well, a little while ago I saw her talking with someone in the restaurant downstairs.' Prasit looked out his office window. 'She's not there now so she probably went back to her room. I've asked her to keep a low profile until things calm down.'

'Thank you. You don't know how happy this makes me.' Nid's adrenaline was pumping.

Leaving her travel bag in the office, she quickly ran across the parking lot and into the old building used as a boarding house. She bounded up the stairs, taking two at a time. Finding a door with a plastic 3 and an A loosely attached by rusty nails, she began to pound. 'Lek? Are you in there?'

No response. She pounded again. 'Lek? Are you in there?'

CHAPTER 48

Lek waited for what seemed like an eternity for the woman to stop pounding on her door. Several times she nearly gave in to the temptation to find out who it was, but was able to restrain herself.

Finally the pounding stopped and for the next few minutes there was a deafening silence. The stranger was obviously listening for movement.

Lek remained frozen to her bed, listening intently to any signs that the stranger was still waiting outside her room. The silent standoff lasted another few minutes before Lek heard the distinct sound of footsteps walking away from her room.

It was so quiet that Lek thought she could hear the footsteps all the way down the three flights of stairs and out into the parking lot. Still, she didn't dare move.

What if there was someone else outside the door, waiting for her?

That was a chance she'd have to take. She couldn't stay hidden in her room all day. Soonton was waiting for her in the cafe downstairs and if there was someone waiting for her outside, she figured at worst she could make it that far. Soonton would know what to do.

Examining every corner along the way, Lek stealthily made her way over to the cafe.

'Where have you been? Do you realize how dangerous it is for us to be here?' Soonton snapped.

'I'm sorry. Someone came to my room looking for me. I had to make sure they were gone.'

'Who was it?' The tone of Soonton's voice changed from anger to worry.

'I don't know. I didn't open the door. I think it was a woman but I didn't recognize her voice,' said Lek.

'They've found us. We have to get out of here, now!'

Soonton rose from the table and made his way toward the exit. Stopping to survey the parking lot, he waved Lek over to join him. Seeing nothing threatening, he led Lek across the parking lot toward a car he had parked near the exit.

Lek snuck a glance into the office on her way by. Prasit was busy talking with a woman inside. Was that the woman who knocked on her door? Lek didn't recognize her.

Nid paced Prasit's office, grilling him for information. 'If she's not in her room, where might she be?'

'I'm not sure,' Prasit replied. 'I can't imagine she would go anywhere. Except maybe the cafe downstairs. Did you check there?'

'No, I just checked her room.'

Both she and Prasit looked over toward the cafe at the same time. The early afternoon sun brightly lit the inside of the cafe allowing the two observers a clear view. A few customers were scattered about, quietly eating and talking amongst themselves. Not one of them even vaguely resembled Lek.

As Nid and Prasit returned their attention to each other, movement in the parking lot behind Nid's back caught Prasit's eye. 'Hey, wait. That's her over there.'

'Where?' Nid yelled, quickly spinning around to see what Prasit was talking about.

'There, across the parking lot.' Prasit pointed toward Lek and Soonton. They appeared to be trying to make it across the lot unnoticed.

Nid bolted out the door after them, knocking over a chair on her way. 'Lek! Wait! Stop!'

'That must be the woman who knocked on my door!' Lek said, panicking.

'Let's go! Quick.' Soonton grabbed her and pushed her into the car in front of him. The keys were already in the ignition and it only took a split second for the engine to come to life.

'Lek! Wait! It's your mother! Come back!' Nid screamed.

'What is she saying?' Lek asked Soonton.

'I don't know and I don't care,' Soonton replied as he floored the accelerator. The tires spun as the car lurched out of the parking lot and into the street.

'Lek! Wait!' Nid continued to scream as she ran after them. The car was too fast, Nid didn't have a chance. Out of breath, Nid leaned on a light pole and watched as her daughter rounded a corner and disappeared from sight.

Nid didn't even notice the two police cars that pulled into the parking lot behind her, but she sure noticed them as they screeched out of the parking lot to give chase to Soonton and Lek.

'They're going after them,' Prasit called to her. 'Come on, we can take my car and follow them.'

Nid didn't hesitate. As they pulled out into the street, Prasit handed Nid a small radio. 'Turn this on,' he instructed her. 'It's a police band radio. We won't be able to go as fast as them but we can keep track of where they are going. Hopefully we won't be too far behind when they catch up with them.'

Nid did as instructed and tried to understand the muffled words that came through the radio. Prasit seemed to know exactly what they were talking about and deftly steered the car down side streets and toward the west end of town.

'They're going to try and head them off before they get into the countryside where there are hundreds of little dirt roads they could use to escape,' he translated.

Escape. The thought sent chills down Nid's back. She hadn't been this close, ever. She secretly hoped they could avoid the police, yet somehow get hung up so that Nid could get to them first. Why was Lek running?

'Finally, we're creating some separation,' Soonton said after sustaining ludicrously high speeds through city streets, busting through intersections, narrowly missing pedestrians and other vehicles.

Now out of the city limits and onto open road, the old car was being pushed to its limits. *Here's our chance*, he thought. *The police are still trying to navigate the city streets and will be held back by any carnage we caused getting to open road. Aaaah!*

He used a little too much speed on a tight corner. When the wheels were no longer able to maintain their grip, the car began to slide sideways.

Trying to regain control, he turned too hard on the steering wheel, and shot across the road to other side. Another correction put him back onto the pavement, but by now all hopes of controlling the uncontrollable sent the car careening sideways into the ditch. With a horrifying thump, the car hit a large boulder, sending Soonton head first into the windshield, killing him instantly and sending the car flipping into the air. The centrifugal force pushing Lek against the passenger door was too much for the latch. When it gave way, Lek was flung out, cart-wheeling through the air, landing in thick underbrush. When the car bounced off the ground and made another terrifying revolution in the air, the passenger door broke loose completely, sending it flying into the tapioca field on the other side of the road, 50 meters away.

The sickening sound of metal, glass, tarmac and gravel mashing together lasted only a few seconds, but seemed to last forever. Then there was silence.

'They see them,' Prasit announced. The radio continued on, but Prasit stopped translating. His face turned ashen.

'What is it? What's happening?' Nid asked, frantic. Although the talk on the radio seemed more like static than words, Nid could tell that the police had become excited. She was able to discern a few words and passages, but they didn't make sense. 'Stop, (static), crash, (static), down the hill, (static).'

Prasit slowed the car. 'There's no reason to hurry now,' he announced quietly.

'Why? What happened?'

'It seems they've crashed. It doesn't look good.'

Nid dropped the radio onto the seat beside her and covered her face with her shaking hands. It couldn't be. Not now.

As Prasit and Nid arrived on the scene, policemen meandered about, talking to each other and directing traffic. Skid marks covered the road. There was no sign of Lek or Soonton.

One officer instructed Prasit to keep moving, which he did until he could find a suitable place to park just past the accident. As he and Nid got out of the car and attempted to walk over to the site, another officer halted them.

'Police business,' he barked. 'Move along.'

'I have reason to believe my daughter was in that car,' Nid pleaded. 'Is she hurt?'

'Ma'am, please. Go back to your car. There was only one person in that car and he isn't going anywhere. If you want to find out about him, come down to the station later.'

'I am the daytime manager of the bus company,' Prasit interrupted. 'The man who was driving that car was one of my drivers. He left the station with this woman's daughter. Now please let us through.'

The officer looked them over and let out a sigh. 'Sergeant,' he called toward a group of officers nearer the scene. 'I think you better handle this.'

The sergeant looked bothered by the request and halfheartedly motioned for them to come over.

'What is it?' he asked, annoyed.

'These people claim to know the victim,' the officer said as he backed away to return to his traffic duty.

As Prasit explained the situation to the sergeant, Nid caught her first glimpse of the car that had sped out of the bus parking lot with her daughter inside. It was now mangled beyond recognition. It's color was the only clue. 'No one could have survived in there,' Nid solemnly thought to herself.

'Well, she's not there now,' the sergeant said to Prasit, interrupting Nid's thoughts.

'But she was when they left the depot,' Nid piped in. 'Maybe she was thrown from the car during the crash. Maybe she's lying in the ditch someplace, hurt. Can we at least look for her?'

'If she was in that car, there is no way she would have made it out alive. Besides, we have men all over the area picking up pieces of evidence. If she was here, we would have found her by now. It's my guess that she was never in that car, at least not at the time of the accident. But, if you want to have a look around, I guess I have no problem with that. If you do find anything, don't touch it. Let us know first and we will take care of it. And please, try to stay out of the way.'

'Thank you sergeant,' Prasit said as he gave him a *wai*.

Nid was already on her way. She didn't cherish the thought of looking inside but she had to see for herself whether or not Lek was there. As she approached the wreckage, a small group of uniformed policemen lingered about, seemingly uninterested in the proceedings. She found it disconcerting that if someone had survived the crash, these men showed no attempt to help.

Nid bent down, peered inside and soon discovered why no one was doing anything to help. Soonton's crumpled body lay tangled in the wreckage. There was definitely no saving him.

Nid hesitantly walked around to the other side of the car. The first thing she noticed was that the passenger door was missing.

Eventually Prasit caught up with her. 'What a mess,' he said, shaking his head in disbelief.

'Where's the passenger door?' Nid asked, ignoring Prasit's comment.

They both looked around. Not far away, a pair of officers stood next to what appeared to be the door. Nid quickly looked toward the woods nearby.

'Are you thinking what I'm thinking?' Prasit asked quietly.

'I sure am,' Nid replied, as she slowly began to make her way through the thick scrub brush leading toward a grove of planted rubber trees.

Prasit followed her through the brush and into the wooded area. Although there were no identifiable trails, the stand was fairly open. If someone had wanted to get away in a hurry, this place offered plenty of room to run.

CHAPTER 49

Nid and Prasit, working as a team, began by searching the thick scrub and tangled weeds that separated the roadside ditch from the grove of planted rubber trees. In some places it was quite thick and could easily have hidden a body. In other places it had been trampled down into foot paths and would have easily allowed an escape.

Splitting up, Nid and Prasit were able to cover about one hundred meters in each direction; well past either side of the accident. They searched intently, using sticks as scythes to beat down the brush. When they met back in the middle, both were convinced that if Lek had been tossed from the car during the accident into the thick underbrush alongside the road, she was no longer there.

They next turned their attention to the rubber plantation. They trudged all over looking for clues between the neatly planted rows of trees. They turned up nothing. No trails of blood. No torn clothing. There were plenty of footsteps, but they went in every direction and were of several different sizes.

'If she was ever here, and if she managed to make it into the jungle, there is no way we are going to be able to find her,' Prasit told Nid, reconfirming her fears.

'I know,' Nid conceded dejectedly. Trying to sound positive she added, 'At least I think it's safe to assume that if she was in the accident, she couldn't have been hurt too badly.'

'I'm beginning to believe she never was in the accident. Maybe Soonton let her out of the car before the roadblock,' Prasit surmised.

'Maybe you're right. Either way, she's not here now. It would be futile to continue to search further.'

'Maybe she returned to her room,' Prasit said hopefully. 'Let's go back to the station. If nothing else, Toi finishes work in about an hour. She can at least let us into the room. If Lek is there, we will find her. If not, maybe she left some clue as to where she might be.'

Nid allowed herself a rather sad smile, and said. 'Okay, let's go.'

Their search had lasted over two hours and when they finally made it back to the scene of the accident, nearly everyone had already left. A few policemen remained to supervise the removal of the wrecked vehicle.

When they reached the station, Nid hurriedly walked up to knock on Lek's door. Still no one answered. She kept trying for about 15 minutes before finally giving up. Dejected, she walked back over to Prasit's office to see if he had heard anything. He hadn't.

'Although you might be interested in this,' he said as he handed her an identification card. 'I had this made up for Lek so she wouldn't run into any problems while working for us. It wasn't easy because the people at the hall of records will only issue ID cards to people who were born in their district. I had to use my home address and family name to get it for her.

'I know the people who work over there. They knew it wasn't true, but I've done favors for them in the past so they put it through. It just arrived this morning. You might as well have it,' he said.

'Thank you, Prasit.' Nid took the new card and looked at the picture. If Lek had only stopped in to pick it up before she ran away, Nid would have been there and none of this would have happened. 'If' is an awfully big word.

Around 5.30 p.m. the buses began to arrive for the shift change. Nid stayed in the office to be near Prasit when Toi arrived. He gave her a reassuring smile and told her it shouldn't be long. Finally, at a little after 6 p.m., Toi's bus pulled into the lot.

'This is Lek's mother,' he introduced them once Toi had disembarked from the bus. 'This is my niece, Toi.'

'Lek's mother? She never mentioned having a family...' Toi seemed delighted. 'Nice to meet you. Lek's a great roommate. She's a bit quiet at times but fun to have around. I'm sure she'll be delighted to see you.'

Nid gave Prasit a quick glance.

Toi caught the exchange. 'What's the matter? Is Lek okay?'

'We don't know,' Prasit answered. 'She and Soonton had a little trouble with the police this morning and we can't find her. We're hoping she's in your room and won't open the door because she's afraid. Her mother has been trying off and on all afternoon but no one answers the door.'

Toi looked puzzled. 'I knew she thought she might be in trouble for the bus accident yesterday, but she told me she couldn't understand why. I'm sure she had nothing to do with it.'

'I believe you,' Nid replied. 'Let's hope she's hiding in your room so we can assure her she's not alone. Together maybe we can straighten out this mess.'

'Sure. Let's go,' Toi said as she led Nid and Prasit across the parking lot. When she opened the door to her and Lek's room, Toi immediately knew something was wrong. Lek's things were gone and there was a note on her pillow. She gave Nid a puzzled glance and handed her the note.

'Toi,

Sorry I couldn't wait around to say goodbye but right now everything is all messed up. I'm sure by now you've read the newspaper and know the police are looking for me. I promise you that I had nothing to do with any murder, I don't even know who that man was. Soonton told me I shouldn't wait around to find out what happened, he said it would be no good for me. I can't tell you where I'm going because I don't know. Take care of yourself and good luck. I will miss you.

Lek.'

Nid stared at the note for a few moments before slowly sitting down on the edge of Lek's bed. 'Now what,' she found herself saying to no one in particular. Prasit and Toi remained silent.

Receiving no answer, Nid continued on, more or less talking to herself. 'I guess the only thing to do now is to rent a hotel room and stick around a couple of days in case she comes back. If she does, I want to be here to help her.'

'Why rent a hotel room?' Toi spoke up. 'Why not stay here? You can use Lek's bed and that way, if she does show up, you will be right here and we won't have to try and find you.'

'Actually, that's not a bad idea,' Prasit offered.

'I wouldn't want to be a burden,' Nid answered.

'No burden at all,' Toi protested 'I'll be working all day anyway, so I can give you my keys and you can come and go as you please. It really wouldn't be a bother.'

Nid could feel the sincerity of their offer. Her new found friends truly wanted to help. Lek surely must be a good kid to have friends like these, Nid thought. She smiled and nodded her head in agreement. 'I'd like that.'

'Then it's settled,' Toi said. 'Let's go get your things.'

'My bag is down in Prasit's office,' Nid tried to sound cheerful. With her unspoken command, the three left the room.

The large busses in the busy parking lot initially blocked their view of the office. When they did get close enough to see the terminal, all three noticed the single police cruiser parked out front.

'They sure don't waste any time,' Prasit commented.

'I wonder what they want,' Nid pondered.

'They' turned out to be just one high-ranking uniformed officer from the Korat police department.

An ominous looking man with dark piercing eyes and a small scar on his jawbone near his right ear, he introduced himself as Police Lieutenant Colonel Chuanon.

'Miss Sawang,' he began once they were all seated inside Prasit's office, 'has your daughter ever been in any trouble with the law before?' His voice was a study of patience and determination.

Nid nervously toyed with the handle of her purse. Suddenly, in Prasit's dimly lit office, she felt as if both she and Lek were being put on trial. As a character witness she may be Lek's only hope of clearing her name. 'Not to my knowledge.' Nid tried her best to sound confident.

'Has she ever been around when others have mysteriously died?' Chuanon pressed on.

'What are you getting at?' Nid immediately became defensive.

'I'm just trying to piece together parts to a very complicated puzzle,' Chuanon answered without changing his expression. He was good at this little game.

'We knew about Soonton and his connections and although we couldn't prove anything, we suspected the bus accident yesterday wasn't an accident at all. Before today, though, I had no reason to believe that your daughter was involved. We assumed she was just doing her job as the conductor of the bus and just happened to be in the wrong place at the wrong time. Yet why did she run away with him? It doesn't make sense.'

'She was scared,' Nid replied.

'Scared of what?' Chuanon inquired.

'I'm not really sure,' Nid replied.

After a moment of strained silence, Nid hesitantly removed Lek's note from her purse and handed it to Chuanon. 'Maybe this will help.'

Chuanon's expression turned contemplative as he read the note. Finishing, he nodded and handed it back to Nid. 'What was her connection to Soonton?'

'He saved her from three boys that tried to rape her last year,' Toi offered. 'Ever since then, he has been teaching her to protect herself.'

Nid tried not to look shocked, but she definitely was.

'I see,' Chuanon paused. 'Do you know where she went?'

'No,' Nid replied sheepishly.

'You're her mother and you don't even know where she is?'

'Believe me, I wish I did. I would like nothing more than to have her here so we could put an end to all this nonsense.'

'That makes two of us,' Chuanon responded. 'I'll tell you what. I still don't think she had anything to do with Anan's mysterious death, but she may have some guilty knowledge. If you happen to find her before we do we would very much appreciate the chance to talk with her.'

Chuanon handed Nid, Toi and Prasit copies of his business card. 'I can assure you she won't be put under arrest. I'd just like to ask her a few questions.'

CHAPTER 50

Deep in the forest and well hidden behind a large rock next to a small stream, Lek sat alone. Shivering, she tried her best to piece together the blur that made up the past few hours. One minute she was yelling at Soonton to stop, seemingly the next second she found herself lying in a ditch. She must have been thrown from the car. But how?

She must have been unconscious, for she vaguely remembered waking up to the sounds of sirens blaring, excited voices and footsteps running near her. She was also entangled in thick brush and as she freed herself, she thought she remembered seeing a smashed car off in the distance.

All she could think to do was run. So she ran. When the grove of planted trees ended and the jungle began, she kept on running.

How did it all happen? When she woke up yesterday morning, life was normal. She had a job. She had friends. She had a place to stay. And now this.

Every bone in her body ached. Still she shivered. She wasn't cold. On the contrary, her body was bathed in sweat. She reached down into the stream and splashed some water on her face. Cool water. It felt good.

Suddenly she felt very tired. She laid back down on the ground and curled her body into a tight ball. With her knees firmly planted against her chest, she laid her head on the ground and continued to shake.

Lek awoke with a start just past dawn. It took her a second to realize where she was and when she did, she looked herself over to make sure she was still all there. She had taken a beating from the mosquitoes and ached from the accident, but no bones were broken.

She went over to the stream and splashed water on her face and arms. It was there that the reality of her situation came back to her. She was lost and alone. She had no food and no money. She also realized she couldn't stay where she was and needed to find a way out of the jungle.

She shook the sleepiness out of her head and convinced herself that she couldn't afford to concentrate on the negatives of her situation. She had to take a minute to figure out some positive things she could use to her advantage. She concluded her small stature was a positive because it would allow her to keep well hidden. She was also resourceful, in good shape and well trained.

The part that bothered her the most was not knowing where she could go. She couldn't go back to Korat, no doubt the police were still looking for her. She didn't want to go back to Buriram either, there was nothing for her there. She decided she would just have to figure it out once she got herself out of the jungle and there was no time like the present to do just that.

She spent the middle part of the morning trekking westward through the thick jungle, the direction she thought would take her further away from the city limits of Korat. Before long, the jungle ended, giving way to tapioca fields, cow pastures and eventually a small dirt road.

When she came upon her first small village, she left the dirt road so as not to be seen. The going was rough as she trekked through thick brush, across several streams and through a few rice fields. After an hour or so, she was able to join up with another small dirt road well past the village.

The second dirt road eventually led her out to a paved road and although it wasn't heavily traveled, she stayed off it lest she meet up with a stray police car out looking for her. On the rare occasion a vehicle did pass by, Lek could hear it coming well before it reached her, allowing her to find some underbrush to crouch down and hide behind.

Luckily the jungle that crept up to the edge of the road wasn't very dense and Lek was able to cover a lot of ground quickly. When she had traveled a kilometer or two she came upon a house set back away from the road. As she prepared to make a detour around it, the more she studied it, the more it seemed as though no one was home.

It was a rather small house with a table and chairs set up behind it. The wooden shutters that would normally cover its windows were wide open, allowing Lek a clear view straight through the house and out the other side. There was no movement anywhere except for some laundry gently blowing in the breeze as it dried in the midday sun.

Lek quietly and stealthily made her way toward the vacant house. As she got close, she noticed that the table was set up with what looked like a basket of food and a container of cooked rice. Whoever lived there must have just left and hadn't planned on being gone for very long. No matter, they weren't there now and Lek hadn't eaten since the previous day. Although it seemed too good to be true, she took her chances and grabbed the food before running away.

She only stopped to inspect her pilfered meal when she was sure she was far enough away from the house for anyone to find her. The basket contained greens, fruit, cooked fish, dried beef and chili sauce. Together with the rice it was culinary heaven. She sat down and ate the entire repast without stopping, momentarily forgetting where she was and what she was up against.

A passing convoy of trucks brought her back to reality. She hadn't realized she was so close to the road. Luckily, she was still far enough back into the brush that no one could see her. Once they had passed, she continued on her way to nowhere.

An hour or two further along she came upon some railroad tracks and decided they might be safer to follow. She diverted her path away from the main road and walked along the tracks that led deeper into the jungle.

After a while she came upon a place where they split off into two different sets of parallel tracks. She recognized from her earlier travel by rail that these places were where trains traveling in opposite directions using the same tracks stopped to let each other pass. It gave her an idea.

She walked a little way up one side of the split, sat down next to a bush and waited. Sure enough, after a couple of hours a westbound train came along and stopped. Lek looked it over and noticed that more then half of the train was made up of passenger cars, the rest were cargo containers. Not knowing nor caring where it was going she climbed aboard one of the cargo cars and found a place to sit amongst the boxes and crates.

A few minutes later the eastbound train sped by, blowing its whistle as it went. When the last car of the eastbound had passed the last car of the westbound, Lek's new found transportation slowly creaked to life.

CHAPTER 51

Lek once again greeted a new day with confusion. For once again she awoke not knowing where she was. She tried to clear the blurriness out of her sleepy eyes by surveying the scene around her. Boxes, boxes and more boxes.

Suddenly the box she was sitting on lurched forward and a loud screech pierced her ears. It was followed by a thump. Then another thump, again, and again. The thumps were getting closer together. Everything seemed as though it was moving when it finally dawned on her that she was still inside the cargo container of a train.

She climbed off her cardboard throne and peered out the half-open door to try and see if she could tell where she was. Except for the tail end of another train headed in the opposite direction, nothing could be seen except rice fields and jungle, offering no clue as to her whereabouts. No matter, as long as she was getting further away from Korat.

After several more hours and what seemed like at least a hundred station stops, the train finally came to rest in a densely populated area. Lek sat and waited for a while just like she did at all the other stops. When the train didn't start up again, she knew it had reached its ultimate destination.

As she peered out the door one last time, she could see a group of workers converge on the container cars, apparently to unload them. Not knowing what else to do, she jumped down onto the tracks and ran.

Lek ran away from the train and the workers as quickly as she could, not bothering to look back to see if they would chase after her. She quickly crossed the street in front of the station and lost herself in the mass of people busily rushing about.

She hadn't seen this many people in a long time. The tuk-tuks and motorcycles noisily weaving in and out of the heavy traffic confirmed what she had thought. This could only be one place: Bangkok.

The last time she was here was almost six years ago, when she and Dow had made their escape from Rattana and Siriporn. After all that time away from the big city, she had forgotten how busy Bangkok was. So many people crowded the streets, so much pollution choked the air. Since she had been breathing clean country air for the past six years, her chest and lungs soon began to tighten. It would take some getting used to if she decided to stay.

Did she have a choice? Without money, food or friends she was at the mercy of fate. The decision to stay or not wasn't hers to make.

As she wandered around aimlessly, trying to decide what would be her next move, she noticed beggars panhandling the streets. She pitied them, surely there must be a better way.

Walking continuously for most of the afternoon without a goal or destination, her path eventually led her to a park in the middle of the city. The answer to what she could do to sustain herself had so far eluded her. Tired and hungry, she found a spot beneath a tree and away from other people. With the evening of her first night in Bangkok upon her, she laid down and fell asleep.

Lek awoke early the next morning without enough energy to move. Tired and sore, she remained beneath the tree, looking into the smoggy sky and drifting in and out of sleep. She tried to keep the hunger off her mind even though at times her stomach hurt so much she wanted to cry. Tears wouldn't come, though. Her body was depleted of water, too.

The image of the beggars on the streets the day before kept coming back to her. How far had she sunk? Could she bring herself to beg?

She remembered that the beggars were at least getting some handouts. Surely they must be able to eat. With hunger gnawing constantly at her stomach, she decided she had come too far to let herself die of starvation on the streets of Bangkok. What else could she do but try for a handout? Telling herself it was only a temporary situation until she found a better way, she set out to try and find a donor willing to give her a small amount of money. She only needed enough to help her stay alive.

She will always remember the first person to give her a donation. She had been walking around for almost an hour with her hand extended in front of her asking everyone she met for the smallest amount of change they could bear to part with. She was just about to give up when a local businessman stopped to look at her.

'It's a damn shame what this proud city has come to when it's gotten to the point where beautiful young women like you are forced onto the streets to beg,' he commented sadly as he reached into his pocket and gave her twenty baht. 'I'm very sorry,' he added, 'I wish I could help more.'

'Kop kun kha,' was all that Lek could muster in response. As soon as the businessman walked away, Lek literally ran over to the nearest food stall she could find. She bought a five baht bottle of water, drank it immediately, bought another and five baht worth of sticky rice. She then sat down on one of the stools and ate it all.

Then the tears came. She didn't know why she was crying but she couldn't stop. She could see the cook and the other customers looking at her strangely yet she couldn't help it. Feeling embarrassed, she gathered herself as best as she could and walked back out into the busy city.

Over the next few days Lek wandered around the city aimlessly. She only begged when she was hungry and the more she did it the less she liked it. At night she slept where she could, sometimes in parks, other times on the sidewalks or on the side streets out of the public's view. Her outfit began to show the effects of living in the streets. Her yellow blouse was now dark tan, her slacks were scuffed and stained.

One afternoon as she was walking down a side street she passed a food stall that had cooked chicken laid out on its stand. For some reason she remembered Dow and her sneaky ways of stashing food. Dow always had a way of doing what was necessary to survive.

Seeing that the cook was busy preparing a meal for another customer, Lek, in the best impersonation of Dow she could manage, grabbed a chicken breast and quickly walked away.

She had found a new way to obtain food. Although it was dishonest, it was less intrusive than begging from strangers. In her mind she justified the act by telling herself that the small amount she needed wouldn't hurt anyone as long as she didn't steal too often and never from the same place twice. Between petty thievery and begging, maybe she could gain enough strength to stay alive.

CHAPTER 52

Lek's aimless wandering through Bangkok eventually led her to Sukhumvit Road. Although she didn't recognize her surroundings, she had been there before. Long ago, she once stared blankly at this section of the city through the windows of Siriporn's car on her way to yet another night of forced child labor on the streets of Patpong.

All she thought about now was where she might be able to obtain her next meal. Hunger can cause even the most honest person to do things they never thought they were capable of, like begging and stealing in order to eat. Lek no longer thought of it as stealing. It was pure survival. No more, no less.

Lek hadn't eaten since yesterday and as she passed a small side street, she spotted a food stall that was ideal for her next pillage. Cooked chicken was left out unattended on a table and plenty of customers kept the cook busy frying vegetables and pounding *somtam*.

Lek began her walk toward the busy food stall to make an attempt at swiping a meal from her unsuspecting prey. The timing seemed perfect—no one appeared to be paying any attention to her or the cooked chicken. Two more steps and she'd be there. Three or four more and she'd be out of sight comfortably devouring a free meal.

Just before she reached out to make her move, someone grabbed her by the arm. 'Lek? Is that you?'

Lek spun around to see who her detainer was. A woman in her mid twenties stood before her with an expression mixed with shock and disbelief. Her face was well covered with makeup, she wore nice clothes and was accompanied by a male foreigner. Not recognizing her, Lek broke her grip and prepared to run.

'Wait! Lek, it is you. You look scared half to death. Don't you recognize me?'

There was something familiar about this strange woman, and she did know Lek's name. Lek paused to study her, but remained wary.

'Don't you remember me?' The woman persisted. 'It's me, Om.'

'Om?' Lek repeated without much confidence. It had been years since she'd heard that name and it took her a moment to realize who it might be. Om was her friend from Patpong who had helped her and Dow escape to Buriram. Although she had changed, the woman before her did bear a slight resemblance to her old friend.

'Yes! It's me, Om,' she said excitedly. 'I knew it was you. Look at you, you've grown up.'

Lek finally began to relax, although living on the streets wouldn't allow her to open up too much. Seeing her old friend was great, but people were not to be trusted. Lek offered a slight smile and remained silent. Her posture resembled a scared animal that had been backed into a corner.

'Relax Lek, I'm your friend,' Om spoke calmly. Over the years working the bar scene she had seen many people down on their luck. She was no stranger to this type of situation, yet never before had it been someone she had once been so close to. She wasn't about to let Lek get away.

Om motioned for her foreign male escort to stay back, then cautiously walked around Lek to the food stall. Keeping an eye on her friend, she bought two pieces of chicken, a small plastic bag full of cooked rice, a small cooked fish and a bottle of water. The vendor, oblivious to the situation, deftly put the food into a larger plastic bag, took Om's money, then went about the business of dealing with other customers.

Without saying another word, Om handed the meal over to Lek. As Lek began to devour the meal, Om led her over to a bench nearby and sat her down.

'You sure were hungry,' Om said after Lek had finished. Seeing how quickly Lek had eaten the meal, how dirty she was and how ragged her clothes had become, Om asked her a question she already knew the answer to. 'Where are you staying?'

The free meal had served its purpose. Lek was no longer wary of her old friend. She was also beginning to regain her strength. 'You're standing in my living room,' she replied, trying to sound cheery.

'Not good enough,' Om said sternly. 'Look, I'm kind of busy right now, as you can see,' she said, tilting her head toward her male counterpart. 'Here, take my keys and go to my room. I'll be back later and we can talk.'

'I can't do that,' Lek protested. She was ashamed at what she had become and didn't want to take advantage of her friend's hospitality. Om had given her a meal. That was more than anyone had done for her in a long, long time, and it was more than enough.

'I won't take no for an answer,' Om said with a smile, yet firmly enough to show Lek she meant what she said. 'Here's some money for a tuk-tuk. Just give the driver this address,' she said as she dug through her purse and produced a card. 'It's room E-4.'

'But . . . I don't know,' Lek was still hesitant.

'Don't even think about it. I'm happy to see you. We've got a lot to catch up on,' Om said as she led Lek over to the side of the street. She hailed a tuk-tuk, denying Lek the opportunity to resist.

Om instructed the driver where to take Lek, not giving her a chance to use the address card Om had given her. 'Make yourself at home. I'll see you later,' Om said just before the tuk-tuk pulled away with Lek in the back.

Shocked at what had just transpired, Lek watched out of the back of the tuk-tuk until her friend was out of sight. She contemplated telling the driver to stop so that she could get out and run, but her instinct told her to stay.

A few minutes later, the driver turned down a side street and stopped in front of a rather new looking building. Lek gave him the money Om had given her, then got out and stood in front of the apartment block. It had clean white walls and through its glass doors, Lek could see a well-dressed woman sitting behind a large reception desk watching a color television.

Lek looked herself over, embarrassed at the condition of her and her clothes. She didn't belong here. Nonetheless, after a few minutes of indecision, she convinced herself that she had been in worse situations before. She swallowed her pride, walked inside and tried to ignore the woman behind the desk.

To her dismay, though, there were no stairs. An elevator provided the only access to the upper floors. Lek had never used an elevator and even though she thought that given a little time she could probably figure it out, Om had told her that her room was E-4. Lek couldn't speak English, much less read it, and had no idea what floor the room would be on.

Feeling embarrassed, she walked over to ask the receptionist where Om's room might be. The receptionist, who seemed bothered that someone had the audacity to interrupt her television viewing, looked at her disdainfully. 'Fifth floor, down the hall on the left,' she said indignantly.

Lek thanked her. 'City people are less polite than country folk,' she thought to herself as she walked over and stood in front of the elevator.

Before she had a chance to teach herself how it worked, the doors opened and a young, well-dressed couple got out. They looked her over as they passed by and once behind her began to chuckle and talk about her condition loud enough for Lek to hear.

She tried not to pay any attention to them as she entered the elevator, found the buttons on the wall and pushed number five. She could feel her stomach tingle as the elevator rose.

When she found Om's room and stepped inside, she discovered it was much nicer than the one that she remembered Om living in near Patpong. E-4 smelled of success. The walls were freshly painted in cheery white, there was a table and two cushioned chairs set up against one wall and a large closet full of nice clothes set up alongside a new vanity table with a big mirror against another wall.

Om's large bed was covered with pillows and stuffed animals. In one corner was an apartment-size refrigerator. On top, a television and video player were set up facing the bed. Even the ceiling fan looked new. To top it off, the room had a door near the back that led to a private bathroom.

Om had come a long way since that night when Lek and Dow had stayed with her during their escape from Rattana and Siriporn.

All this grandeur didn't exactly make Lek feel at ease. On the contrary, she now felt even more out of place. Her clothes were still so filthy she didn't dare sit down on anything for fear of ruining it. But Om did tell her to make herself at home. So, ever so cautiously, Lek removed her clothes and stepped into the bathroom. 'I hope you don't mind,' she said aloud.

For her entire life, Lek's bathing consisted of dipping a bowl into a *klong* jar to splash water over herself. Now she was faced with yet another new dilemma; there was no bowl and no *klong* jar full of water. Instead, the room contained a large bathtub with two knobs and two nozzles, one of which was perched high above her, pointing down into the tub.

Lek stepped inside the tub and turned one of the knobs. Almost immediately, a strong gush of water came pouring out of the showerhead above her, catching her completely off guard. Much to her surprise, unlike the cold water she was accustomed to, the water that splashed down upon her was hot.

She quickly turned it off and tried the other knob. Same result, only this time the water was cold. Feeling brave, she turned the other knob again and sure enough, the temperature of the water became comfortably warm. Lek felt absolutely heavenly as the strong flow of clean warm water washed the filth of the city streets away from her.

When she finished washing, she wrapped a towel around her wet body, went back into the bedroom, turned on the television and laid down on the soft bed. It was the first television she had seen since the one she and Toi used to watch in the cafe in Korat.

Lek became completely absorbed in a Chinese movie that had been dubbed into Thai and lost all track of time.

CHAPTER 53

Lek was startled by a loud knock on the door. Opening it very cautiously, she was greeted by Om's smiling face on the other side.

'Great, you found it!' Om said as she burst into the room. 'You found the shower, too. Good thing, you were beginning to smell quite strong.'

'You don't mind?' Lek asked her hesitantly.

'Of course not!' Om replied with vigor. 'You did us both a favor, really.'

'Was I that bad?' asked Lek.

'Well, the lady downstairs wants to know which *klong* my friend fell into. They're all polluted now, you know. The *klongs* I mean. It's not the same as before. But never mind all that, how are you? What have you been up to? Where's Dow?'

Lek was sorry to admit that none of the questions Om asked had happy answers. Om stayed stoic, trying her best not to show her emotions as Lek retold the happenings of her life over the past few years.

After Lek had finished her depressing life story, she finally managed to turn the conversation back to Om.

'Enough about me, how about you? It looks as though you've done well. What have you been doing for the past, what has it been, five or six years?'

'My life hasn't been as exciting nor as depressing as yours. I'm still working the bar scene and as you can see it's been pretty good to me. I don't work in Patpong anymore, I've moved over to Soi Cowboy. You remember the place, don't you?'

'Of course, how could I forget? I take it you're no longer worried about Rattana and Siriporn.'

'No, they were arrested for breaking child labor laws a while back. I'm sure they paid their way out of it somehow but never mind, they haven't returned to Soi Cowboy. It was a happy day when I found out,' said Om.

'That's the first good news I've heard in a long time. That's great!' Lek was starting to feel better.

Seeing the mood shift, Om decided to try a new topic. 'So, what is it that you want to do now that you're here? Are you going to stay a while or are you moving on to someplace else?'

'To tell you the truth, I have no place else to go. I was sort of hoping now that I'm here I might be able to find some kind of work.'

'Have you thought about what you might like to do or where you might be able to find a job?'

'I've thought about it a lot,' Lek admitted, 'but I haven't been able to come up with anything. Do you have any ideas?'

'As a matter of fact, I do. Come here,' Om said as she brought Lek over to a spot in front of her full length mirror. Standing behind her so that Lek had a full view of herself, Om quickly removed the towel from her body.

Lek immediately covered herself up with her hands.

'What are you doing?' she protested.

'Trust me,' Om said as she gently took Lek's hands and moved them to her side. She then took Lek by the shoulders and pulled them back to straighten her posture. 'Look in the mirror. What do you see?'

Lek was too embarrassed to answer. She did manage to look up at her image.

'A beautiful young woman,' Om answered for her. 'Look at your body. It's incredible. Full firm breasts, your muscles are toned, your belly is flat. I'll bet there's not a gram of fat on you.'

'What are you getting at?' Lek asked her disapprovingly, as she grabbed the towel back and wrapped it around herself.

'Lek my friend, your soul is sitting comfortably inside a gold mine. I'm not half as pretty as you are and look where I am. With what you've got, the possibilities are endless. A year from now, hell a few months from now, you could be wallowing in wealth.'

'Are you trying to say I should work in bars like you?' asked Lek.

'You make it sound so terrible. It's not. It's the only way girls like us can get ahead. I've known girls who have traveled all over the world. Girls who have bought their families houses, set themselves and their families up for life after just a few years of working in the bars. The best part is that it's easy and fun. Dazzling men take you out to dinner, to the movies, buy you things and treat you like a princess.'

'Yeah, but to get all that you have to sleep with them.'

'So what? It's only your body. When you die you get a new one anyway, right? As long as you stay strong and keep your faith there's no way anyone can touch your soul. If you've got it, use it, and believe me when I tell you, you've got it,' proclaimed Om.

'You make it sound so ... easy.'

'It is! Besides, think about what you've been doing so far in your life. You have worked hard and where has it got you? Living on the streets of Bangkok, that's where. Think about it.'

She struck a nerve with her last line of reasoning. Lek lapsed into deep thought about her life, where she was now and where she was heading. No alternative seemed to be presenting itself at the moment and if she could beg and steal to keep alive, why couldn't she sell her body to get ahead? Which was worse, stealing from those who were not much better off than she was or providing sexual gratification to those who had enough money to be able to afford it? It was a tough decision.

'I've never slept with a man before,' Lek admitted sheepishly.

'How old are you?' Om asked.

'Eighteen,' Lek replied.

'An 18-year-old virgin as good-looking as you? I didn't think that was possible in this day and age. What about your boyfriend in Buriram, Chatchai?'

'I think he wanted to but we never had time enough alone to do anything.'

'Never mind. It won't be a problem if we don't tell *mamasan*. She's not too keen on hiring inexperienced girls and might think twice about hiring you if she found out you were a virgin. Don't worry, though. We can get around that little problem because I can fill you in on the details. Can you speak any English?'

'No, but wait a minute. I didn't say I'd do it,' said Lek.

'I know, but you will. What else can you do? Besides, you're too smart to turn down an opportunity like this. Tomorrow night I'll take you in to meet *mamasan* and the girls. You won't have to work, just sit there and see how it's done and how easy it is. Agreed?'

'I'll give it a look,' Lek conceded.

The next afternoon Lek sat and watched as Om carefully and with much skill applied makeup to her face. Lek had never before used makeup and was having a little trouble following all the intricate steps it involved.

'This is the hard part of our work,' Om said, 'getting ready to go.'

When she was finished with herself she sat Lek down in front of the mirror and performed her practiced skill on Lek's face. Lek rather enjoyed being pampered and she enjoyed the end result even more.

Om then went over to her closet and pulled out two outfits. She handed one of them to Lek. 'Try this on and see if it fits you.'

'I don't know, that's a little bold for me,' Lek responded.

'Nonsense. I think it will flatter you,' Om persisted.

Lek tried it on and although it was just a bit too big, she liked the way it made her look. Om put on her outfit, threw a bikini into her bag and cheerfully announced that it was time to go.

'Two sexy girls like us, I'll bet we'll turn some heads on the way to the bar,' Om said as she gave Lek a nudge with her elbow.

Once outside, Om hailed a tuk-tuk, negotiated a price, then climbed into the back and encouraged Lek to do the same. Lek hesitantly complied.

When the driver stopped the tuk-tuk on Asoke Road and dropped off his passengers at the west end of Soi Cowboy, bad memories of Lek's past came rushing back. Her stomach began to get queasy and her head began to swim as she and Om walked through the area that Lek had tried so hard to forget.

It had been a long time since she was last there, yet some of the old bars were still operating. Though it was still early and not yet crowded, there were still enough people milling about to increase Lek's uneasiness.

Long since accustomed to the area and all that went on there, Om obliviously led Lek down the bar-lined street and into her bar.

Once inside, she introduced Lek to some of the girls, all of whom remarked how pretty she was. Lek acknowledged them but didn't have an answer to their question of whether or not she would be working with them.

Just past 7.30 p.m., the working girls disappeared into a back room to change their clothes. Om reappeared first, dressed in a skimpy bikini. She took a seat next to Lek on one of the couches that lined the perimeter of the bar.

'That's *mamasan* over there,' she said, pointing to an older woman seated at the other end of the bar. 'I'll introduce you later if she doesn't come over here first.'

Around 8 p.m. the D.J. started playing rock and roll and disco music. As the first few foreigners appeared, some just peering through the door before moving on, others coming inside and taking seats on one of the couches or on a stool at the bar, a handful of the girls climbed up on stage and began to dance.

It wasn't long before one of the foreigners sat down next to Lek and put his hand on her knee. Lek froze as he started talking to her in a language she didn't understand. Om, still seated next to Lek, began to translate, bringing back memories of the first time Lek was in this bar. It was Om who had brought her in here when she was only five years old on her first night selling candy and cigarettes. Just like the first time, Om filled the role of translator.

'He says you're pretty and wants to know where you come from.'

'Tell him I'm not interested,' Lek said nervously.

Discouraged, Om made the translation and waited for his response. He looked like a big spender and Om hated the thought of letting him get away.

The man rose to leave, but not yet willing to give up, Om quickly grabbed his arm and sat him back down next to her.

Her quick response appeared to have worked for it didn't take long for him to get over his initial disappointment. After a few minutes of small talk, he ordered another drink for himself and one for Om.

For the next 30 minutes or so Om directed all her attention to him leaving Lek alone to sit and watch the happenings around her.

Everyone seemed to be having a good time. No one seemed to be in any kind of danger. Most of all, it looked as though all the girls were making money, as was evidenced by the big tip the foreigner had given Om before he left. It didn't appear as though Om had exactly worked too hard for it, either.

About an hour later, when Om was busy dancing on stage, *mamasan* came over and introduced herself.

'Om tells me you are new in town,' *mamasan* said to her.

'Yes, I just arrived at Om's place last night,' Lek responded as politely as she could.

'Have you ever worked in a bar before?'

Lek thought the question might be coming and had dreaded the thought. She didn't know how to answer, especially after what Om had told her last night. In typical Thai fashion, she avoided the issue by asking a question of her own. 'How many girls do you have working here?'

'Never enough,' *mamasan* answered. 'Would you like a job? If everything works out, I can pay you two thousand baht a month.' *Mamasan's* expression showed she was gauging Lek's response.

Mamasan seemed friendly enough. All the girls seemed friendly, too.

'Sure. Why not?' Lek said without giving it much further thought.

'Great. When would you like to start?' *Mamasan* seemed relieved.

'How about now?'

'That would be fine. Do you have a costume?'

'A costume?' Lek responded, confused.

'Yes, a costume. You know, a bikini or bathing suit to wear?'

'Oh, a costume,' Lek said as if she knew what *mamasan* had been talking about all along. 'No. I, ah, left it in Om's room.'

'No problem. Follow me,' *Mamasan* said as she led her out to the back room.

After rummaging through a pile of clothing, mamasan produced a one piece bathing suit and handed it to Lek. 'Try this on.'

Lek undressed slowly, still uncomfortable about being nude in front of a stranger. *Mamasan* took it all in her stride. She had seen hundreds of girls in the raw. She watched intently as Lek squeezed into the tight fitting suit and marveled over how well it highlighted her curvaceous body.

'You are going to be the best-looking woman in the bar. Now go out there and knock 'em dead.'

With *mamasan*'s urging giving her a new found pseudo-confidence, Lek marched out into the bar, climbed up onto the stage and took a place next to Om.

It didn't take long for her to figure out she had no idea what she was doing. She had never tried to dance before much less dance to foreign music. Her first few awkward steps caused Om to burst out laughing.

'I'm glad to see you've decided to join us. We'll have to do something about your dancing, though,' she said, as she started to gyrate her body wildly.

Lek watched intently and tried her best to imitate what she was doing. Her attempts were so feeble, though, that even *mamasan* laughed.

Lek spent the rest of the night talking with Om and the other girls and trying her best to dance. She also tried to converse with the many foreigners that sat with her and attempted to win her over. It would take a while to get good at that part of the job. As she watched a few of the other girls leave with foreigners, she realized it would take even longer before she was ready for that aspect of the business.

She and Om stayed until closing, which didn't come soon enough. However, when the night was finally over, Om took her over to the cashier and showed her how to redeem her drink tickets. Lek produced ten little pink slips of paper that the waitress had given her after foreigners had bought her 'ladies' drinks. The cashier counted them twice, then handed Lek two hundred baht, ten baht each for every ticket.

Lek had actually made some money of her own. She was so delighted, she talked Om into stopping for a bite to eat on their way home. It felt good to be able to buy her own food again. Her road to recovery had begun, or so she thought.

CHAPTER 54

Lek's second night in the bar started out similar to the first. The major difference was that Lek now knew more about what to expect. Her dancing was still poor, but each song she danced to saw a little improvement. The customers didn't seem to mind and even though her English was negligible they bought her drinks and seemed to enjoy being with her.

Later in the evening a handsome young man with curly blonde hair walked into the bar and received a round of 'woos' and 'yays' from some of the girls. Om leaned over and told Lek that his name was Craig and that he was a favorite customer of *mamasan*'s. She hadn't seen him around for a while, he must have just arrived from America.

Out of curiosity, Lek watched as he made his way over and sat down next to *mamasan*. She seemed especially delighted to see him and it looked as though he ordered drinks for the both of them. Lek thought he was good-looking but shrugged him off as just another customer and paid no more attention to him before she returned to her current foreign friend.

That was until Om nudged her arm. She looked up to see him standing directly in front of her, with *mamasan*'s arm linked through his. They were saying something that she didn't understand. The two English words she was able to pick up were 'new' and 'pretty'. Craig nodded his head and agreed with everything *mamasan* said. Then, before Lek knew what was going on, *mamasan* took her by the arm and led her over to where they had previously been sitting.

Craig seemed more interested in talking with *mamasan* than paying attention to Lek. He did buy her a drink, though, so she sat with them and tried to pick up what they were talking about. They spoke English and talked too fast for her to understand, so she finally gave up trying. Bored, she looked around the bar and made faces at some of her friends and other customers. The next thing she knew, *mamasan* told her to go and get dressed.

Fearing that she had done something wrong and was being fired, Lek tried to convince *mamasan* into giving her one more chance. *Mamasan* only laughed and told her not to worry, she could come back the next night. For now, though, Craig had paid the bar to take her home with him. She warned Lek to treat him good, he was a valued customer.

Still confused, she turned and looked at Om as she went into the back room to change. She was just pulling off her bathing suit when Om entered the room.

'I just heard, you lucky devil,' Om remarked.

'What's going on?' Lek queried, perplexed.

'The most valued customer of the bar just paid *mamasan* to take you out,' Om announced enthusiastically, 'and it's only your second night. I told you that you were beautiful. This guy is a regular big spender around here. Treat him right and you'll go places. Do you realize how many of the girls who work here have been trying to get him? I'm jealous.'

'Treat him right, that's what *mamasan* told me. What's that supposed to mean?'

'Aaaah! You're so dense sometimes. Just do what comes natural. Most of all, have a good time and make sure he has a good time, too,' said Om.

Lek finished dressing and as she emerged from the dressing room, Om playfully pushed her towards the man everyone coveted so much. When he saw her, he grabbed his chest in mock surprise and spoke something to her she again didn't understand. He let it ride, paid his bar tab and led her out the door.

He continued to talk to her even though she didn't understand a word he said. She tried not to let on that she didn't understand by shaking her head in agreement and laughing when he did. She had no idea if he knew or not but it didn't seem to matter. He hailed a tuk-tuk and before she knew it they were in his hotel room.

Once inside he turned on the television, handed her a towel and disappeared into the bathroom. She was as nervous as a schoolgirl on a first date. After all, this really was her first date. Without a clue as to what to do, she sat on the edge of his bed and clutched the towel for support.

A few minutes later he emerged from the bathroom wearing only a towel around his waist. He parked his wet body in front of her for a moment as if he expected her to do something. When she only looked at him in confusion, he motioned for her to go use the shower. She could only smile nervously and nod in assent.

When she came out of the bathroom he was already in bed beneath the covers. She noticed his towel had been unceremoniously thrown over the back of a chair and without thinking twice about it, she walked over and straightened it out. She also bent down and picked up his clothes that he had thrown on the floor, folded them neatly and put them on the chair next to his towel.

He thanked her in Thai when she had finished, then turned down the top sheet and motioned for her to join him. His face was lit up with a bright smile but Lek noticed a strange look in his eyes that she had never seen in anyone before. Keeping her towel wrapped tightly around her, she climbed in bed next to him and pulled the sheet over her.

Craig reached over and slowly removed her towel. She tried to resist but he persisted.

'Treat him good,' *mamasan* had told her so she gave in. He then peeled back the top sheet and revealed both of their naked bodies. She almost gasped when she saw what was between his legs. Too scared to do anything else, she lay still with every muscle in her body tense.

To his credit he tried everything he could to lessen her tension. He tickled her, whispered in her ear, gently kissed her cheek and caressed her body.

None of it worked. She stayed stiff as a board, unresponsive to his advances. Mentally, it did wonders for her, though. She could see he was doing his best to help her. Physically, she just wasn't able to let go.

He finally gave up trying to get her involved, and rolled over on top of her and forced himself between her legs. For the next five or ten minutes he pushed and pushed until Lek thought she was going to split in half. When he finished, he rolled off her and immediately grabbed his towel, went into the bathroom and took another shower.

Lek could hear the water running as she lay in bed wondering about what she had just done. Even though she hurt, she felt a strange feeling in her heart. It reminded her of how she used to feel about Chatchai. Craig was a nice guy, she told herself, and sex wasn't that bad. She wondered about how she had done, if she was able to please him like everyone told her to do.

He came out of the bathroom with a smile and as he started to get dressed he threw her a towel and pointed to the bathroom. Lek took the hint and showered again, too. As the warm water brought new life to her tense muscles she began to think she really liked this guy. He had been smiling, too, so she must have done okay.

By the time she finished her shower and reentered the room, Craig was already fully dressed. She didn't know what was supposed to happen next so she quickly put on her clothes to prepare for anything. As she was dressing, he pulled out his wallet and produced a thousand baht note. Without saying a word, he handed it to her. Lek gave him a *wai* before gratefully accepting it.

When Lek finished dressing, Craig escorted her out into the hallway, kissed her on the cheek, then closed his door behind her.

Lek stood alone in the hallway of his strange hotel. She had followed him in and didn't notice how they had gotten there so it took her a minute to get her bearings and find her way out. Not knowing what else to do, she hailed a tuk-tuk and returned to Om's room.

Lek was anxious to tell Om all about her first experience and could hardly wait for her return. Yet when the hour grew late and Om still hadn't come home, Lek realized she must have been bought out of the bar and was probably spending the night in a hotel someplace with her own customer.

Without Om to talk to, Lek resorted to telling the stuffed animals about her dreamy new boyfriend. She told them how nice he had been to her, how much money he had given her and how maybe someday he might take her with him to visit America. She allowed these thoughts to follow her into a comfortable sleep.

Om didn't come home until late the next afternoon. When she finally arrived she seemed in a hurry and even though she asked Lek how it had gone the night before, she didn't wait around for the answer before she jumped in the shower. Even as she sat down in front of the mirror and put on her makeup, Lek's description of the past evening's events didn't seem to register with her. Lek's suspicions were confirmed when she told Om she had a scorpion on her back and Om only responded with an inattentive 'uh-huh'.

'I've got to run,' Om said when she was finished with her preparations. 'I'll see you later at the bar and we can talk all about it.'

Disappointed, Lek watched as Om stormed out the door. The entire interaction had lasted less then a half an hour and left Lek wondering whether it had actually even taken place.

That night Lek was greeted at the door of the bar by *mamasan* who took her by the arm and told her they needed to talk. She led her over to a corner seat away from the rest of the girls and sat her down.

'What happened last night?' she asked in a rather accusatory tone of voice.

'It was wonderful,' Lek tried to sound reassuring. 'He took me back to his place, we showered and, you know. After we were done he gave me a bunch of money and sent me home. He's a really nice guy. It was a good time for both of us . . . I think,' she said.

'Not according to him. He said you lay there like a dead fish, never once talked with him and then left on your own. He came back here and wanted his bar fine back.'

'What? He asked me to leave, didn't he?' Lek was now completely confused and her feelings had just been crushed.

'He said after he gave you the money you got dressed and left. It doesn't matter what you think happened, obviously something didn't go right. He's a valued customer here and we try to take care of our good customers. I gave him his money back, now you have to pay me for your night off last night.'

'Night off? I worked last night.'

'Worked, huh? Why didn't you come back here when you left his hotel? Were you afraid we might find out what happened? I've been in this business a long time and I know all the tricks, girl. You were just trying for some easy money and a quick night off. I've heard it all before, lay there and act dumb, don't let him get too excited and it's out the door in a couple of minutes with a pocket full of money. The only other possibility is that you're a virgin, but I doubt that. Are you?'

Lek was trapped. If she admitted she was a virgin she thought she might get Om in trouble for getting her a job there. Om had told her *mamasan* didn't like to hire virgins. But if she told her she wasn't a virgin she might get fired for something she didn't do, a trick she didn't know about that she had supposedly played on a valued customer. Since she had done it with Craig the night before, she decided it wouldn't be a total lie to say that now she wasn't a virgin. That's the angle she decided to take and she would just have to weather out whatever storm *mamasan* blew at her.

'No, I'm not a virgin,' she told her with mock indignation.

'So what were you up to last night?'

'I really like Craig a lot. I was just having a bad night last night. I promise it won't happen again,' said Lek.

'Four hundred baht. That's what it will take to convince me. That's how much I had to give back to him. Do you have four hundred baht or will I have to take it out of your salary?'

'I have it here." Lek reached into her pocket and pulled out some of the money that was left over from what Craig had given her the night before. She counted out four hundred baht and handed it over to her boss.

'I feel confident that a matter such as this will never come up between us again. Am I right in thinking this way?'

'Absolutely,' Lek assured her. 'Never again.'

'Good, I didn't think so. Go ahead and change, it's time to go to work,' *mamasan* said as she got up and left.

'What was that all about?' Om and a couple of the girls came over to join Lek in the corner. They had already changed into their bikinis and the music had already started.

'I'll tell you later,' Lek told them. 'I've got to go get ready, I'm late.'

When she came back out of the dressing room she went directly up on stage. She was still confused about her talk with *mamasan* and didn't feel like talking with any of the other girls quite yet.

The question that dominated her thoughts was what had she done so wrong to cause Craig to demand his money back from the bar? Was she really that bad?

She tried not to look anyone in the eye as she danced and was able to divert the other girls' looks by gazing around the bar. While doing so, she noticed Om over talking with *mamasan*. When the two had finished their conversation, Om joined a group of the other girls who were eagerly waiting close by.

Lek's set finished too quickly, for now she knew she would have to answer a lot of questions from Om and the others. She tried to avoid this scenario by finding a seat by herself in a dark corner but as soon as she settled in Om came over with a few of her friends.

'What happened last night?' They all wanted to know. 'Why was *mamasan* so upset and why did Craig come back to the bar alone?'

'I don't know,' Lek said uncomfortably. 'I thought everything went okay. I guess it didn't.'

It suddenly occurred to Om that it had been the first time for Lek. She remembered her first time and it became clear to her exactly what had happened.

'You didn't know what to do, did you?' she asked. The three or four other girls who had gathered around listened intently for Lek's response.

'No,' she replied. 'I thought I was doing okay. I mean, I let him do it to me and when he finished he was smiling.'

'She's a virgin?' Geow, one of the other girls, squealed in delight.

'No way!' Meow said in disbelief. 'How could a sex bomb like her have escaped being broken in for so long? It's not possible!'

To Lek's embarrassment they began to laugh and giggle at the news. Om quickly changed the course of the conversation when she announced that it was up to them to teach her how to handle herself in those kinds of situations. She reminded them that they were all in this together and needed to stick up for one another.

'You've got to move your body, girl,' Gook began by writhing around in front of Lek. 'Make him think you're enjoying yourself. Let him hear it, too. Oooo, yes, oooo, yes.'

'Ah, ah, ah!' Meow chipped in as she caressed her body.

'Uhm, uhm, ah, yes,' Geow joined in the fun.

Soon all the girls were gyrating and moaning in front of Lek, causing her to break out in restrained laughter. When Jiap faked an orgasm so loud it caused all those sitting within a few meters of their table to stop what they were doing and look over to see what was going on, their whole crew burst into laughter.

'You girls are great!' Lek said, still laughing. 'Who needs a real family when they can have you?'

'Yoooooo!' Jiap screamed with her arm raised high in the air. She peeled off from the group, walked over to a foreigner sitting at the bar and began to rub her body against his back. She didn't even look at him as she did it, her gaze was still fixed on Lek. She gave Lek a wink, then bent over, and with an exaggerated display, licked the patron's ear. He turned around to grab her but she expertly slipped out of his reach. Still not looking at him, she pranced up onto the stage.

CHAPTER 55

Nearly ten months had passed since Nid had left Korat after Lek's accident. She had waited around for a few days in case Lek returned. When she never showed, Nid bade farewell to Prasit and Toi, then made the journey back to her room in Pattaya.

Unfortunately, good news did not await her there. Not only was Termsak still refusing to take her calls, but Malee had already left to return to her village up north as well.

Malee did leave Nid a farewell letter explaining why she hadn't waited for Nid to return. In it, she explained how she was not good at saying goodbye. She also predicted that they would meet up again someday, so saying goodbye was unnecessary. She wished Nid and Lek good luck and looked forward to the day they would meet up again.

Those ten months that followed her return from Korat were rough on Nid, for she was now truly alone. She whiled away the lonely hours by taking long walks on the beach, writing new songs and singing at the Malee Cafe. All three activities combined to slowly bring her back into the mainstream of life. It was the latter two that began to revive her career.

The management of the Malee Cafe had taken her back without hesitation. Although it had been a while since she had been in the limelight, she was still a proven attraction. Cuts from her first and only album were still getting occasional airtime on local radio stations, and customers who visited the Malee Cafe often came just to hear her sing.

An added attraction for the management of the Malee Cafe was that Nid came cheap. Since she was still receiving small royalty checks from her album, she earned enough to pay her bills and live in relative comfort. She was therefore willing to accept her old job back at the same pay.

Some of the songs she wrote only received moderate praise, others became crowd favorites. One in particular became a nightly request. She had written it from deep inside her heart and each time she performed it her dedication shone through. She titled it: 'Lek, I Miss You' and it was this song that brought her back into favor with Termsak.

Many attempts were made by the management of the Malee Cafe to get Termsak down to Pattaya. Without telling Nid, they had called him several times to let him know what a hit Nid had become at the club with her newly written material. They insisted he come and have a listen. Eventually, he conceded.

The night Termsak arrived to see her perform, Nid didn't know he was in the audience. He sat at a table out of sight just to see if what the management had told him was true. If it wasn't, he had planned to make an early departure without letting anyone know he was there. He was a busy man and couldn't waste his time on someone who wasn't committed to her profession.

It didn't take long into her first set before he realized he had been wrong about her and her talent all along. She worked the crowd well and they remained absorbed in the show throughout her performance. Termsak began to chastise himself for being so stubborn in his refusal to let an old wound heal. Sensing his mistake he began to order shots of whiskey to get up enough courage to approach her with his apology.

When she sang 'Lek, I Miss You' it brought a lump to his throat. He considered himself a good judge of music and if that song had that much of an effect on him, it was sure to be a hit. If, that is, he could convince her to record it. The waitress poured him another shot.

A couple of shots later, when Nid finished her set, Termsak watched to see where she was sitting. He then sent a dozen roses and a bottle of champagne to her table. He gave her a couple of minutes to ponder where they had come from, then walked over to join her.

'Termsak? Did these come from you?' Nid asked in shock.

'They are my humble way of apologizing for being so bad to you. I'm truly sorry, I was wrong. Can you ever forgive me for being so stupid?' he said.

'There's nothing to forgive, Termsak. It was I who caused the problem. I should be sending you flowers and champagne.'

'That's not true. You tried to make amends and it was I who was so stubborn. Until I heard you perform tonight I refused to remember how talented you are and what a beautiful voice you have. Maybe you would consider giving me another chance?'

'Sit down Termsak, please. Give you another chance for what?'

'I'm sorry, I'm a little drunk,' Termsak said when he had some trouble negotiating the chair Nid offered him. 'But I wasn't drunk when I heard you perform and told myself I've got to get that woman back in the studio, fast.'

'Do you really mean that?'

'Of course I do,' Termsak slurred. 'On one condition. You have to promise me that you won't disappear before a concert again. If you can promise me that, I want you back in the studio as soon as you can get your pretty little voice up to Bangkok.'

'I think you know by now, Termsak, that whatever happens, finding my daughter takes priority in my life. I will promise you this, if the situation arises again I will handle it differently.

I don't know exactly what that means, but I won't leave you in a bad position like last time.'

'Good enough. Never let it be known that Termsak doesn't know how to be accommodating to his stars,' he announced loudly.

'I don't think that was ever in question,' Nid reassured him.

'Nid, Nid, Nid. You're such a forgiving individual. Give me a call tomorrow when I'm sober and we'll set something up for next week, okay?'

'Where will you be tomorrow?' she asked.

'Who cares? Just call my secretary, she'll take care of everything. Did I ever tell you what a good secretary I have?'

'Termsak, I've never seen you this way, are you all right?'

'Sure, I'm fine,' he half sung to her. 'It's just that it's not often when I realize I've been a fool. Apologizing is not one of my fortes, as you can probably tell.'

With that spoken, Termsak got up and left Nid to ponder what had just transpired.

'How was it that Termsak just happened to be in the audience that night?' Nid wondered. 'Usually when he comes to the club he arrives with singers to show off on stage. Tonight he seemed to be alone.' The answers to her thoughts were not long in coming.

'I saw Termsak over here a little while ago, is everything okay with you two?' the manager of the cafe asked after rushing over to join Nid at her table.

'Yes, he came over here to apologize. I'm not really sure why, though,' she said.

'Did he like your new songs?'

'As a matter of fact, he liked them enough to ask me to come back into the studio.'

'I thought he might.'

'Wait a minute, what do you mean by that? Did you have something to do with his being here tonight?'

'I've been calling him every few days to tell him he had better come down here and hear your new material.'

'You mean it was you who called him? You did that for me?'

'I did it for the both of us. My conscience wouldn't allow me to let you sit here and wilt. Nid, if anybody is ready for the big time it's you. I couldn't see you two feuding over a meaningless incident that happened such a long time ago. It wasn't doing anybody any good keeping you a secret stashed away in a nightclub here in Pattaya. Don't get me wrong, you're the best thing to come along to our club in a long time and I love having you around, but your time has come. You've worked long and hard and you deserve to enjoy the fruits of your labor.'

'Does that mean you won't mind me leaving to go record with him in Bangkok next week?'

'Of course I mind! You are the biggest attraction my business has and I'll mind losing the customers you bring in here. But there's no way I'd be able to live with myself if I didn't let you go.'

When Nid called Termsak's office the next day his secretary, Phanee, was her usual friendly self.

'I'll set up a meeting for you next week,' Phanee told her. She broke off the conversation for a moment and Nid thought she could hear her flipping through some pages.

'How's Tuesday? Will that be okay?'

'Sure, Tuesday's fine.'

CHAPTER 56

Still hopeful to conclude her monumental task, when Nid arrived in Bangkok she took a side trip over to the police station just to see if they might have heard anything about Lek.

She asked to see the officer in charge of missing persons and was led to a room on the second floor. An older gentleman with colorful bars on his uniform looked up from behind his desk as she entered the room. A smile of recognition emerged on his face. Nid thought she recognized him, too, but couldn't place him.

'Hello, I'm Nid Sawang.'

'Yes, I know. I'm Officer Wichai.' He could tell she was having difficulty remembering who he was. 'You're the singer, right?'

'Yes, thank you for noticing,' Nid responded politely. She reasoned that since her picture had been on her first album, no doubt he had seen it. That was probably the reason why he looked as though he recognized her.

'My guess is you're here because you still haven't found your daughter.'

'How did you know that?'

'It's my job. Actually, I probably wouldn't have remembered you at all if you hadn't made an album and had a flash of success. You and I had a little talk about six years ago after we arrested Rattana and Siriporn Chokul.'

Nid let out a long, 'Oh, of course. Officer Wichai. I thought I recognized you.'

'I guess you didn't find your daughter in Buriram,' he said.

'No, she ran off before I ever got there.'

'I'm sorry to hear that. Do you have any new information or leads for us to follow?'

'A lot has happened since then but I'm afraid I don't have anything concrete to go on. She worked for a bus company in Korat for a while. They made an identification card for her.' Nid reached into her purse, pulled it out and handed it to Officer Wichai.

'Unfortunately, something came up and she had to leave before she picked it up. I don't know where she went. I thought there might be an outside chance that she came to Bangkok to work. If she did, or does, she might need to apply for a new card. If she does, maybe you could flag it somehow and find out where she is,' Nid suggested.

'Sounds like a good plan, in theory. I'll have to tell you, though, identification records around here are somewhat less than fully organized. There are literally thousands of them in this station alone. I'll give it a try. If you'd write down your current address and phone number for me, I'll go make a photocopy of her card and get the process started.'

As he left the room, Nid wrote down all the information she could think of including her hotel room and the phone number of the studio. When Officer Wichai returned, he handed Lek's identification card back to Nid.

'I'll let you know as soon as anything turns up. It may take a while, but you never know.'

'Thanks, I'm sure you'll do the best you can.'

'I feel funny asking you this, but there is something you could do for me if it's not too much trouble.'

'Sure, what is it?'

'My wife and I truly enjoyed your album. We always wondered why there wasn't a second one. Now I think I understand and I can hardly wait to get home and tell my wife. Would it be too much to ask for you to give us your autograph?'

'Not at all.' Nid was a bit taken aback. She could feel the goose bumps rise on her arms as she scribbled down: 'Thank you for all you've done for me' and her signature.

'This is great, thanks.'

Nid left the police station feeling ten feet tall. Other than people in the music industry, it was her first direct feedback from anyone about her album. It had been a year and a half since she recorded it and she had just found someone who still remembered it.

She was still riding high when she entered the studio. It was then and there that she committed herself to a promise to work as hard as she could to make her second recording session more of a success than the first.

Nid discovered that since she had already experienced one recording session, everything seemed to go much smoother the second time around. Termsak was still a perfectionist and had them doing nearly as many takes as the first time, but Nid knew as well as everyone else to expect it so it wasn't nearly as painful.

By mid-March she had wrapped up the final take and the new album had only to be mixed before it was ready to be released. At the end of their final session Termsak brought them all into the lounge across the hall for his usual post-recording get together.

'I'm especially excited about the "Lek, I Miss You" track. It turned out even better than I thought, and I had high expectations to begin with. I'm going to push it hard. Hopefully, by the end of next week all the radio stations in Bangkok will have a copy of the single. The week after that I'm going to start sending it out to stations throughout the country.

'Thanks again everyone for your hard work. Now, everyone go home, relax and keep in touch. I predict big things will be happening soon so fasten your seat belts, we're in for a fast ride to the top.'

By mid-May, Termsak's predictions proved to be prophetic. Every time Nid turned on the radio she heard her song at least once an hour on various stations.

Her new found celebrity status began to wear on her, though. She loved her room at the Charoen Guest House and wanted to keep it, but security there was nil. Each time she wanted to go out, the lobby contained a handful of well wishers and autograph seekers which made every trip an effort.

What bothered her most, though, was the young women of various ages who began to appear from nowhere. All of them claimed to be the Lek in the song that she was looking for. Their appearances only served to remind her that the real Lek was still nowhere to be found.

On the last day of May, Termsak called Nid to tell her the song had made it to the top of the charts. It was now the number one selling record in the country. He also said he was trying to line up a concert tour for her and the band, and wanted to check with her first before he made any commitments to the other band members or the promoters of the tour.

'Termsak, I'm really sorry about what happened the first time and I promise it won't happen again,' she said.

'Don't apologize, just let me know if you have anything planned so I can go ahead and try to book this tour.'

'I don't have anything planned right now and if you book this tour I will make sure not to do anything that will screw it up, okay?'

'That's what I wanted to hear. We have a tentative opening date scheduled for sometime in the middle of June. I'm sorry, I know that's not a lot of time to prepare. I'm just hoping it's not enough time for something out of the ordinary to pop up.'

'If it does you'll be the first to know.'

'That's not very comforting.'

On 16 June, which happened to also be Lek's 18th birthday, Nid waited with Termsak, Phanee, the band members and crew members backstage at the Huamark Indoor Stadium in Bangkok. It was the opening night of Nid's concert tour. Everyone was a nervous wreck, although no one was quite as nervous as Nid. Outside, it was a warm and overcast evening with intermittent downpours threatening a low turnout.

Despite urgings from the others not to do so, Nid kept peering out at the huge crowd that had gathered for the show. At least a thousand people ignored the weather to be there and all were clapping and cheering, attempting to bring the show to an early start. It was the most people Nid had ever seen in one spot and the thought of performing in front of them made her sick to her stomach with pre-performance jitters.

At 8 p.m. sharp, the stage hands led the band out to their positions leaving Nid just off to one side behind some speakers. The concert's promoter, who doubled as the M.C., walked out and grabbed the microphone in front of the cheering crowd.

'Thank you all for braving the rain to be here tonight,' he began, causing a rousing cheer. 'It's now the time we've all been waiting for. The concert premier of the talented and lovely, writer and performer of the nation's number one hit. PLEASE ... WELCOME ... NID ... SAWANG!'

The band began to play and the crowd went wild. Immediately all the butterflies left Nid's stomach as she ran onto the stage and grabbed the microphone. She thanked the audience and the M.C. and began to sing.

The crowd never stopped cheering throughout the entire first number. When she finished, the decibel level of their cheering was deafening.

When the band began to play her second song, the crowd calmed down a little so they could clap and sing along. When she was done, the crowd once again erupted into thunderous applause.

About halfway through the show she announced she would sing 'Lek, I Miss You', which caused an ecstatic cheer. Then, when she began to sing, the crowd became eerily quiet. It wasn't until she was about a third of the way through the song before Nid realized that the reason it seemed quiet was because almost the entire crowd was singing along with her. They all knew every word.

Throughout the song people continually came to the edge of the stage to hand her roses. Those who couldn't reach her settled for throwing them up onto the stage. The stage hands were kept busy for the rest of the song, keeping Nid's arms free from all the roses she was receiving and trying to clear them away from the floor around her.

Nid was absolutely overwhelmed by the response she received from the audience. Never in her wildest dreams had she thought it would be anything like this. She continually looked to the members of her band for support, but could see they, too, were overcome by it all.

When she had sung her last song and the concert was finished, Nid gave the audience a deep *wai* then led the band off the stage.

The audience in front of the stage didn't want to let her go and gave her a standing ovation that lasted ten minutes.

A chant of encore began to spread until the entire crowd was screaming it as loud as their lungs would allow.

Nid was emotionally exhausted, in tears and in no way did she want to go back out to sing another song. But the crowd wouldn't let up and soon even Termsak and some of the stage people joined in the chant.

The promoter finally approached Nid. 'No one is going to leave until you go out there and sing another song.'

'I can't,' Nid protested. 'I just . . . can't.'

'I think you can probably muster up enough willpower to go out there just one more time.'

'But what will I sing? I've already done all my songs!'

The promoter motioned the band to go back out and nodded towards Termsak. Then, whispering in her ear that she knew damn well what it was the crowd wanted to hear, he and Termsak physically picked her up and carried her part way out onto the stage. The crowd erupted again and the stage was again showered with roses.

Nid tentatively walked out to the center of the stage and looked at the band, then over at Termsak and finally toward the promoter. She tried to look at anything but the crowd.

She finally picked up the microphone off its stand and with tears in her eyes and her voice cracking, she turned to the crowd and asked them what it was they wanted her to sing.

Another chant started and didn't stop until the band began to play and Nid began to sing.

'LEK . . . I . . . MISS . . . YOU . . .'

'LEK . . . I . . . MISS . . . YOU . . .'

CHAPTER 57

Everyone involved with the tour told Nid it had been a success, especially considering it was her first time on the road. Nonetheless, it had been a hectic and somewhat trying experience for her. Even though she and the band only performed five shows, Termsak and the promoter had her on the move constantly. She made special appearances at club meetings, social gatherings and civic conventions. She was a special guest on television and radio shows. For the entire trip, she never felt as though even one minute was her own, and at times felt a bit like a puppet in a sideshow.

It wasn't all bad, though. She had flown in an airplane for the first time, an experience she wasn't likely to forget soon. She also saw more of Thailand, and from a better perspective than she could ever have hoped for. She was constantly surrounded by roses and flower arrangements. She stayed in the best rooms at the best hotels and had as much of the best food as she could possibly eat available to her 24 hours a day.

Her song, 'Lek, I Miss You' had stayed in the number one spot on the charts for six weeks before it fell to number two. As singer and writer of the song, the royalty cheques Nid was now receiving were more than she thought she would ever see in two lifetimes. The problems that came with stardom didn't exclude her, though, and soon began to wear her down.

The simple life Nid had enjoyed so much before was now a thing of the past. Whenever she tried to take her favorite walk along the beachfront promenade in Pattaya she was mobbed by fans and autograph seekers. She couldn't just pop into the Malee Cafe to see her friends and former co-workers, either. Her entrance to the club was always met with pomp and circumstance.

Her room at the Charoen Guest House was still her favorite place to stay, but living there was fast becoming a burden on the family that owned and operated it. They had always been very good to her and treated her well. Now, though, in addition to their regular duties, they had to try and act as security for all the people that were constantly trying to get in to see her, secretary for all the calls she received every day and mail room attendants for all the fan mail she was now receiving. Nid came to realize she wasn't being fair to them, even though they never complained and acted as though they enjoyed the extra attention.

Nid began her search for a house in and around Pattaya with the help of a local broker. She must have looked at one hundred different houses, none of which fit the image Nid had of the place in which she wanted to spend the rest of her life. It didn't help that everywhere she went in Pattaya, people recognized her. Pattaya had become so crowded, too, that it was never long before any house she happened to look at was surrounded by fans.

It was Termsak who finally convinced her to take a look outside of Pattaya. He suggested a place called Hua Hin, another beachside town on the opposite coast of the Gulf of Thailand. He described the town as a seaside community that in many ways resembled Pattaya from ten years ago. He spoke of unspoiled beaches just south of Hua Hin that seemed to go on forever, cool ocean breezes and lush vegetation.

He also claimed it wasn't as crowded nor as polluted as Pattaya had become. One of the big selling points for him was that it was close enough to Bangkok to be convenient, yet far enough away to be removed from Bangkok's overcrowding. He told her it was his favorite place to go and get away from it all and thought, with her affinity with Pattaya, Nid might like to at least have a look at it.

Hua Hin turned out to be everything Termsak had said it would be. Nid fell in love with the area immediately. She spent a few days in relative obscurity in a nice hotel near the beach before a local broker showed her a house on the southern outskirts of town, just on the northern end of Big Sand Beach. It was located close enough to town to make it easy to pick up supplies, and far enough away so that her fans would have a difficult time finding it.

Only one dirt road from the main thoroughfare ran down into the compound and a locked gate at its beginning would provide plenty of security. A row of small cottages to house the staff nestled in the woods, comfortably hidden behind the main grounds.

The main house was rather new, built in old style Thai tradition. It was made mostly of teak and had beautifully carved eaves. There were several bedrooms, a large kitchen and several more sitting rooms.

A large, manicured garden out front reached all the way down to the beach. The facade faced the open ocean and offered a beautiful view.

Nid at first thought the house was probably too big for her to live in alone, but later considered that when and if she ever found Lek, it would be perfect for the two of them. The more she looked at it and the more she thought about it, the more she realized it fit the image she had of the perfect place to live.

The necessary paperwork was finished within a couple of months. All that was left was for Nid to move in.

Her departure from Pattaya was anything but smooth. Bittersweet memories occupied her thoughts as she gathered her things to leave. She had arrived in Pattaya nearly 14 years ago to find an unknown tribal woman who she thought might be able to help locate her missing daughter. Fourteen years later, after she had become good friends with this woman, Malee had since left to fulfill her own personal dreams, yet Nid's dream of finding Lek still hadn't been realized.

Now she was leaving the town she had loved so much for a place she could love even more. She wanted to make a quiet departure, but her local fans wouldn't allow that to happen. About fifty well wishers crowded around the front of the Charoen Guest House to see her off. Most wanted her autograph or to touch her one last time. As much as success could have changed her, Nid remained as humble as she was on the day she arrived and couldn't turn them down.

Nid had the help of the staff of the guesthouse when she loaded her belongings into the equipment van that Termsak had loaned her from Bangkok. It still took over an hour to get all her things through the crowd.

Although no one from the guesthouse ever said anything about it, with all the extra work they were doing, Nid could sense that they were silently relieved to see her go. Now they could go back to living a normal life without the sideshow of having a live-in celebrity.

The first thing Nid noticed after she left Pattaya and was finally brought to her new home in Hua Hin was how quiet and serene the surroundings were in comparison to what she had just left. After unloading the van and bidding farewell to the help Termsak had hired for the move, Nid sat out on her veranda and fell asleep in a chair while listening to the soft sounds of waves lapping the shore.

Over the next year Nid turned her house into her own private palace. She furnished the place with a combination of old style Thai furnishings and modern conveniences. She bought herself a television and a stereo, a car and a small rowboat that she could paddle around when the seas weren't too rough.

She hired a full-time cook, maid, driver and grounds keeper, all of whom she was able to house in the row of cottages out back. All her servants were good people and Nid enjoyed talking with them, but they wouldn't allow themselves to become close to their employer. It wasn't the proper way to act.

Without any close friends in the area, Nid led a life of seclusion. The only contact she had with the outside world was with Termsak, her band members, the people in the music industry and the Bangkok police. She checked with the latter often to see if they ever came up with any leads about Lek. The answer was always the same negative response.

Her favorite acquisition became the piano she put in her large living room. She taught herself how to play and within a year she had written enough material to record her third album. When it was completed, she embarked on her second tour.

Her third album was just as successful as her second. Over the preceding year the media had begun to label her as a one hit wonder, but they soon retracted every word. They now called her one of the best singer/songwriters to have come along in a long time. Her schedule became full and hectic again, meaning she had less time to spend at home and checking with the police as to the whereabouts of her daughter.

CHAPTER 58

Lek lay motionless with her eyes closed. An old bath towel and the corner of a bed sheet covered only a small part of her body. The air conditioner was turned off, leaving an overworked oscillating fan on the bedstand to make a futile attempt at relieving the stifling heat. It wasn't enough. A sheen of sweat covering Lek glistened in the faint light of the room.

It was Mike's bed. Mike was an American who worked in Bangkok, one of the many expats of various nationalities who seemed to be passing Lek around between them. Not that she minded. After all, it was the slow season and the expats who worked in town paid her rent, allowed her to eat and even kept a balance in her bank account.

She was in no hurry to let it be known that she was awake. She could feel Mike stirring next to her, a prelude, she knew all too well, to her 'customer' fulfilling his primal urges. That would come soon enough. For now, Lek was content lying still, letting the slightly cooled air from the fan flow over her, and letting her mind drift off to her current situation at the bar.

She had been working out of the same bar for nearly a year. During that time she had picked up enough of the English language to be able to hold her own in conversations with *farangs* in almost any situation. That, along with her good looks, had made her one of the most popular dancers in the bar. She was also quite popular with her coworkers. Except, of course, for Moo the bartender. No one got along with her.

Moo had been working in the bar longer than any one of the current employees and never hesitated to use the position of seniority to her advantage.

Moo was rather large and, unfortunately for those who had to work near her, had a mean disposition. Although up until recently she hadn't paid much attention to Lek, no one escaped her bullying.

Most likely out of jealousy of Lek's popularity, Moo had begun to play mean-spirited tricks on Lek and her customers. She began by making them wait an unusually long time for their drinks. When that ploy didn't seem to achieve its desired effect, Moo started giving them smaller drinks.

Being the lighthearted, easygoing person that she was, Lek never confronted Moo about her antics, opting instead to wait her out. Surely she would give up sooner or later. But the situation had been going on for a couple of weeks with no end in sight. Lek was beginning to realize that if she didn't do or say something soon, things might get out of control.

Mike was definitely awake now. He reached over and gently caressed Lek's breasts and whispered in her ear that it was already 4 p.m. The news didn't exactly surprise her. After a night of heavy drinking, the two of them had stayed up playing video games until 8 a.m.

Lek had become accustomed to the routine. Even though all the men she had been with liked to consider themselves different, in reality they were pretty much all the same. Not knowing when they might have the chance to see her again, they all wanted that one more sexual fix before they sent her off to work.

If they happened to wake up early, say, before noon, chances were that they would probably still be drunk and the sex might last a long time. In cases like the present, when they didn't wake up until late in the day, chances were pretty good that they would just be hungover and the sex would be fairly quick and painless. Lek wasn't disappointed.

Without so much as a hint of foreplay, Mike reached down and pulled one of Lek's legs over his waist. With her still on her back and he on his side, he made his entrance. The hangover must be draining all his energy, Lek thought, he doesn't even have the strength to climb on top or pull her on top of him.

When he had finished quivering, Mike kissed her on the cheek and grabbed her towel. After one more quick fondle of her breasts, he arose and headed for the shower, leaving her lying on her back, staring at the ceiling tiles. She was neither smiling nor frowning. Her expression was impassive, true to her thoughts, for her mind had already drifted back to her work at the bar.

Everyone who worked at the bar could see that Lek was being harassed by Moo, yet none was willing to step in and help her for fear of Moo's wrath. It would be up to Lek to try and figure out a way to bring things back to normal. How she would go about accomplishing that feat was anybody's guess.

When Mike emerged from his shower, he turned on the television, flopped down on the bed beside Lek and lit a cigarette. Lek took his actions as her cue to shower and prepare to leave.

Fifteen minutes later when Lek emerged and began to get dressed, Mike feigned protest, 'You have to leave so soon?', even though he knew full well that the hour was growing late and Lek needed to prepare for another night at work.

'You pay my barfine and I stay with you all night,' Lek said slyly.

'I would, but I have to work tomorrow,' Mike replied. 'I really need to get some sleep tonight.'

'Okay, I go now,' Lek said as she attempted to pull on her clothes while Mike tried his best to fondle her one more time before she left.

The irony of Mike's statement wasn't lost on Lek. He has to get some sleep so he can go to work tomorrow, Lek thought. I have to go to work tonight. And until three in the morning, probably. They were all the same. None of them seemed to realize that after a hard night out, they could take a night off and sleep. We have to go back to the bar and be cheerful to a new set of customers, most of whom have had a good night's sleep before coming out, and be ready for anything they might want to do. Never mind, it was what she chose to do. Besides, the money was good.

The evening began as it normally did with a few foreigners straggling in now and then, and by 10 p.m. the place was beginning to fill up. Moo continued her silent harassment of Lek and her customers, short-sizing their drinks and making them wait unusually long times to be served. Although she was a little extra tired and not quite as cheerful as normal, Lek was still unwilling to make a scene out of the situation.

About an hour later, Moo tried a new ploy. The man who had taken up a position next to Lek had ordered himself a beer and a lady's drink for Lek. After a lengthy wait, the waitress brought the man a glass of whiskey and ice, and Lek a shot of tequila. The order not being even close to what they had wanted, Lek sent the waitress back to get the correct drinks.

Instead of sending the waitress back with the correct order, Moo personally brought the same drinks back to Lek's table. 'If you order the wrong drinks, don't expect me to cover for you,' Moo snapped at Lek as she roughly slammed the drinks on her table. 'Liquor costs money. Someone has to pay for your mistakes and it's not going to be me.'

'These aren't what we ordered,' Lek tried to sound polite. Moo was embarrassing her in front of her customer.

'Are you calling me a liar?' Moo leaned in close to Lek's face.

Lek started to get up to protect herself. 'Why are you doing this?' she asked as innocently as she could.

Moo pushed her back into her seat. 'Don't you threaten me!'

The man who had been sitting next to Lek made a hasty retreat to the other side of the bar. He didn't understand a word of Thai, but he could definitely see what was going on. He also knew enough never to get involved in a dispute with the locals.

Seeing the worsening situation, Meow and Om came running over to step in between the two. 'Don't do it, Moo,' Meow said once she was in position.

'Stay out of this,' Moo snapped at them. 'It's got nothing to do with you two. It's between me and her,' she said as she tried to reach past them to get at Lek.

Lek had about all she could take. Without warning, she thrust her arm between Om and Meow and pushed Moo on the shoulder. The outburst caught everyone by surprise and sent Moo sprawling backward into and over a bar stool. The loud crash caught everyone's attention, including *mamasan*.

'What's going on here?' *Mamasan* asked as she hastily came over to get between the two combatants. Her presence immediately defused the situation.

'Just a misunderstanding,' Moo said quietly as she picked herself up off the floor. 'We will handle it later, after work,' she added staring at Lek.

'That suits me,' Lek said defiantly.

'I won't stand for any fighting between my employees,' *mamasan* spoke harshly. 'This is over. Finished. There will be no more of this at work or after work. Do you understand me?' she said looking between Lek and Moo.

Both women nodded their assent even though both knew it was far from over.

'Now get back to work, all of you!' she shouted at the assembled crowd. She then went about the work of trying to repair the damage done to the image of the bar. This little outburst would cost her dearly, for, in the interest of goodwill, she would have to go around and buy most of the bar's regular customers a drink on the house.

As closing time grew near, the tension in the bar mounted. Even though the other dancers took turns ordering for Lek and her customers, Moo had managed to get a message through that she was prepared to meet Lek outside after work. Lek accepted without hesitation.

'What are you trying to prove?' Om was adamant in trying to dissuade Lek from taking on the challenge. 'She's twice your size and will probably kill you.'

'I'm not afraid of her,' Lek replied defiantly. 'We'll see who is going to kill who.'

When the time finally arrived, the tiny Lek and the massive Moo were kept apart by a group of bargirls as they left the bar. The entourage walked down the street that made up Soi Cowboy, picking up other workers and customers filing out of the bars that closed at the same time. Seeing the crowd of people heading in the same direction could mean only one thing: a fight was on.

The army of spectators grew to a few dozen people as the group rounded a corner and headed into an alley off the beaten track. When a suitable place was finally found, the onlookers formed a large circle, creating a makeshift arena.

'I'll give you a chance to save face,' Lek told Moo once they stood facing each other. 'If you want to back out, now's the time.'

Lek's taunting caused Moo to lose her temper, something Lek was counting on. Moo let out a nasty growl, raised both her fists high in the air, and made an uncontrolled charge.

Lek deftly stepped off to one side as Moo brought her fists crashing down, striking nothing but air. Her forward momentum, helped by a timely push from Lek, caused Moo to lose her balance and crash into the crowd. Her clumsy maneuver brought jeers from the crowd.

Meanwhile, tuk-tuk drivers and locals had joined the crowd and bets were being placed at a feverish pace. Most of the odds had the fight lasting no more then five minutes before Moo pummeled Lek into submission.

'Had enough yet?' Lek taunted Moo again.

'Never,' Moo snarled as she pushed herself away from the spectators. She made another charge, again with her fists raised high above her head. Only this time she anticipated Lek making the same side step maneuver and directed her blow toward where she thought Lek would move.

It was just what Lek was hoping for. Using a move that her old friend Soonton had taught her, Lek concentrated her energy and unleashed a ferocious kick into Moo's unprotected belly.

Moo doubled over immediately. Before she had a chance to recover, Lek once again concentrated her energy and let loose a savage left, right combination to Moo's face.

Her nose broken, Moo fell to the ground, struggled to get up, then flopped unceremoniously back down. Lek stood over her, waiting for another attack. When it didn't come, she relaxed.

The fight was over almost as quickly as it had begun. The crowd fell completely silent. All had expected a quick fight, but none had expected this outcome. Stunned, a few began to clap. A few more followed, and gradually the applause built until the entire audience was cheering.

Om ran over and grabbed Lek. 'We have to get out of here before the police come,' she said as she steered her through the throng of people. 'Where did you learn to fight like that?'

'I told you I could take care of myself,' Lek answered, her adrenaline pumping. She was as surprised as anyone. Even though Soonton had taught her well, this was the first time she ever had the need to use what he had taught her.

'I'm just glad you're still alive,' Om said sincerely.

When she finally managed to get Lek past the crowd and out onto the side of Soi Asoke, the major thoroughfare leading past the Soi Cowboy area, a younger Thai man approached them.

'Follow me,' he said excitedly. 'I'll give you a ride home.'

Om and Lek looked at each other, confused. 'No thank you,' Om told him. 'We can make our own way home.'

'No, really,' the Thai man persisted. 'I drive a tuk-tuk. I'll give you a ride home for free.'

'Why would you do that?' Lek asked incredulously.

'Because I bet on you to win the fight. Everyone called me stupid, but I could see it in your eyes. I could tell you had what it would take to win. I bet all I had and you didn't let me down. You made me a lot of money tonight, more than I make in an entire week. So please, let me give you a ride home.'

What could they say? He already had Lek by the arm and was leading her over to his parked tuk-tuk, so Om followed along and the two climbed aboard.

After giving the driver directions to their room, Lek began to shake. The intensity of what had just taken place was beginning to sink in.

'That was a stupid thing to do,' she said solemnly.

'You're right, it was,' Om responded. 'She could have killed you. But she didn't. You won and you're not hurt, so try not to think about it. Tomorrow is a new day.'

'Tomorrow,' Lek repeated, trying to rub the pain out of her hands. 'Tomorrow I have to face *mamasan*. She warned me not to meet up with Moo after work. I can imagine what she will say to the both of us when we get to work tomorrow.'

'*Mamasan* is not stupid,' Om retorted. 'Even she could see that Moo's antics were getting out of control. Something had to be done. What you did should have been done a long time ago.'

'Not by me,' Lek said remorsefully as the tuk-tuk swayed around the final corner leading up to their building. When their journey came to an end and the two women disembarked, they instinctively reached for their money to pay the driver. He just smiled and waved them off, then drove away.

Lek dreaded going to work the entire day following the fight. Would Moo be there? What would *mamasan* say? The two questions caused her to throw up twice as the time to leave approached. She considered not going at all, but decided she would have to face the situation sooner or later. She might as well get it over with tonight.

When she walked through the front door to the bar, Lek was immediately embarrassed by the large amount of adulation the other dancers were heaping upon her. Her achievement the night before had made her a heroine in their eyes. Then *mamasan* walked in.

'We need to talk,' she said sternly to Lek as she walked by on her way to her usual perch at the end of the bar.

'Here we go,' Lek said to her followers, sensing the worst.

'I don't want to know what happened last night,' *mamasan* began once Lek took a seat beside her. 'I already heard that you beat up Moo. I don't know how and I don't care. I just want you to understand that my job isn't an easy one. Sometimes I have to make decisions that may not be the most popular with the people who work for me but must be made for the good of my business. It's important for me to keep control of my employees. If I lose that control I might as well find another occupation.

'Dancers come and go faster then anyone can keep track of them. Some get married, some move to other bars, some just quit and return to their villages. Good bartenders, on the other hand, are hard to come by. It takes a long time to train a bartender. I know that at times Moo is a little hard to get along with, but she's a good barkeeper. I need her back and I don't think she will return as long as you are here.'

'What are you trying to say?' Lek asked hesitantly. She didn't like the direction the conversation was heading.

'Lek, you are a good worker and popular with the customers. You have done very well here and I appreciate the business you have brought in. But Moo is my niece. I think you know how families have to stick together and take care of each other.'

'I wish I did,' Lek interjected quietly.

'I'm afraid I'm going to have to let you go,' *Mamasan* continued, ignoring Lek's comment. 'Effective immediately. Here's five hundred baht for the part of your salary that you've earned so far this month. Now get dressed and get out of here.'

'That's it?' Lek protested. 'No second chances?'

'That's it,' *Mamasan* said without remorse.

Lek looked at the crumpled five hundred baht note in her hand. Here we go again, she thought.

Looking around and seeing many eyes fixed upon her from the darkness of the bar, she slowly climbed off her bar stool and walked into the back room to gather her things.

'What happened?' Om said as she burst into the room.

'Moo is her niece,' Lek informed her.

'So? She started it. Did you tell her that?'

'No need. She said she didn't want to know. "Families have to stick together" she said. "Get your things and get out." So that's what I'll do. Who needs this job anyway?'

'You're right. I'm going with you,' Om said excitedly as she began to change out of her bikini. She made the decision on the spot and the excitement it generated showed clearly in her hurried actions.

'What? No, you stay here,' Lek protested. 'There's no need for both of us to get dragged down by my stupidity.'

'Hey, I got you into this mess and I'm going to stick with you to get out of it. *Mamasan* was right. Families do stick together and we are family, right?'

'Thanks Om.' Lek gave her a hug. 'I needed to hear that. But one of us has to keep working. We have bills to pay.'

'No worries there. With your good looks and my experience we won't be out of a job for long,' remarked Om.

CHAPTER 59

Om had been correct in her assessment of their situation. After she and Lek had taken a few well deserved nights off, they easily obtained jobs working in a small but popular bar in the Nana Plaza Entertainment Complex called Sexy Nights.

As is usually the case when bargirls change their place of employment, it took a few months to get settled into their new surroundings. Being new arrivals, most of the established hands viewed them as potential threats to their already established territory.

After that initial breaking in period, both Lek and Om were accepted into the family of the bar. They became popular with their co-workers and before long it was back to business as usual.

Then one night a group of rowdy customers stormed the bar. These American soldiers would eventually change Lek and Om's lives forever, although neither would have guessed it from their introduction.

There were about 15 of them and even though they had their choice of any one of the many bars in the three storey, horseshoe shaped complex that made up Nana Plaza, they seemed to concentrate their escapades inside the tiny Sexy Nights Bar. Before the night was over, almost all of them had paid a barfine for the girl of their choice.

Lek and Om were bought out of the bar by a pair of friends, Paul and Tom, who kept them out all night. Together they hit other bars, the all night disco in Patpong, and when the sky began to brighten with the early morning sun, they returned to Paul and Tom's hotel to eat breakfast in the coffee shop. By the time they finished their meal, all four of them were exhausted.

Om accompanied Tom to his room and Lek retired to Paul's room where they slept away the rest of the sunlit portion of the day.

The second night the soldiers were in town was much like the first. Tom and Paul accompanied Om and Lek to Sexy Nights, and after several hours of uninhibited drinking, they once again paid the girls' barfines. Once again, they stayed out the entire night.

Their itinerary on that second night included a trip to Soi Cowboy to patronize several of the area's bars, including a quick stop into their old bar. Moo was still working inside, but didn't pay much attention to Lek and her entourage.

When Soi Cowboy closed down for the night, the foursome meandered over to a coffee shop to continue their party. A massage parlor by day, the dingy basement was turned into an all-night gathering spot for bargirls who either hadn't been bought out or were through with their short-time customers, and imbibers who hadn't quite managed their fill of alcohol.

It was a popular, rowdy place that remained open all night. Owned by an influential local policeman, the bar seemed immune from the national laws that determined closing times for places of entertainment. After 3 a.m., it was packed almost every night of the week, even though it was the only bar in the city where customers had to enter through the bathrooms.

The third night the Americans were in town was much calmer than the first two, for the boys had to go to work the following day. Just the same, Tom and Paul bought Om and Lek out of the bar to spend the night together. Only this time, they were all in bed before midnight.

The pattern continued for the rest of the week. Paul and Tom would work during the day and visit the girls at night.

While the boys were off at work during the day, Lek and Om would return to their own room to talk or sleep and prepare for the night of work ahead.

Lek thought Paul was a 'nice guy' and had a good time with him, yet when pushed about it by Om, Lek had to admit that he was just another customer. Om, on the other hand, was beginning to fall for Tom.

Lek was quick to pick up on it. 'I know the feeling is mutual,' she told Om. 'I can tell by the way he looks at you when you're not watching him. He doesn't even look at the other girls when he's around you. Not like Paul does.'

'Do you really think so?' Om was fishing. She hoped it was true but didn't dare believe it. It was dangerous to fall in love with anyone in this business. With so many other girls for the foreigners to choose from, chances for a monogamous relationship were slim at best.

'I don't think so, I know so,' Lek stated confidently. 'He's lost when you're not by his side. Lady, you've set the hook. All you need to do now is reel him in.'

By the end of the week, Tom and Paul were through with their current assignment in Bangkok. Both came to Sexy Nights on the night before their departure. Since they were due to leave so early in the morning, neither paid barfines for Lek and Om, opting instead to say their goodbyes in the bar.

Paul's goodbye to Lek was rather quick and unemotional. Lek's assessment of him had been fairly correct, he was just another customer who didn't seem interested in pursuing the relationship any further. He rather hastily handed Lek a five hundred baht note, more so because he felt it was the right thing to do rather than because he actually wanted to.

Lek awkwardly accepted his gift. Reading his body language, she didn't follow him to the door. It had been a fun week but she wasn't exactly broken up over the fact that he was leaving.

Tom, on the other hand, seemed to be having trouble leaving Om. He didn't even want to address the situation, but seeing Paul's impatience to leave, he realized if he wanted to say anything at all to Om, he would have to hurry.

'I promise I'll come back as soon as I can,' he told her. 'It might even be as early as next month. I'll write to you often if you promise to write back,' he said.

Om had heard it all before. Why would this time be any different? He did seem sincere, though. 'I promise,' she agreed without much conviction. She would, too, but only if he wrote to her first. With those few words spoken, Tom gave her a quick peck on the cheek and was gone.

The next couple of weeks were unusually quiet in the bar business. Apparently the global recession, along with the renewed scare campaign about AIDS were keeping tourists at home. Once again the survival of the many bars in the area was left up to the working expat community.

Three weeks after the American soldiers had left, a letter arrived for Om. Tom had kept his promise. As soon as she received it, Om rushed it over to one of the translation shops that specialized in bridging the language barrier between bargirls and their foreign punters. Most of the translations were rudimentary at best, but they served the purpose of getting the general point of these love letters across to their receivers who would otherwise have no idea at all what they said. Two hours and one hundred baht later, she could read what he had written.

The letter itself was rather short, mostly concentrating on the usual 'I miss you' and 'I can't wait to see you' routine. However, it did say that he would indeed be returning to

Bangkok. The date he wrote as his scheduled arrival was the very next week.

Trying to keep herself from getting too excited, after all she had received similar letters before only to be disappointed, Om nonetheless kept her end of the promise and wrote him back. Before she had the chance to translate and send it, though, Tom arrived.

As soon as he was able, Tom went over to the bar to be with Om. Seeing she was already busy with another customer who had bought her a drink, instead of complaining, he waited patiently off to one side of the bar. He didn't have to wait long. As soon as Om saw him, she downed her lady's drink, apologized to her customer and went rushing over to be with Tom.

Tom's second stay in Bangkok turned out to be quite similar to his first. When he didn't have to work the next day, he would buy Om out of the bar and the two would party all night. When he did have to work, he still paid her barfine just so that he could be with her. At the end of the week, when it was time for him to go, he once again promised to return to her and to write as often as he could.

Over the next few months 'the army', as the bargirls were fond of calling them, would come to Bangkok for one week every month. Neither Lek nor Om knew for sure what they did there, something about looking for lost soldiers in Vietnam. As far as they could figure out, the army would spend one week in Bangkok, one week somewhere else in Southeast Asia, then two weeks at their home base in Hawaii. Actually, it didn't really matter to them what it was they did, the girls were just happy to see them whenever they arrived.

During that time, Tom and Om became an item. Whenever Tom was in town he would spend all his free time with Om.

When he was out of town, he wrote her often, occasionally sending her money. After seven months of this routine, Tom finally proposed to her. Om accepted without hesitation.

The two were married by Buddhist monks in a small Thai ceremony at *mamasan*'s house. A handful of Tom's army buddies in their dress outfits and a select few bargirls made up the guest list.

Their honeymoon lasted just one weekend on the island of Koh Samui before Tom was called back to duty.

Three months later, Om had a passport, a plane ticket and all the necessary paperwork to join Tom in Hawaii. After nearly 22 years working in bars, seven of them selling candy and cigarettes as a child and almost 15 years working as a dancer, now at the ripe old age of 27, Om was finally able to make a graceful exit.

'This is great! I'm so happy for you,' Lek told her as she tried to help Om cram all her belongings into a large suitcase and a small carry-on bag.

'I'm so nervous I think I'm going to wet my pants,' Om responded.

'Don't worry, it will be wonderful.'

'I know. I'm not worried about Tom. It's just that I've never been in an airplane before.'

'It's only a bus that flies,' Lek tried to reassure her.

'I'm going to miss you so much, Lek. Why don't you come with me? I think I have some extra room in my suitcase. Maybe you can fit inside.'

'No thanks. You go ahead. I've got to take care of things around here. Now that you're leaving, someone has to make sure this place doesn't fall apart.'

'Are you going to be okay?'

'Why do I always have to remind you that I can take care of myself?'

'I know,' Om was resigned. Not able to hold back any more, Om reached out and grabbed Lek. The two hugged each other so tight neither could breathe. Both burst into tears. Just before they passed out from lack of oxygen, there was a knock on the door. Tom had come to get Om.

'Time to go,' he announced excitedly.

'Come to the airport with us,' Om demanded of Lek.

'No, you two go ahead. You know me, I hate long good-byes. I have to get ready for work anyway. I don't want to be late,' she said.

Lek tried to help Om with her luggage but it was so heavy Tom had to come over and relieve her of its burden. Lek walked Om and Tom to the door of the room and stopped. Afraid of what she might do once Om left, Lek didn't want to go outside for fear of someone seeing her break down. She didn't want to lose face.

Om tried to stay cheerful as she exited the room but even Tom could see the pain in her face at having to leave her best friend behind. 'Write to me,' she said with a poor attempt of a smile. Fight as she did, the tears just wouldn't stay inside her eyes.

'I promise,' Lek said with the same problem. 'Write to me first and send me your address.'

'I'll do that,' Om replied as Tom shut the door behind them.

Lek stood and stared at the back of the door for a long time. She wanted to open it and run after her friend. Instead, she stood still as the same empty feeling of losing a loved one came rushing back, paralyzing her. The only positive thought she could muster was knowing that this time her loss was leading toward a happier life for her friend.

CHAPTER 60

Lek plopped down on her bed and began reading a newspaper to try and get her mind off Om's departure. Blinking her eyes to fight back the tears, she flipped through the pages without paying much attention to what was in front of her.

There's no reason to be sad, she told herself. Om was moving on to bigger and better things. Besides, it wasn't like she would never see her again. They were bound to meet up some day.

Lek continued to flip through the pages of the daily newspaper, still not paying much attention to what she was looking at until an advertisement for a classical Thai dance school caught her eye. Reading it merely to divert her attention away from Om, Lek learned that the school was advertising openings for its next term. It promised its graduates jobs with the Superstar Dance Troupe, the best of whom would be sent on assignments performing the ancient art of Thai dancing in foreign countries. Out of curiosity, Lek clipped the ad out of the paper and placed it on her dresser.

That night at work, the owner and *mamasan* of Sexy Nights, known to her customers as Nok, could see the effect Om's departure was having on Lek. Nok had come from a somewhat similar background. After escaping from a brothel in the northeast, Nok had made her way to Bangkok. With the financial support of a friendly American, she had bought Sexy Nights with the resolve to make life as bearable for her employees as she could. Seeing Lek sitting alone in a back corner of the bar, as unhappy as she was, worried her.

'It's not the end of the world,' she tried to reassure her once she had taken a seat next to her. 'I'm sure you two will keep in touch. She will probably be back to visit sooner than you know.'

'Thanks,' Lek replied. 'It just seems so strange that she's actually gone. We've been together a long time.'

'Well, you're young. You will make new friends soon enough. In the meantime, let Om be a happy memory. I'm sure she is doing quite well for herself and wouldn't want you to be unhappy on her account.'

'You're right,' Lek replied, fiddling with a newspaper clipping.

'What's that you have in your hand?' Nok asked when she caught sight of it.

'It's nothing,' Lek answered. 'Just an ad for a dance school.'

'A dance school,' Nok repeated approvingly. 'Mind if I have a look?'

'Not at all.' Lek handed her boss the clipped advertisement.

'*Now accepting applications*,' Nok read aloud, '*for a Thai dance troupe*. Not a bad idea,' she added.

'Do you think so?' Lek had been thinking about it and reassurance from Nok seemed to make it sound like it might actually be a realistic possibility.

'Sure,' Nok said without hesitation. 'You are one of the best dancers I've ever seen.'

'You wouldn't have said that if you saw me a year ago,' Lek told her.

'Maybe not. But if that's the case, then you have obviously improved a lot. That proves to me that you are a quick learner. Why not give it a try? It might be fun.'

'Maybe you're right,' Lek agreed. 'Maybe I should give it a try. At the very least, it might take my mind off Om for a while and give me something to do during the day.'

'That's the spirit,' Nok reassured her.

The next morning Lek awoke at 11 a.m., which was quite early for her. The first thing she thought about wasn't the empty bed next to her. She had had plenty of nights sleeping alone when Om had gone to stay with Tom when he was in town. What came to her mind first was the advertisement for the school.

'Now accepting applications,' she read it aloud again. 'Maybe I should give it a try.'

After a quick shower, Lek stood in front of her closet trying to pick out the least revealing outfit she owned. She tried on at least three before she settled on one she thought would be the most acceptable. Donning it, she primped herself in the mirror, then set out to find the school.

When she arrived there, it wasn't at all like she had pictured it from the words in the advertisement. It was rather small, dirty and had relatively few people inside. Noticing a receptionist, Lek approached her to introduce herself.

'I'm here to find out about the ad you placed in the newspaper,' Lek informed her.

'Sure,' the receptionist responded cheerfully. 'The requirements for being accepted into the program are rather simple. Basically, all you need is time, one thousand baht a month, and a willingness to join.'

Lek thought about it. She had all three of the requirements. It sounded too good to be true. Surely there must be some catch. Not seeing what it could be, Lek decided to press on. 'Okay. How do I sign up?'

The receptionist pointed toward a register on top of her desk. 'Just sign here and give me one thousand baht. I'll write you out a receipt. The next class begins at nine on Monday.'

'Is that nine in the morning or evening?' Lek asked hesitantly. Neither possibility was overly enthusing. 9 p.m. meant she couldn't afford to join for it would mean quitting the bar. 9 a.m. would be a painful time to attend dance classes, especially since the bar didn't usually close until 3 a.m.

'That would be nine in the morning,' the receptionist responded. 'Is that a problem for you?'

'No. Not at all,' Lek couldn't believe her own voice. Nine in the morning. Ugh. Never mind, she would give it a try and if it turned out to be too much she could always quit. She handed the woman one thousand baht and signed her name in the register.

'See you Monday,' the receptionist announced cheerfully.

Over the next few months, Lek learned a lot about herself. One of the most important things she learned was that she wasn't a quitter. As difficult as it was, she worked her job at the bar during the night and trained in classical Thai dancing during the day, taking short naps when she could between the two. There were a few days when she wasn't able to do one or the other, but for the most part she kept up her new schedule.

She also realized that for the first time in a very long time she was able to fraternize with other people her age that weren't in the bar business. Although she liked her second life, at times the people seemed pretentious. There was no way she could let the other students know how she made her living.

Their snobbery made her realize just how unpretentious the people were that she worked with at Sexy Nights. They would always be the ones she considered family, especially *Mamasan* Nok now that Om was gone.

Another important thing she learned about herself was that she actually had a talent for Thai dancing. Usually the best Thai dancers were taller women, but Lek's quick comprehension, dogged determination and keen aptitude earned her high marks with her instructor despite her small stature. Best of all, she truly enjoyed it. Before long she found herself positioned near the top of her class.

A couple of months after Om had left, Lek received her first letter. To her relief, Om wrote that Tom was very good to her and that she enjoyed her new life very much.

'We just moved into a big house off base. It has a room for sleeping, a room for cooking, a bathroom and a room just for relaxing and entertaining guests. Tom says it's a tiny house. I don't agree. Compared to what you and me are accustomed to living in, it's a mansion.

Hawaii is the most beautiful place I've ever seen. Everything is green and lush, the air isn't full of smoke like Bangkok and the streets aren't full of garbage. Last week we even went to see a waterfall. It was so romantic.

All the people here are rich. Everyone complains about not having any money but everyone has a car, a television and either a big house or a big apartment.

Tom told me he is going to stay in the army for two more years. After that, we are going to move to Neuwhamper, wherever that is, to be close to his family.

I miss everyone very much, especially you. Maybe some day you can come and visit me in America.

Say hello to everyone for me. Please write back soon. I want to know everything that is going on back in Bangkok.

Your best friend, Om.'

In mid-October, Lek's teacher gathered the class to make an announcement. 'Sometime in mid-December we will be sending a group of dancers on a working trip to Japan to perform in a dinner club. The group we send will be joining other dance troupes from other countries for the show. It will be a six month commitment. Those selected will receive a salary of thirty thousand baht a month which will be deposited directly into your bank account in Thailand. All hotel room costs will be paid by the Japanese firm hiring you. Each dancer will also receive a healthy allowance for meals and expenses.

'There are currently two openings to join the already established dance troupe from Bangkok. I have lobbied for and received permission to send two of you from this class. Who will go will be based on who performs the best over the next few weeks. Also, due to tough Japanese immigration laws, you will need to pass a thorough background check. Evidently the Japanese are worried about losing some of you to the lucrative prostitution trade.

'I will post the results inside the front door of the school on the first day of December. I warn you not to bother trying to check with me before that date. It won't help your cause and I don't need the headache of having you pestering me for the next few weeks. Interviews for interested candidates will begin after today's class.'

The announcement sent a murmur through the class. Every dancer hoped they would be chosen, including Lek. It would have been a dream come true for her. Twice as much money as she had ever earned and the chance to travel to a foreign country. The problem was, as Lek realized, there was no way she could ever pass the background check given her upbringing and her current occupation.

The following week, when class was over for that particular day, Lek's teacher called her aside. 'I have been going over the applications for the Japan trip and I didn't see yours anywhere. You are one of my most promising students. Why haven't you signed up for consideration?'

'Because I wouldn't pass the background check,' Lek replied quietly. She didn't want to go any further and tried to excuse herself to leave.

'Wait,' her teacher persisted. 'Why do you think you can't pass the check?'

'Because I'm an orphan. I have no family. And,' Lek hesitated. 'And because I work as a "bartendee" at the Sexy Nights Bar in Nana Plaza. Since I have no family, and therefore no family records, the only records of my existence are the identification papers I had to file with the police in order to work at the bar,' she said.

Lek's teacher sat back in her chair and contemplated what Lek has just told her. She had been around a long time and had seen many different types of people from many different backgrounds come and go from her school over the years. She was a perceptive woman and knew what Lek was getting at but was too embarrassed to admit.

However, lately almost all of her students had come from rich families who could afford the tuition. She herself had come from a poor family up country. She had worked hard to get to the respectable position she now enjoyed. She understood that opportunities for the smart but poor were hard to come by, especially for women.

She also knew many people and had solid contacts in many places both high and low. Staring at a possible rags to riches story sitting across the desk in front of her reminded her of her own hard work to get to where she was.

She knew that if she could convince Lek to give it a try, and if Lek continued to progress at her current rate, if she pulled the right strings and received a tremendous amount of good luck, she might be able to pull it off.

'Let's fill out an application together, just in case,' she instructed her.

CHAPTER 61

On the last day of November, Lek received her second letter from Om. She was pregnant! She was writing to say that she and Tom had just returned from the doctor.

It took a minute or two for Lek to stop dancing around her room in delight over the news. When she finally calmed down enough to continue reading the letter, she found out that Tom had agreed that if it was a girl, they would name it Lek.

'I wish there was some way you could come visit us in America to be with me while I have our baby,' she wrote. 'But Tom said we don't have much money right now. He said that we have to save all we can for the baby.'

She ended the letter, 'Please write, I miss you terribly.'

The letter made Lek realize how much she missed Om, too. She immediately sat down to send her congratulations.

The next day, the first of December, was the day her teacher was scheduled to post the names of the two dancers selected to go to Japan. Lek was still riding high from the news from Om and couldn't care less whether she made it or not. Actually, she was so confident she hadn't passed the Japanese immigration check that, when she went to school in the morning, she didn't bother to look at the list.

Before she was able to walk into the classroom, however, Sa, one of the other dancers in her class, came running up to her. 'Did you see?' she screamed. 'We made it!'

'What?' Lek was stunned. 'We made it,' Sa repeated. 'We're going to Japan. You and me! Everyone knew you would be chosen, I can't believe they actually chose me, too!'

'What are you talking about? I'm not going, am I?'

'Of course you are. Didn't you see the list?'

'No, I, uh . . .' Lek stuttered.

'Come on. I'll show you.' Sa seized Lek by the arm and led her over to the bulletin board just inside the front door. Sure enough, two names were written on a piece of paper tacked to the board. Lek's name was at the top.

Lek nearly fainted. She wandered into the classroom in a state of shock, still thinking someone must have made a mistake. She drifted over to her usual spot to warm up and was greeted by a host of other dancers offering their congratulations. A few seemed a bit jealous, but most told her they knew she would be selected because she had truly earned it. She had worked the hardest and had become the best in their class.

When the teacher entered the room she called the class to order and began to teach just like any other day. Sa could hardly contain her enthusiasm while Lek was still too confused to let it all sink in. When the class was just about over, the teacher finally acknowledged the winners to the rest of the students.

'I'm sure you have all seen the list by now and know who has been chosen to represent this class in Japan,' she began. 'It was a difficult choice. This is the best class I've ever taught and many of you earned the right to go. All of you have worked hard and progressed wonderfully. There will be more opportunities in the near future so I encourage all of you to keep trying. I'm sure that we will be able to place everyone somewhere soon enough.

'Right now I'd like to offer my sincerest congratulations to Lek and Sa. They proved themselves to be the best of the best. Good luck ladies. Make us proud,' she said.

The entire class erupted into a unanimous cheer. Sa ran over and hugged Lek who was still too stunned to allow herself to appreciate the moment. When the rest of the class filtered out of the room, Lek stayed behind to talk with her teacher. She had so many questions.

'How? Why?' she asked her.

'Never mind how. It's just that I couldn't let a silly background check get in the way of sending my best dancer. You did your part and earned it, Lek. Leave the rest to me.'

It was finally beginning to sink in. One of the first good things ever to happen to her in her entire life was actually becoming a reality. Lek could feel the excitement nearly bursting inside her.

She rushed straight home, ripped open the letter she had written to Om the day before and added her own terrific news.

For the rest of the afternoon Lek sat in her room and thought about the upcoming event and its possible ramifications. She had now come to a crossroads. Her two separate lives were tugging her in opposite directions. The only family she knew was made up of her 'sisters' at the bar. The thought of leaving them was not a happy one. She almost felt she would be betraying them if she left, even though she knew they wouldn't see it that way.

She finally convinced herself that it was just the fear of change that was bothering her. She'd had so many major changes in her young life, now that she had found a place where she was happy, Sexy Nights, she was having a hard time letting go.

In the end she decided that 30,000 baht a month salary without having to sleep with strangers, along with the travel and the fact that she had done it all on her own combined to make the opportunity too good to pass up.

CHAPTER 62

On 15 December, Lek went to her bank and withdrew 18,000 baht from her savings account and paid off six months rent in advance for her room, happy with the thought that she would have a home to come back to when she returned.

She then packed her suitcase with her best clothes and the three costumes she would be wearing when she performed. When she was done she prepared herself for her last night working at the bar.

When it was time to go, she looked around her room and became a little queasy. She hated long goodbyes and knew the night ahead would be full of them. Locking the door behind her, she made the short walk over to Nana Plaza.

Sexy Nights was positioned near the end of the walkway and it looked like a table covered with food and flowers had been set up outside the door. She could see *Mamasan* Nok and some of the dancers mingling with a handful of customers outside. All seemed to be smiling and eating.

As she moved closer, someone announced 'Here she is!' setting off a round of cheers. The announcement prompted Lek's co-workers to come running up to greet her. Each one gave her a big hug and put a flower lei around her neck. As she was led forward, she could see they'd had a large cake made with 'Congratulations Lek' inscribed in the icing. They had also catered a large table full of assorted food and had outdone themselves with the flower arrangements.

For the rest of the night, Lek was never left alone. She constantly had someone by her side talking with her about Japan and what they thought it would be like living there. Literally everyone in the bar bought her drinks and as closing time arrived, Lek had a stack of drink tickets to cash in as well as an enormous buzz. She was definitely having the time of her life and at least once every hour she would look over to the Buddha statue in the corner of the bar and thank it for allowing her to have her current stretch of good luck.

When the bar did close, Lek was led by a large group of well wishers over to a side street food stall where they ate until they were stuffed. That was followed by a march over to a nearby coffee shop where they ate even more, drank heavily and talked until the sun came up. Lek finally said her last goodbye and broke away from the crowd at around 6 a.m., knowing full well her friends would continue the party without her long after she had left.

Lek stumbled home to her room, set her alarm for noon and thanked Buddha for giving her the foresight to have already packed her things. Her flight was scheduled to leave at 4 p.m. and she knew she would need all the extra time she could find to try and sleep off what was sure to be a major hangover when she woke up.

Six hours later she slept right through her alarm, and was nearly late for the scheduled meeting with the rest of the dancers. Luckily, she arrived only 10 minutes late, and was there before her teacher.

She found the rest of the group without much trouble. They were all mingling around by themselves waiting on the teacher. Lek set her luggage down and said a quick hello, then ran into the bathroom to throw up.

She came out of the bathroom a few minutes later just in time to see the teacher arrive.

'May I have your attention, please,' she shouted to be heard above the noise of the busy airport lobby. 'I'm sorry I'm late, I hope you didn't have to wait too long.'

'She's always late for these things,' one of the other dancers said to Lek in a raspy voice. 'I think I'd faint if she ever came on time.'

Lek was a bit taken aback by the obvious disrespect this woman was showing her beloved teacher. She didn't offer a response. The other dancer smiled and shook her head. 'You will learn soon enough.'

'Since we are a little behind schedule we will have to hurry a bit so I'll try to make this brief,' the teacher continued.

'That will be a first,' the other dancer said to Lek.

Lek tilted her head to look at her yet still refused to respond.

'As most of you know, I won't be going on this trip,' Lek's neighbor said in unison with the teacher.

'Shh!' Lek scolded her. She didn't know the teacher wouldn't be going along and wanted to listen to find out all the other things she didn't know about.

'Once you arrive in Japan your contact at Narita airport will be Mr Fujimoto.' Lek was finally able to listen to her teacher without her neighbor's interruptions. 'He should be waiting for you there with a sign that reads: *Constellation Dance Troupe.* It will be in English so those of you who can read English should look for it and help those who can't.

'I'm going to start calling out names. When you hear your name come up and get your ticket, then proceed over to the baggage X-ray station. After that's done, go over and get yourselves checked in. I'll meet with you just outside the passport control area. If there are no questions, let's get started.'

'My name is Pin. Is this your first trip?' Lek's neighbor introduced herself as the teacher called out names.

'I'm Lek,' she answered. 'Yes, this is my first trip. What do X-ray and check-in mean?'

'You are new,' Pin said with a hint of exasperation. 'Don't worry. I'm an old pro. Stick with me. It's kind of a hassle but we'll get through it.'

After they picked up their tickets, Lek followed Pin through all the necessary steps to passport control where they were again met by their teacher.

'This is it ladies. Once you pass through those doors you are on your own until you get to Japan. Those of you with experience please try to help out the others.

'Remember, you are representatives of your country. Ambassadors of Thailand. Make us proud. Good luck to all of you. I'll see you in six months.'

When it was Lek's turn to have her passport and visa checked, the officer behind the desk looked at her passport, then at her, back at her passport and back at her. It seemed as though he was giving her strange looks and she began to get nervous. When she looked around, though, she noticed they were doing the same to everyone.

After a minute or two of flipping through pages and checking his computer, the officer mechanically asked her where she was going and what she intended to do. Apparently satisfied with her answers, he made a couple of stamps in her passport and waved her through.

The next thing she knew they were in the middle of a group of passengers that were being herded down a long gangway that led to the waiting jet. Once inside, Lek showed her boarding pass to the flight attendant and gave her a confused look. The stewardess smiled and led her directly to her seat. Moments later she was joined by Pin.

What seemed like only a few minutes after that, the jet taxied down the runway, gained speed and lifted into the air. As Lek watched out her window with amazement, she could see

Bangkok below her as she had never seen it before. It looked so small and far away. The image was fleeting, though, and soon gave way to water soaked rice fields before thick clouds engulfed the jet and robbed her of her view.

Looking around her, Lek noticed Pin had tilted her seat back. It looked so much more comfortable than sitting upright so Lek tried to figure out how to do it herself. She pushed and pulled the seat, but couldn't figure out how to get it to work. Just as she was about to give up, Pin finally noticed what she was trying to do and showed her how. In this position, with the hum of the engines and the lack of sleep from the night before, Lek was soon dreaming of faraway places.

She was awakened almost six hours later by a stewardess telling her they would be landing soon and she needed to put her seat back up in its upright position. Still groggy from sleep, Lek slowly complied, then looked out the window to see if she could get a glimpse of where she was.

Any view she might have had of the ground below was blocked out by a thick bank of clouds in the black of night. She became mesmerized by the eerie display the lights from the airplane produced as they illuminated the clouds rushing by.

Before long the clouds began to break up and she could see tiny lights dotting the dark land below. The plane landed moments later, and they disembarked.

Just as her teacher had promised, a short, well-dressed man with thick glasses and a sign that read Constellation Dance Troupe was waiting for them near the luggage pick up area. He spoke very little Thai and most of his instructions were given in English. Lek's previous job had taught her to speak the language well enough to enable her to translate to those few dancers who had trouble understanding him.

'Hello everyone. My name is Mr Fujimoto. Welcome to Japan,' he addressed them. 'We are most happy to have you here. There is a bus waiting outside to take you the rest of the way into Tokyo. Please pick up your luggage and follow me.'

As he led the dancers outside to the waiting bus, the first thing Lek noticed about Japan was how cold it was. It was mid-December and winter had not yet fully set in, but the temperature of the air was still colder than the drinks she used to serve in Sexy Nights.

The heating on the bus was intermittent at best and by the time they arrived in downtown Tokyo two hours later, Lek thought her toes were going to fall off. If it hadn't been for the excitement of being in a new country for the first time, the ride might have been unbearable.

It was mass confusion when they arrived at their hotel. Mr Fujimoto immediately scurried off to a back room someplace and left the dancers by themselves to unload their luggage and mill around in the lobby. None of them knew what was going on and conflicting rumors about what they were supposed to do spread fast.

The nine dancers that made up the Thai dance troupe soon split into two groups. The first group's consensus was to go ahead and check in by themselves. The other group agreed it would be better to wait until they were told what to do.

Mr Fujimoto reappeared about fifteen or twenty minutes later and handed the dancers keys and room assignments, giving merit to the group that had opted to wait. He instructed them to take their luggage to their rooms and get settled in. Since it was already 2.30 a.m. they should try and get some sleep. He announced there would be a meeting in the lobby at 11 a.m.

Three dancers were assigned to each room. The rooms were rather small and had a set of bunk beds, a single bed, two small closets, one desk with a chair and a mirror, and a small bathroom.

As it turned out, Lek's roommates were Sa and Pin. Lek and Sa shared one closet since Pin had seniority and wanted the other closet for herself. Having all that settled and out of the way, they hastily unpacked their nightclothes, took showers and went to bed.

CHAPTER 63

Mr Fujimoto was assisted by his wife when he called the meeting to order at a little past 11 the next morning.

'May I have your attention, please,' he began. 'Please settle down, we have a few things we need to go over before we take you in and introduce you to the other dance troupes.'

'Orientation time,' Pin leaned over and told Lek. Her voice was still raspy.

'Do you have a cold or something?' Lek asked her.

'Excuse me. Would you two like to conduct the meeting this morning?' Mr Fujimoto interrupted. All eyes were now focused on Lek and Pin.

'No, thank you. I'm sure you could do it much better,' Pin replied. Lek just bowed her head.

'Thank you for allowing me that. It was most kind of you,' Mr Fujimoto said sarcastically. 'Now, if I may continue, the club you will be working in is only a few blocks away. You will be escorted there nightly by approved staff members only. Our mini-buses leave every night at 7 p.m. sharp. I urge you to be on time.

'You will perform in two shows nightly. The first show will begin at 8 p.m. and the second at 11 p.m. Mrs Fujimoto will be in charge of scheduling which group will perform at which time during the program.' Mr Fujimoto pointed to his wife seated next to him. She responded with a quick bow.

'When you aren't performing you are urged to mingle with the audience. Part of our club's attraction to its customers is to give them a chance to meet the performers. To encourage you to do this you will be paid a commission for each drink a customer buys for you and each plate of food they order while you sit with them. This will be payable at the end of the night and is yours to do with as you wish.

'Tonight all nine of you will perform. Starting tomorrow night only eight of you will be on stage at a time. This will give each of you three nights off a month on a rotating schedule, once every nine nights. During the daytime when you're not working as well as when you have a night off you will be allowed to do only one of three things. Either stay in your rooms, go on an organized tour or go out only when you are escorted by an approved staff member. There will be no exceptions. Immigration laws here are stringent, but more importantly, we don't want to have a difficult time keeping track of you. Any questions?'

After a short question and answer period, the meeting broke up around noon. The Thai dancers were then led into the hotel restaurant for lunch and to mingle with some of the dancers from the other countries who also performed in the nightly shows. There were no formal seating arrangements and the dancers were encouraged to sit with people they didn't know.

Lek, Sa and Pin stuck together, not only to try and get to know each other better, but for security, too. They found three empty seats at a large table that looked to them as though it had a good mix of nationalities. After introducing themselves, they discovered they were sitting with two dancers from Malaysia, three from the Philippines, and one blonde woman from Brazil. English turned out to be the common language amongst them. As each nationality had a different accent, at times it was difficult to understand what was being said.

The dancers they sat with had been working in Japan for at least a month or two already. All had signed six month contracts and told the Thais that when their contracts finished, more dancers from their home countries would arrive soon after they left to replace them. All seemed to have liked the group of Thais that had just left a few days earlier and were looking forward to working with the new group.

The conversation was rather dull and formal until Maria, the solo dancer from Brazil, began to loosen them up with anecdotes from her work at the club. Lek took a liking to her immediately because of her animated personality and wild stories. She especially liked the way Maria rolled her R's when she talked. Each time she did it, Lek would do an exaggerated imitation of her. Sa was quite embarrassed by Lek's fun but the others laughed and Maria actually enjoyed Lek's sense of humor. The two hit it off instantly.

When the luncheon finished Maria followed Lek, Pin and Sa up to their room where the four sat around and talked for a couple of hours. Maria did most of the talking and kept the Thais entertained for most of the afternoon with stories about Brazil and the wild parties she had attended in Rio. Pin and Sa didn't have much to contribute but Lek told stories about life in Bangkok.

Maria took her leave around 4 p.m. to go and join her roommates. Just after she left, a bored Sa turned on the television. Lek and Pin watched as she flipped through the channels trying to find something interesting, only to find all the programming was in Japanese, which none of them could understand. The three decided their time would be better spent getting to know each other.

Sa started off by announcing she had been born and raised in Bangkok.

'My *Por* owns a big woodworking shop over near Pratunam. I don't go there very much because *Mae* says I should stay away from the people who work there. She said they are dangerous because they were living on the streets before *Por* gave them a job. They seem okay to me, though, but what *Mae* wants, *Mae* gets.'

Lek bit her lower lip. She had met the same type of people as Sa's mother when she was living on the streets. She didn't see them often and figured it was because they probably spent most of their time locked up in their beautiful homes afraid to venture out lest some of the dirt from the city should stain their perfect souls.

'What kind of things do they make there?' Pin asked. She noticed Lek's strange reaction but let it pass without comment.

'Hand carved wooden tables, chests, bars and things,' Sa replied as if everyone should know about what had so dominated her sheltered life. 'We sell most of them to people from foreign countries. *Por* has regular buyers from Germany and America who own shops to sell them. I'm not supposed to know this and I probably shouldn't tell you, but I was left alone in the office one day and I managed to sneak a peek at the real books. You know, the ones we don't show to the tax people. The most expensive thing we sell costs us about 1,000 baht to make. We sell it for over 50,000 baht! The cheapest thing we sell goes for about 10,000 baht.'

'The rich get richer and the poor struggle to survive,' Lek muttered.

'Where do you live?' Pin asked Sa. She could tell the conversation was bothering Lek and tried to change its course.

'We have a big house off Sukhumvit Road. We have two full-time cooks and four servants who all live in cottages out back. We've a big yard, a swimming pool, two Mercedes Benz, a red one and a yellow one, both with drivers, and ...'

'Dream life,' Lek interrupted her.

'Not really. It's all so boring,' Sa complained. 'Everyone tries to act so perfect all the time. I don't have any real friends, only the one's I'm supposed to have because they're like us. What I'm doing here in Japan is a dream life come true for me.'

'Me, too. But for different reasons,' Pin stated.

'Yeah, tell us about you,' Lek urged her. She was getting weary of Sa's poor little rich girl story.

'Well, I live with my mother, three sisters and four brothers in a small house not too far from the school. My parents split up about five years ago when *Mae* found out that *Por* had a mistress. It probably would have been okay. Lots of women put up with their husbands having minor wives and stay with them just to keep the family together. But when *Por* found out *Mae* knew, I guess it must have taken the fun out of having one. He made up his mind that living with the younger woman would be a more attractive lifestyle than living with us. So he left. Too bad for him, though. The younger woman left him after only a couple of months living together. I figure she probably had a younger man on the side all along and was just using *Por* for his money. It must have cramped her style when *Por* moved in with her.

'Anyway, he's been trying to get back with *Mae* ever since. *Mae's* great, we love her. She won't take him back. She told him, "you made your bed now you have to sleep in your own stained sheets," she said.

'He will do anything to get back with her now. He agreed to send me to dance school just to please her but it backfired on him. Since I got this job I make more money than he does and I can support my whole family. Now that *Mae* doesn't need to worry about money she doesn't have to take him back. He's probably angry with himself for sending me to school. He can't seem to win, no matter what he does. I mean, he keeps doing things to please *Mae* and they keep backfiring. I wouldn't even have been able to go to dance school if he hadn't agreed to pay for my sex change.'

'What?' Lek and Sa said in unison.

'Don't worry. I've had all my hormone shots and the operation is complete. I really am a woman now.'

'Oh my ... No ... You used to be a boy?' Sa said, completely aghast.

'I should have known,' Lek said smiling. 'Your voice. That's wonderful. I have many friends who have had the operation.'

'Yeah? Well, I'm a lot happier now. It was a mistake of nature to be born a boy in the first place. I just righted a wrong. With the help of medicine, of course.'

'You don't have to justify it with me,' Lek reassured her. 'You are who you are no matter what you are. A person is defined by their heart not their gender.'

'I thought you would understand, Lek. You seem a little different to the other dancers.' Pin threw a glance over at Sa who was still transfixed in a dumbfounded stare. Pin looked back at Lek and asked, 'Why is that? What's your story?'

'Uh-hem,' Lek cleared her throat. She had been dreading talking about herself, but now that Pin had revealed her shocking secret, she thought it might not be so bad to tell her story.

'I have no family. I'm an orphan. I've been a lot of places and done a lot of things trying to grow up and survive on my own. I've met a lot of good people along the way but nothing ever seems to last. Somehow I ended up in Bangkok going to dance school and now, here I am.'

'You're being awfully vague. What was it you did in Bangkok to support yourself while you went to school?' Pin asked.

'Let's just say I worked in the tourism trade. I was a guide of sorts. I showed our foreign visitors around Bangkok and made sure their stay was a pleasant one,' she said.

'I thought so,' Pin said, with a knowing smile and a nod of her head. 'I've been there and know exactly what you're talking about.'

'What?' Sa interjected. Every bit of the conversation went over her head and it was making her dizzy.

'Never mind, Sa. We will explain it to you later,' Pin replied. 'Right now it's almost six o'clock. We have to get ready for work.'

The announcement caused both Lek and Sa to sit straight up and take a deep breath. Their first night of work in Japan was slowly creeping up on them.

'Don't worry. It will be easy. You have already done the hard part just to get here. The rest is fun,' Pin told them when she saw their reaction. It hadn't been so long since her first night of work in a foreign country that she couldn't remember the initial fear it caused.

'Why don't you two get your costumes ready while I take a shower?'

'Good idea,' Lek said and the tedious process of primping and preparing for work was set in motion.

A little before 7 p.m., someone knocked on their door. 'Hurry it up in there. The vans will be leaving soon.' All three quickly gathered their things and headed for the lobby to meet up with the other dancers.

The trip from the hotel to the club was short and soon they were all herded through the back door, down a short hallway and into a medium sized dressing room that became a lot smaller when it was filled with dancers trying to change into their outfits.

Confusion reigned as they hurriedly changed, applied makeup and halfheartedly attempted to practice some of their dance steps in the crowded dressing room. Mrs Fujimoto popped her head through the door and announced, 'The Philippine dancers will be the first to go on tonight. The show starts in five minutes so get ready and get in place as soon as possible. In other words, NOW!'

After the Filipinas rushed by her to move into position, she announced, 'The Thai dancers will be next. As soon as you're ready, go out and stand in the wings. When the Filipinas are done the curtain will go down and you should waste no time taking your positions on stage.' She then left to prepare the Philippine dancers for the raising of the curtain.

Fifteen minutes later, the Thai contingent gathered themselves and walked out to the waiting area. Each one was pacing around back stage with opening night jitters. Sa told Lek she thought she was going to throw up. Lek could only nod her head, she was too nervous to respond.

Just before 8.30 p.m. the curtain went down on the Philippine dancers and they rushed off stage to get out of the Thai dance troupe's way.

Nine Thai dancers with their bright golden costumes ran out and took their positions on the dimly lit stage. Within seconds the curtain rose and the spotlights hit their targets. Lek stood still in the front row, too nervous to move.

When the music started, Lek's instincts and training took over. Her legs and hands moved automatically and perfectly. Together, all nine dancers performed as one.

CHAPTER 64

Although mangoes grow throughout the year, in Thailand the largest crops ripen in late January or early February, often when temperatures begin to approach their yearly highs. Just as the mangoes are ready to harvest, the rains come. For two weeks in the middle of the hot season, people can expect daily showers and thunderstorms to cool things off, at least temporarily. This reprieve from the heat is seen by some as an omen that positive changes, although often temporary, are on the way.

While Nid never forgot about her search, she didn't call the police as often as she used to. When the mango rains reached their peak in 1992, change was in the wind and she rang the police station in Bangkok once more.

'May I speak with Officer Wichai, please?' She was all too familiar with the routine that followed. Her call was transferred several times to different offices before she was finally connected with her intended party.

'This is Officer Wichai. How may I help you?'

'This is Nid Sawang. I'm just checking in to see if you have any news for me.'

'Nid? Yes. I have been trying to reach you. I think we might have something here. Can you come up to the station?'

'What have you got?'

'It may be nothing. A woman who goes by the name of Lek who fits your daughter's description applied for a new identification card. If you have the time, I think you ought to come up here and check it out.'

'I'll be there in a couple of hours.'

Nid called for her driver as soon as she hung up the phone. He initially didn't hear her because he was fast asleep in the garage. When Nid found him and started screaming at him to hurry, he knew he'd better comply. And quickly. Nid never acted that way toward anyone, not even her employees. One time she caught him drunk before he was scheduled to drive her into town and he thought for sure it would be the end of his job. Even then she hadn't gotten angry with him. Now she looked like a woman possessed and he knew he had better sharpen up.

At her urging, he broke every speed limit along the way and made it to Bangkok in record time, despite the wet, sometimes slippery conditions. When they pulled up in front of the police station, Nid apologized for being so rough on him and explained that it could be a very important meeting. He knew then that something had come up concerning her missing daughter.

Officer Wichai was ready and waiting for her when Nid entered his office. 'I'm sorry about all this but I've been very busy lately and it took a long time for this to come across my desk,' he apologized as he handed her a photocopy of an application form for an identification card.

'It's her!' Nid exclaimed when she saw the picture attached to it.

'After looking at the ID you gave me before I'm inclined to agree. It's a little old, though. If you check the date you will notice she made out the application more than a year ago. I'm sorry it took so long for me to get it. Believe me, it wasn't for lack of trying. It's not my job to screen applications but you made an impression on me when you were in here last time.

'How did you ever find this, then?'

'I was bragging to a couple of my buddies about you the other day,' he said sheepishly. 'I told them I knew you from when you came in looking for your daughter. I always keep a copy of Lek's ID you gave me to prove it and I was showing it off. One of my friends works in the records department and part of his job is screening applications. When I told him the idea you had about how she might come in here for a new ID, he said it was a little slow in his office and he'd check around for me. This is what he came up with. If I'd only known, I would have checked with him sooner. Like I said, it's been busy in my department. We don't have the luxury of much free time to search records.'

'You're wonderful. Thank you. Does it say anywhere on here where she was going to work?'

'It sure does but I don't think you're going to like it. Right down near the bottom of the page it says we approved her application for an ID last year to work at a bar called Sexy Nights in the Nana Entertainment Plaza on Sukhumvit Soi 4. It's a go-go bar. Maybe she's a barkeeper or something,' he said.

'It doesn't matter as long as I can find her. I've waited a long time for this moment and I want to thank you for all you've done. How can I ever repay you?'

'Don't thank me yet. She might not be there any more. If she isn't, you'll probably hate me for not finding this sooner,' he remarked.

'Even if she isn't there I'm sure this is recent enough that someone will know where she went or how to find her.'

When Nid left the police station and rushed outside, she found her driver standing to attention holding her door open. She jumped into the back seat and couldn't help but think how comical it was, the way her poor driver was reacting to the way she had yelled at him earlier in the day. He never even flinched when she told him to hurry over to Nana Entertainment Plaza.

He pulled the car past the open air bars at the entrance to the ground level of Nana Plaza and into a parking spot under an overhang. It took Nid a few minutes of looking before she found Lek's bar and when she finally did, it wasn't yet open. So, she walked back down the stairs and took up a position on a stool of one of the open air bars below.

The bartender informed her the go-go bars usually didn't open until 8 p.m.

It wasn't long before people began to recognize Nid. Her quiet little drink was soon interrupted by a swarm of onlookers. With all the people gathered around, Nid's previously unobstructed view vanished.

Realizing the impossibility of her situation, she graciously excused herself, climbed back into her car and told her driver to try and find a quiet spot where they might be able to eat something without being a part of a mob.

Nid returned to Nana Plaza at 8 p.m. With an extra effort, she managed to make her way up to Sexy Nights without being noticed. Once inside, though, she was almost immediately recognized. Although not many customers had arrived, there was a full compliment of dancers who seemed nervous and scared to approach her.

Not seeing Lek anywhere, Nid asked one of the dancers to tell her where the proprietor might be. The chosen dancer giggled nervously as she led Nid to an office in a back room behind the bar. A woman slightly older than Nid was bent over with her back turned to the door picking up papers she had dropped on the floor. She didn't notice Nid come in and was swearing at her clumsiness.

When she did realize someone else was in the room, she turned around quickly to apologize for her rudeness. Both women's eyes bulged when they saw who they were looking at. The *mamasan* was Nid's older sister Nok, who she hadn't seen since the foreigner took her out of the *songh* in Surin over twenty years ago.

'Nid? What are you doing in here?' Nok recognized her immediately.

'Nok? Never mind me, what are you doing in here?'

Nok screamed. The two women dropped everything they had in their hands and ran over to embrace each other.

'I didn't think I would ever see you again. Where have you been all these years?' Nid demanded, tears streaming down her face.

'It's a long story,' Nok said as she cleared away a stack of papers from a chair so Nid would have a place to sit. She then turned to the dancer who had escorted Nid into her office. 'Go out to the bar and bring back a bottle of the best spirits we have in stock.'

'Where do I begin?' Nok said when she turned back to Nid.

'You could begin with what happened to you and that foreigner who took you away from Surin.'

'Jack? He was a wonderful man. He brought me here to Bangkok and tried to make sure I was taken care of. He was just a friend trying to help a person in need, nothing more and nothing less. He tried to buy me a passport and a visa to come work for him as a maid in America but I was too young.'

'Why didn't he marry you? He could have gotten you a passport then, couldn't he?' Nid asked.

'It wasn't like that. He was already married with two children. We were never lovers or anything like that, we were just friends. I'm not sure why he chose to help me, but I'm glad he did. His heart was as big as the sky. He sent me money for years to help me get set up. I saved all of it and eventually I was able to buy this place. It's not making me rich but it provides me with a comfortable living.'

'What about his wife? Didn't she mind him sending you money?'

'Not at all. She was a good person, too. I even received letters from her every once in a while. Jack had told her what the situation was like over here and she wanted to help, too. She understood that there was never any funny business,' she said.

'So, with the money they sent you, you were able to buy this place? They didn't mind the fact that you used the money to buy a go-go bar?' Nid asked.

'Actually I never told them. All I said was that I had started my own business. With the money this place has brought in I was able to pay them back. I finished a couple of years ago. It was one of the greatest feelings I've ever had when I put that last payment in the mail. I don't hear from them much anymore. They have probably found another lost cause somewhere to try and help.'

'I always wondered what happened to you. Back in the *songh* we used to dream that you were living in a big house somewhere in America.'

'No, I've been right here in Bangkok. It wasn't easy. The hardest part was leaving you in Surin. I felt terrible about it. I tried to get Jack to go back and get you but he said that there was no way they would let him back in after what he did for me,' she said.

'He was right. They called him every name in the book after you two didn't return. They even talked for a while about hiring a cheap gun to track you down and shoot you. We all thought it was just their way of scaring us out of trying to escape. None of us ever believed they would actually do it but we worried just the same.'

The door to the office creaked slowly open and the young woman who had shown Nid into the office peeked her head inside. When Nok waved her over she brought in a bottle of Chivas, a bucket of ice and two glasses. Constantly smiling and dipping her head, she filled the glasses with ice and poured both women a drink. The two women were engulfed with emotions. They were overcome by joy and happiness, but also despair for all the years they had lost.

'I thought about you often back in that pit of hell all by yourself, Nid. I wanted to get you out of there but I was afraid to return by myself because of what I thought they would probably do to me. I did go back about ten years ago even though I knew you were long gone.'

'You did? I went back there, too. Do you know what happened to the place?'

'I heard something about the police chief catching a social disease from one of the girls there. Is that what you heard?'

'Yes, fitting isn't it? They used and abused us until they finally got what they had coming to them, then they shut the place down.'

'Yes, well, I shouldn't talk. I have women working for me that go home with customers every night.'

'It's different here,' Nid said philosophically. 'The women working here aren't slaves and since you went through what you did in the *songh* I'm sure you don't treat them that way. They work here of their own free will and do so because it's about the only way they can get themselves and their families out of total poverty. We did it because we were sold into it by our mother. I have to tell you that when I finally escaped I came here to Bangkok and worked out of a coffee shop for a couple of years. Speaking of our mother, I've never been back there. Have you?'

'Yes, I went back about five years ago. Did you know she died?'

'It serves her right after what she did to us,' muttered Nid.

'Don't be that way, Nid. Do you remember our brother Somsak? He has taken over the farm and he told me *Mae* thought we went off to be maids, not to work in a brothel. He said that for years *Mae* stuck up for us in front of the townsfolk who used to tell her and our family that we were whores. I told Somsak that *Mae* was right, that we were maids. I didn't want him to think any less of us.' Nok sighed then quickly changed the subject. 'Now look at you. A big star.'

'Are you trying to tell me that you knew all along where I was and never came to tell me you were okay?'

'Sure I knew. I followed your career since your first album just like everyone else. But I wasn't like everyone else because I knew the famous Nid Sawang was my sister. I watched your rise to stardom from inside my bar, never able to say anything to anyone about who you were and what you meant to me. It's been tough at times,' said Nok.

'Why didn't you come forward and talk to me? I can't believe you knew all these years and you never gave me the peace of mind knowing where you were and that you were okay,' Nid responded.

'I did it for you, little sister. I didn't want to ruin your career. Do you think the bigwigs would have given you a break if they knew your sister ran a go-go bar?'

'Maybe it was noble of you to think that way but your fears were unfounded. I worked hard and earned what I became. No one has ever asked me where I came from and I never volunteered the information. I don't think it would have made any difference. If I'd only known where you were I could have shared my success with you and you could have helped me by being a needed friend and sister.'

'How did you find me?' Nok asked.

'Actually, I didn't know you would be here. Do you know this girl?' Nid handed her Lek's picture.

'Sure. That's Lek. She used to work here. Why do you ask?'

'Damn it! You mean she doesn't work here now?'

'Not any more. Why?'

'She's my daughter. I've been trying to find her ever since she was stolen from me as a baby. The police finally came up with her application to work here and that's why I came. I always get so close but I've never been able to be in the same place at the same time.'

'Are you trying to tell me that our Lek is your daughter? Is she the Lek in your song?'

'That's her.'

'I always thought that song was just someone's creative imagination. I never knew you had a daughter and that the song was real. It makes sense, though. Lek is always talking about how she never had a family and how she has adopted us to fill in.'

'You mean you still talk to her? Do you know where she is?'

'She's working as a Thai dancer in some dinner club in Japan. Tokyo, I think. You should be proud of her. She worked very hard to become the best student in her class. Her work was rewarded by her selection to an elite team of dancers that went to Japan a couple of months ago. She never did say what the name of her school was or how to get in contact with her, but don't worry. Her contract is for only six months. She will be back in June and I'm sure she will come straight here to tell us all about it. Now that I know about you two I'll make sure you get together this time.'

'June is still four months away. Are you sure there is no way I can contact her before then? After all the times I've been this close before only to miss her, I don't want it to happen again,' said Nid.

'I wish I'd known sooner. I would have found out for you before she left. That's a silly thought, isn't it? If I knew before she left, you two would have been together already. Anyway, she called here last month to say hello. If she calls again I will make sure to have her call you,' Nok promised.

'Thanks, Nok. It's so good to see you and know that you are doing well. Why don't you take some time off and come stay with me in Hua Hin? I have a great place on the beach and I'm sure you would love it. I'd love to have you around, too. It gets so lonely there sometimes.'

'I'd really like that. But now is not a good time. It's very busy and I want to be around in case Lek calls again. After she gets back the three of us can get together for a few days. Right now let's just have another drink and celebrate our reunion.'

'Good idea.'

CHAPTER 65

Nid rented a suite in the Nana Hotel across the street and spent the next few days visiting Nok. After the initial shock of seeing each other for the first time in over twenty years, the two almost immediately returned to being as close as they were before time and fate had separated them for so long. It was almost as if the gap in time had never existed.

On her third night in Bangkok, Nid arranged to have dinner with Officer Wichai and his wife.

'Did you find Lek?' Wichai wanted to know.

'No, not yet. I know where she is, though. She's working in Japan.'

'I'm sorry to hear that. Will you be going to Japan to find her?'

'No, I don't know her address and I don't have any way to find her. Not to worry, though. She will be back in June and I'm sure I will be able to catch up with her then. Besides, you'll never guess what happened. The information you gave me led me straight to my sister Nok. I haven't seen her in 20 years. You really are a hero. I don't know how I can ever thank you enough,' Nid said.

'I'm no hero. I should have gotten the information to you a lot sooner. You owe me nothing,' the officer retorted.

'Nonsense. You have led me to two of the most important people of my past. Your diligence has changed my life.'

'Thanks. Tell that to my boss,' Wichai said and chuckled. 'You've already made me a hero with my wife.'

On the fourth day of Nid's stay, she began to feel as if her presence was hindering operations at the bar. She got to know the young women that worked in Sexy Nights and enjoyed being around them, but noticed they were spending more time with her than with the customers. Business began to drop off somewhat and since Lek wasn't due back for another four months, Nid decided it would be better for everyone if she took her leave.

Despite Nok's insistence that her presence was not a problem, Nid said a tearful goodbye to her sister and promised she wouldn't let nearly so much time pass before they could be reunited.

She spent the next few months pacing her empty house, impatiently waiting for June. A person with wealth and prestige can do many things, but time can neither be bought nor hurried. She spent many an hour sitting on her veranda listening to the sea, but the waves that gently lapped the shore were little comfort for her growing impatience.

She called the bar often to talk with Nok and to find out if she had heard any news from Lek. It was always the same; nothing yet. Nid should have been accustomed to it after having spent so much of her life waiting. This time, deep down inside her heart, she knew it might be her last chance to find Lek.

Her staff gave her a wide berth because they could see the toll the helpless situation was taking on her. Her moods became erratic. One moment she would snap at her staff for the smallest reason, the next moment she would apologize and buy them gifts. More than once she ordered her driver to prepare the car for a trip to Bangkok only to cancel moments later.

She spent many long hours at her piano, trying to immerse herself with writing more songs. It was good therapy, but she was so distracted by her thoughts of Lek and Nok she couldn't concentrate. As a result, she started a handful of new songs that she never finished. She finally gave in and stopped trying.

At the urging of her maid, Nid took on a project to help pass the time. She refurbished two of her spare bedrooms, one for Lek and the other for Nok. It was the perfect endeavor as it enabled her to feel as though she was doing something positive instead of waiting around doing nothing.

She put her heart and soul into the project, sparing no expense. She painted the walls, put in new beds, built new closets, installed new dressers and coordinated it all with new bed linen and curtains. The project was completed by late May.

On 10 June, Nid could wait no more. She once again ordered her driver to prepare the car for a trip to Bangkok and this time she actually went. After checking into a hotel, she went over to Nana Plaza and into Nok's Sexy Nights Bar.

'Lek called last night,' Nok greeted her at the door. 'She said she will be back on the sixteenth. That's next week!'

'That's great news! What did she say? Was she happy? Did you tell her I was here?'

'I'm afraid I wasn't here when she called. The bartender took the call and neglected to say anything about you. Lek still doesn't know.'

Nid looked disappointed initially but soon a smile crept across her face. 'That's okay. We will just have to make it a surprise.'

This time Nok's eyes lit up. 'Lek loves surprises. This will be great. Some of the girls suggested we have a coming home party for her, similar to the going away party we threw.'

'Good idea. Let's throw the biggest and best coming home party anyone could ever imagine!'

For the rest of the week, Nid spent every night in Sexy Nights. She became friends with all the women who worked there and sat for hours listening to stories about her daughter. It made her proud that Lek had been accepted so well by her friends and co-workers. She felt as if she was getting to know her, even without having seen her for such a long time.

When 16 June finally arrived, Nid and Nok spent the early afternoon getting everything ready for the party. Nok wanted to help with the expenses but Nid insisted that since it was her daughter and it was going to be such a special night, she would foot the entire bill.

They decorated the bar both inside and out with dozens of roses, carnations and tropical flora. Buckets were strategically placed around the bar and filled with ice and bottles of champagne. It was the dual meaning of the large cake with WELCOME HOME LEK written in the icing that Nid took the most pride in. Not only would Lek think it meant welcome home to her friends at the bar, but when she found out Nid was her mother it would mean welcome to her real home, too.

When they finished at about 6 p.m. the place was transformed from a bar into a tropical paradise. Everything was ready to go two hours before opening time even though no one knew for sure exactly when, or even if, Lek would arrive. Both Nid and Nok were nervous wrecks and were only able to take solace in the fact that tension loves company.

The two women sat inside the bar sipping cola, not wanting to spoil the night by getting drunk in case Lek did arrive. Time was still their unrelenting enemy. All they could do now was wait and hope.

CHAPTER 66

The sixteenth of June 1992 was an indescribably beautiful late spring, early summer day in Tokyo, Japan. The sun shone brightly, unobstructed by even a single cloud in the sky. The temperature outside Lek's hotel was comfortably warm, not nearly as overbearingly hot as it tends to be in Bangkok at that time of year.

Pin and Sa were out running around somewhere in the hotel saying goodbye to all their friends. This left Lek alone to do her last minute packing and reflect upon the experiences she had lived over the past six months. Tokyo had been good to her. It had introduced her to some fun people who she was sure would become lifelong friends. It had also given her valuable experience performing professionally on stage.

Lek took Maria's picture out of her purse and tried to read the address Maria had scribbled on the back.

Thinking about Maria induced Lek to remember Om as well. She wondered if Om had delivered her baby. It had been almost seven months since Om had written to tell her she was already two months along. If she hadn't had it yet it should be any day now. Maybe there would be a letter waiting in Bangkok informing her whether it was a boy or a girl.

Lek had developed an affinity for the Japanese. She could identify with the hard work they always seemed to be involved in. Once they allowed themselves to settle down and enjoy their free time they were the friendliest and most gracious people Lek had ever met.

She began to think about the men that frequented the club. Most who had asked her to join them at their table were big spending successful business types. One regular customer of hers was the head of the local Yakuza. Although the other dancers were scared of him, to Lek he was just a nice old man who enjoyed her company. None of the men were allowed to take the dancers out of the club with them, and although many tried, Lek's Yakuza friend never asked for special favors and never complained.

Lek was gazing out the window, lost in thought at a little before noon, when Pin and Sa returned to the room. Their laughing and joking brought her back to the reality of where she was and the time that was now at hand.

'It's almost time,' Pin announced in her gravely voice.

'*Chai Yo!*' Sa screamed as she flopped on Pin's bed. 'I love Japan but I can't wait to get back home and tell my family all about it.'

'Me too,' Pin said. 'It's always fun to go home. Everyone treats you like a heroine. And the food! I really miss Thai food. When I get back I'm going to eat for days.'

'My mouth is watering already,' Sa added. 'What are you going to do when you get back, Lek?'

Lek had been watching her roommates' excitement with amusement. She thought a moment about what she might do upon her return to Bangkok. She had no family to return to but she did have plenty of friends.

'Tonight I'm going to take a long hot shower in my own room, then curl up with my stuffed animals and sleep. Tomorrow I'm going to wake up late, go down to the bank and find out about my new found wealth that should be waiting for me after working here for six months.'

'Ah, money only means anything if you don't have any,' Sa commented.

Lek and Pin both gave her a condescending look. Each knew what it was like to be poor and both knew that Sa had never been in that position.

'After that,' Lek continued, ignoring Sa's comment, 'I'm going to go find my friends and get drunk.'

'Sounds like a good idea,' Pin agreed.

Sa looked at them both and shook her head. Obviously she had never been drunk and didn't think it proper for women to consider it.

'And then,' Lek continued, 'I'm going to go to the school and sign up to do this again. Maybe after a couple more trips doing this I will be able to save enough money to start my own business.'

'What would you do?' Sa now sounded interested.

'Who knows? Maybe I'll buy my own bar. I'll figure something out,' she said.

'You sound like I did when I first started,' Pin said. 'Japan does that to you. You always dream big in Japan but you always seem to wake up when you get back to Bangkok.'

'I've got an idea,' Sa announced. 'Let's practice together while we're waiting for the next assignment. You can come over to my house. It has a big room with a stereo and plenty of space to dance.'

'That sounds like a good plan. What do you think, Lek?' Pin asked.

'It sounds like fun. Do you think it will be okay with your family?'

'No problem. I'm sure they would love to meet you.'

A knock on the door ended the girls' conversation.

'Time to go,' a voice announced from the other side.

All three women grabbed their luggage, checked the room one more time in case they forgot something, then joined the others waiting in the lobby downstairs.

Under the supervision of the Fujimotos, the Thai contingent boarded the bus that would take them to the airport. Not without the mass confusion that usually goes with trying to coordinate the moving of a group of people, they managed to get underway shortly past noon.

The road leading out of downtown Tokyo was extremely crowded and slow moving. Once they were out in the countryside, however, the pace quickened. The beautiful scenery of the surrounding area kept the travelers occupied and made for a pleasant journey to Narita airport.

What impressed Lek most about the view outside of Tokyo were the occasional Buddhist temples set up on the hillsides overlooking the towns around them. Although the architecture of the buildings was different to the temples in Thailand, the large Buddha statues that dominated their grounds were very similar to the ones in her home country.

Thai Airways lifted off the runway at 4 p.m. sharp. Lek set her watch back two hours and calculated that the six hour flight would put her back in Bangkok at around 8 p.m. Bangkok time. She then adjusted her seat where she felt most comfortable and instructed her neighbor how to do the same. It didn't matter that her neighbor already knew how, she was just showing off her knowledge of the idiosyncrasies of flying.

As the massive 747 glided gently through the air, Lek sat back and thought about how much fun it was going to be to see all her friends at Sexy Nights. She wondered if they had something special planned for her return just like they had when she left. She decided it was a silly thought. The bartender she talked to last week was new and didn't even know her. Chances were, no one knew she was coming home.

It didn't matter. The women she worked with at Sexy Nights had always been very close and had become the best substitute for a family she'd ever had. They shared their hopes and dreams, their successes and failures, in both good times and bad. Lek was especially close to *Mamasan* Nok, as she had become somewhat of a surrogate mother. She could hardly wait to get back and tell them about her exploits in Japan.

Nonetheless it was still always in the back of her mind that even though they were as close as they were, there was still a big difference between them. Each of them had a real family to go back to if the need arose. Even if they weren't accepted by their family, as is often the case with the women who work in bars, they at least knew where they came from.

Lek couldn't understand why she still thought about it. She had given up hope of finding her real family a long time ago. She dared dream big enough to allow herself to escape the confines of her restricted existence, to realize the potential of her own abilities and explore the opportunities that led her to foreign lands, but she didn't dare dream big enough to find her roots.

She knew that by thinking about it she was only torturing herself. Yet, for some unknown reason during this flight home, it was a nagging thought. Maybe she was just tired or maybe it was the fact that she was returning to her home country but not to a home.

CHAPTER 67

Just as Lek had predicted, the jet touched down on the runway at Don Muang International Airport in Bangkok at 8 p.m. Once inside the terminal, Lek noticed the long lines the foreigners had to wait in to have their passports checked and marveled at how quickly the residents were swept through the stopping point. It didn't matter a great deal as all the passengers were forced to battle for position as they waited for their luggage to appear on the revolving pick-up belt.

Once it finally arrived and everyone had their luggage safely in hand, all the dancers passed through customs quickly and were greeted on the other side of the exit doors by the dance instructor from Lek's school. She gathered them together in one corner of the airport lobby to give them a speech.

'If you will all follow me, I will arrange transportation home for everyone,' she said as she led the dancers over to the public taxi queue at the south end of the airport terminal. With a little effort, she managed to secure a taxi for all.

'I'm going to miss you two,' Lek said as she hugged Pin and Sa.

'No need. We're going to keep in touch anyway,' Pin countered, even though she knew the chances of that happening were slim at best.

'Yeah, we have each other's addresses and phone numbers. I'll call both of you next week to see if you want to come over and practice,' Sa added.

'Okay, we'll do that,' Lek replied. 'Bye for now, then.'

Lek's taxi dropped her off in front of her apartment building just after 9 p.m. It felt as though it had been a long time since she had passed through the glass doors leading into the lobby downstairs, and indeed it had. The receptionist working the desk was new and gave Lek a strange look as she struggled to get her luggage over to the elevator. Lek paid her no heed, she would get used to seeing her around. Lek had neither the energy nor the patience to introduce herself at that particular time.

It was the same slow elevator that took Lek up to the fifth floor, she had no trouble remembering that. Once again she struggled to drag her luggage down the hallway. She slid her key into the lock of the door that read E-4 and was only a little surprised that it still worked. When she pushed it open and turned on the light, she was greeted by a dusty and musty smelling room. Other than that, it was the same as she had left it.

She dragged her bags inside and flopped down on her bed. It was a familiar feeling that she liked very much. Did she want to leave it and go over to the bar to see her friends tonight? She was quite worn out from the trip. Maybe she would take a shower and see how she felt afterward, but right now she didn't feel much like going anywhere.

When she finished her shower, Lek put on a loose fitting set of clothes and crawled on top of her bed again. She curled around her pillow and thought about how little energy she had. She wasn't even sure if she had enough to go downstairs and check her mail. She couldn't think of anything that might be happening that necessitated her presence that evening. It could all wait until the morning.

As Lek lay on her bed and looked around her room she realized it was the first time in months that she had been completely alone. She had no friends in the next room, none down the hall and she shared her room with no one. There would be no one knocking on her door or joining her for the night. She couldn't decide whether she liked that idea or not, for she had grown accustomed to having people around and suddenly everything seemed so quiet.

Maybe she could muster up enough energy to go over and have just one drink with her friends. Maybe, just maybe, the new bartender she had talked to on the phone last week had remembered to tell someone that she would be coming home today. If she had then perhaps they might be wondering about her. Lek dragged herself up off the bed, changed into more presentable clothes and began the walk over to Sexy Nights.

As she entered the lower level of the Nana Plaza Entertainment Complex, Lek noticed that nothing much had changed there, either. The same open-air bars crowded what used to be the parking lot. The same loud music that boomed out of all the bars merged into an incomprehensible buzz that saturated the area. The same white railing that guarded the steps to the second floor still needed to be painted. The first bar at the top of the stairs had the same older women sitting in front of it looking bored, only showing signs of life when a foreigner wandered by.

What wasn't the same was what Lek saw when she reached the top of the stairs and looked down the walkway toward the entrance to Sexy Nights. Either they were trying to change their image or there was a party going on because the entrance was nearly buried in flowers. As she slowly walked toward the scene, Lek began to realize that it was indeed a party. She didn't think it was for her because the decorations were so extravagant. Whoever it was for, *Mamasan* Nok had outdone herself.

As she walked closer to the bar some of her friends saw her, but instead of coming to greet her, they started cheering and ran inside. Something strange was going on. She knew they had seen her. Why didn't they come over to say hello? Had she done something wrong?

The first evidence to the contrary was the large cake that sat on a table just outside the front door. Although a few fingers had been dipped into the frosting, it hadn't been cut yet and the professional writing on top was still intact. It read: 'Welcome Home Lek'.

She was just looking at it when the door swung open and a teary eyed *Mamasan* Nok came out and gave her a big hug.

'What's all this?' Lek asked as she swept her arm around at the extravagant set up.

'It's for you. Welcome home,' Nok replied in a shaky voice.

'All this is for me? You didn't have to go to all this trouble. It's only me, Lek.'

'I didn't. She did.' Nok pointed to Nid who had appeared in the doorway. Nid stood with her hand clasped to her mouth and tears flowing down her cheeks.

'Isn't that Nid Sawang?' Lek asked in astonishment.

'That's exactly who it is,' Nok replied. 'She's my sister that I haven't seen in more than twenty years. But I have better news than that. Let me introduce you.'

'Hello. My name is Lek.' Not waiting to be introduced, Lek burst away from Nok and *waied* the famous singer. 'I love your music. I've got all your albums on cassette. I just love the song "Lek I Miss You" and have always kind of identified with it. It's very nice to meet you.'

Both Nid and Nok were half-laughing and half-crying.

Lek wondered what she had said to cause such a reaction.

Nid was too dumbfounded to move, much less say anything. Her lifelong mission was now standing in front of her, bigger than life itself. All her dreams, all her ambitions, everything she had lived for, for so many years, was now standing right there in front of her, a surreal image brought to life.

Lek stood there, still wondering why this famous singer was crying and speechless. What had she said to offend her?

Nok could see that Nid had lost her courage to speak and that her condition might last all night if she didn't do something. 'This is your mother,' Nok finally said. 'She has been searching for you since you were a baby.'

'What?' Lek took a step back in astonishment, not able to comprehend what was happening. Were these women crazy? This wasn't her mother. This was the famous recording star Nid Sawang.

Still unable to speak, Nid reached into her purse and pulled out all the pictures of Lek she had saved over the years and thrust them toward her daughter. She gave her just a quick moment to look at them before she reached out and grabbed her, pulled her close and hugged her so tight Lek thought she would suffocate.

Lek finally started to believe that it was a possibility that this woman might indeed be her mother. The bargirls who had been standing around watching them let out a cheer so loud that everyone in the entire area stopped what they were doing to look.

The loud popping of champagne bottles being uncorked joined the cheers and the music to create a dreamlike atmosphere that overwhelmed everyone at the festivity.

Nid finally broke the hug and pushed Lek out to arms length. She didn't let go of her, though.

'We have so much to talk about.'

Lek agreed, still stunned.

'Where do I begin?' Nid thought for a moment. 'How about, did you know that today, the sixteenth of June, is your birthday?'

'No, I didn't. The orphanage in Pattaya told me the twelfth of April was my birthday.'

'Well, today is the true anniversary of your birth.'

Nok handed Nid and Lek glasses of champagne, took one herself and proposed a toast. 'Happy twenty first birthday, Lek. Welcome home.'

AFTERWORD

After their emotional reunion, mother and daughter, Nid and Lek, two strangers, did their best to catch each other up on all that had happened in their lives up to that point. There were many similarities between present day Lek and what Nid went through before becoming a singer, but somehow they never were able to form a close bond.

It was not for a lack of trying. Lek stayed with Nid in Hua Hin for a few months, during which time Nid tried to smother her with love and affection. It all was a bit much for Lek. Every time she did anything, every time she left the house, Nid, perhaps afraid of losing her again, wanted to know every detail of where Lek would be going and what Lek would be doing. It didn't take long before this began to annoy the extremely independent Lek.

Nid began to realize that Lek was not the same person Nid had dreamed her to be. She wasn't the cuddly, dependant little baby that was stolen from her so long ago.

It was a great relief for Nid to have found Lek, and for Lek to know what had happened, but evidently Lek ended up holding some resentment towards Nid. Like her mother, Lek had lived a hard life on her own, and had managed to become a self-made woman. But at that point in her life she had become obsessed with money and when Nid didn't lavish cash and gifts on her, instead only offering her free room and board in lavish surroundings, Lek decided that sitting around in Hua

Hin with this stranger claiming to be her mother just wasn't for her, so she went back into her old life in Bangkok.

The two kept in touch, but over time began to see each other less often. For Lek, knowing who her mother was, and knowing that she was a famous singer, and being able to regale her barroom and Thai dancing friends with this fact, was much better than actually living with Nid. I can only guess what effect this had on Nid, for she eventually married and moved away to Europe.

Nid's story is second hand, as told by Lek. It was all fresh in her mind and she was more than willing to tell me, this aspiring writer, back in the early 1990s. It took a couple years for the entire story to unravel, and I obviously filled in a lot of details. Plenty of literary license was taken throughout the book, but the basis of the story is true according to Lek.